Welcom... P9-CDI-477

As innkeepers and entrepreneurs, each of us has a story to tell. I remember when my inn, the Inn & Spa at Cedar Falls, was but a dream envisioned by my mother, Anne Castle.

My mother single-mindedly pursued her goal of establishing an inn, but her real legacy was her ability to draw people in and involve them in her plans and ideas. She was never shy about reinventing herself. In 1985, my mother was a single woman in her 50s with no business experience, no credit history and no bank willing to lend her money. She formed a team of people who shared her vision, and didn't take no for an answer.

Private contractor Terry Lingo (who is now my husband) entered my mother's life at that time. Terry said, "I told my parents that I had met a truly crazy woman. She owned only a little, run-down cabin and a hand-dug well on a one-lane gravel road, and this woman told me she was gonna build an inn. I wondered who the heck would want to visit Hocking County?"

Thanks in part to SELECT REGISTRY and its loyal customers, the Inn & Spa at Cedar Falls is a successful property located in the Hocking Hills in southeast Ohio. Nearly 350 interesting tales are waiting to be shared when you visit our member inns. Each offers a truly unique experience.

Terry and I visit many inns as we travel. We continue to learn from each other and enjoy long-term friendships with the innkeepers. You, too, will learn about the rich history of each inn and make new friends with your hosts and other guests. Of course, it goes without saying that you will be treated to delectable breakfasts and relaxing accommodations during your stay.

We invite you to explore SELECT REGISTRY's guidebook and website, **www.selectregistry.com**. Our rigorous inspection process ensures that each of our members offers the best of the best in distinctive lodging experiences. Our members' hospitality and stories will keep you coming back.

On behalf of our member innkeepers, Board of Directors and the staff at SELECT REGISTRY, please enjoy this complimentary copy of our directory. We hope you come back often to visit our member inns. We would love to hear about your experiences as well!

Regards,

Ellen Grinsfelder
President, Select Registry
Owner, Inn at Cedar Falls, Logan, Ohio

For four decades, a brand and a directory you can count on...

Select Registry, Distinguished Inns of North America—the premier guide to exceptional travel and lodging for 40 years—invites you to find that special place that will make your next trip unforgettable.

Whether you're traveling for business or pleasure, by yourself or with your family, this guidebook will help you to locate extraordinary places to stay throughout the U.S. and Canada. And, no matter what the season or the type of property that you find most appealing, Select Registry likely has something for you.

Most importantly, you can rest assured that our member properties have been selected as among the most comfortable and welcoming—unique and quality assured lodging alternatives in an increasingly cluttered and impersonal travel marketplace.

In years past, the registry book in the lobby of hotels and inns welcomed guests and provided a connection between innkeepers and travelers. The historical registry "quill"—the original instrument of guest registration—has been incorporated into our Association's graphic identity, and the predicates of hospitality, comfort, and authenticity establish our members as "the best of the best"—select properties that will exceed your highest expectations when it comes to lodging.

Look for the plaque with the quill on it when you visit our members' inns, and you'll know that you are "traveling the Select Registry way..."

SELECT ⎔ REGISTRY
DISTINGUISHED INNS OF NORTH AMERICA

se·lect (sĭ-lĕkt') v. -lect·ed, -lecting, -lects. —tr. To choose from among several; pick out, —intr. To make a choice or selection. —adj. Also se·lect·ed (-lĕk'tĭd). 1. Singled out in preference; chosen. 2. Of special value or quality; preferred. —n. One that is select. [Lat. seligere, select-: se-, apart+legere, to choose.] —se·lect'ness n.

In the late 1960s, one man had an interesting idea. A travel writer named **Norman Simpson** drove throughout North America in a paneled station wagon. He identified unique places offering exceptional hospitality and what he called good honest lodgings, good honest food, and good honest feeling. He was hailed as the father of country inn travel. Through his pioneering book, *Country Inns and Back Roads*, Simpson introduced an entirely new type of lodging experience to the traveling public.

What we consider routine in the travel industry in 2012 is certainly different than in 1972 when Norman Simpson first organized our association. Airline travel is commonplace. Gasoline is no longer 40 cents per gallon. Computers, smart phones and tablets accompany business travelers as well as tourists.

The association begun by Norman Simpson with just a handful of New England properties now includes nearly 350 of the finest country inns, B&Bs and small hotels from California to Nova Scotia.

Simpson was an innovator, and his vision and tireless promotion fundamentally changed the public perception of inns in North America. Today, SELECT REGISTRY, the association that was his brainchild, is alive and well, and we continue to represent the very best the travel industry has to offer.

How to use this book

This guidebook is organized in alphabetical order, by state and province (our Canadian members have a separate section that begins on page 378). A map of the state or province at the beginning of each section shows the location of each property relative to major cities and highways. For larger map images, please go to the SELECT REGISTRY website, **www.selectregistry.com**.

Generally speaking, properties are grouped within each state or province by travel area, north to south, east to west. All Camden, Maine properties for example are listed together.

For the convenience of our guests, an index of properties by state and province is provided at the front of the book. At the back of the book, you'll find an alpha-listing of all member properties.

Each SELECT REGISTRY member property is represented with its own page of information in this guidebook. The page includes two pictures, a brief description of the experience a guest can expect at that property, contact information, and a QR code to that inn's page on the SELECT REGISTRY website. The owners/innkeepers are listed so you know who your hosts will be. ❶

The Rooms/Rates section gives the number of rooms and pricing structure for the property. ❷ Cuisine describes the food and beverage specialties for which our members are famous, including whether the property serves only breakfast or is full service. ❸ The nearest Airport(s) tells you where you might fly in. ❹

Because food and wine are important compliments to many of our properties, some members are proud to have received prestigious DiRoNa (Distinguished Restaurants of North America) as well as *Wine Spectator* Awards. These awards are noted on participating Inns' guidebook page(s), as is any AAA Award the inn has received (confirmed by Official Appointment by AAA.) ❺

Each of our inns has a slightly different mix of food and beverage services. Although these are often described in more detail in the Cuisine section for each inn, we want to give our guests a quick snapshot of what each inn offers in-house. The icons near the top of each page tell you whether the inn serves breakfast, lunch, and/or dinner, and whether or not wine or cocktails are available. ❻

Breakfast   Lunch   Dinner   Wine/Cocktails

For quickly moving from this guidebook to the member inn's page on the SELECT REGISTRY website, a QR code is provided for each member inn. Using a QR code reader application on a smartphone, you can take a picture of the code and link directly to that inn's page on the SELECT REGISTRY website. ❼

We hope these instructions help you utilize your guidebook as you plan your travels. For many additional pages of information on each member property, visit us online at: **www.selectregistry.com.**

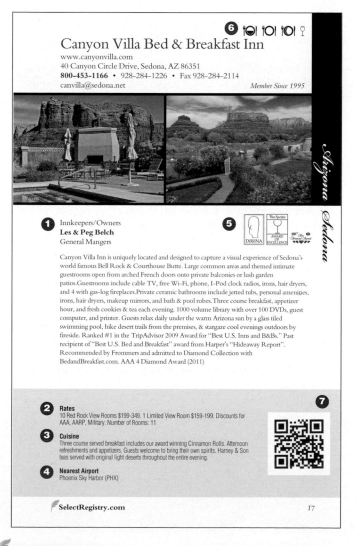

❻ ❼❼❼ ♀

Canyon Villa Bed & Breakfast Inn
www.canyonvilla.com
40 Canyon Circle Drive, Sedona, AZ 86351
800-453-1166 • 928-284-1226 • Fax 928-284-2114
canvilla@sedona.net

Member Since 1995

Arizona Sedona

❶ Innkeepers/Owners
Les & Peg Belch
General Mangers

❺ DiRōNA | AWARD OF EXCELLENCE | Wine Spectator

Canyon Villa Inn is uniquely located and designed to capture a visual experience of Sedona's world famous Bell Rock & Courthouse Butte. Large common areas and themed intimate guestrooms open from arched French doors onto private balconies or lush garden patios. Guestrooms include cable TV, free Wi-Fi, phone, I-Pod clock radios, irons, hair dryers, and 4 with gas-log fireplaces. Private ceramic bathrooms include jetted tubs, personal amenities, irons, hair dryers, makeup mirrors, and bath & pool robes. Three course breakfast, appetizer hour, and fresh cookies & tea each evening. 1000 volume library with over 100 DVDs, guest computer, and printer. Guests relax daily under the warm Arizona sun by a glass tiled swimming pool, hike desert trails from the premises, & stargaze cool evenings outdoors by fireside. Ranked #1 in the TripAdvisor 2009 Award for "Best U.S. Inns and B&Bs." Past recipient of "Best U.S. Bed and Breakfast" award from Harper's "Hideaway Report". Recommended by Frommers and admitted to Diamond Collection with BedandBreakfast.com. AAA 4 Diamond Award (2011)

❷ **Rates**
10 Red Rock View Rooms $199-349. 1 Limited View Room $159-199. Discounts for AAA, AARP, Military. Number of Rooms: 11

❸ **Cuisine**
Three course served breakfast includes our award winning Cinnamon Rolls. Afternoon refreshments and appetizers. Guests welcome to bring their own spirits. Harney & Son teas served with original light deserts throughout the entire evening.

❹ **Nearest Airport**
Phoenix Sky Harbor (PHX)

❼

⌁ SelectRegistry.com

17

⌁ **SelectRegistry.com**

5

Guest Loyalty: *Golden Quill* LOYALTY PROGRAM

We believe that loyalty should be rewarded. That's why we developed the **Golden Quill Loyalty Program**. This rewards program allows you to accumulate points toward a reward certificate by staying at any SELECT REGISTRY inn or B&B.

For each night of lodging at a SELECT REGISTRY property, you earn one Golden Quill. Once a total of twelve (12) Quills are earned, you will receive a $100 reward certificate for use at ANY SELECT REGISTRY inn or B&B in North America.

Visit **www.selectregistry.com/goldenquill** for complete details and to register, confirm and track your Quills online.

Are you on Facebook? As a special incentive for Facebook users, you can earn an extra Quill FREE, just for "Liking" us. Visit **www.facebook. com/selectregistry.com** and click on "Golden Quill Rewards" to register and receive your free Quill.

Vacation of a Lifetime:

In early 2013, we're awarding one lucky winner the Vacation of a Lifetime, a FREE overnight stay at each of our nearly 350 Select Registry inns and B&Bs across North America. That's a year's worth of FREE lodging and it could be yours!

Entering the sweepstakes is easy and no purchase is necessary. Once you register for the Golden Quill Loyalty Program, you're automatically entered. It's that simple. Plus, for each Golden Quill you earn with a night's stay at a Select Registry inn or B&B, you'll also earn an additional entry in the drawing. The more times you stay, the better your chance of winning.

Visit **www.selectregistry.com/Vacation-of-a-Lifetime.asp** for official contest rules.

SelectRegistry.com

Gift certificates

The gift of an overnight stay or a weekend at an exceptional inn or B&B can be one of the most thoughtful and appreciated gifts you can give your parents, children, or dear friends. Employers are discovering that a gift certificate for a "getaway" is an excellent way of rewarding their employees, while at the same time giving them some much-needed rest. A few ideas:

- **Weddings** • **Anniversaries** • **Holiday & Birthday gifts** •
- **Employee rewards/incentives** • **Retirement** •
- **Thank you or Appreciation** •

Our gift certificates are valid at any of our nearly 350 member properties. We process orders daily, packaging certificates with our complimentary Association guidebook and your personal message. If you need a gift certificate immediately, you can order our online electronic version. The next time you think about gift giving, think about our collection of celebrated properties and our gift certificate program—the perfect gift for that special person, **1-800-344-5244** or online at **www.SelectRegistry.com/gift-shop**.

Quality Assurance

Watch a behind-the-scenes video of an undercover inspection online at www.youtube.com/stayselect.

Perhaps the most important distinction between a SELECT REGISTRY member inn and others is our system of quality assurance. SELECT REGISTRY periodically conducts a quality assurance inspection of each of its nearly 350 inns. This program involves independent inspectors—not employees of SELECT REGISTRY—with years of experience in the hospitality industry.

The inspectors arrive anonymously, spend the night, and evaluate the inn based on a detailed point system, which translates into a pass/fail grade for the inn. Inns applying for membership are inspected as are existing member inns on a regular basis.

No other organization of innkeepers has a comparable inspection program.

Not all inns have what it takes to pass inspection. Thus, this practice provides a guarantee to the traveling public that a SELECT REGISTRY inn is in a class of its own. A recent Internet directory identified over 20,000 country inns and B&Bs in the United States and Canada, and only a select few are members of SELECT REGISTRY. No other online directory or organization of innkeepers has a comparable inspection program. In fact, a recent *New York Times* article noted that the proliferation of "inns" has resulted in an industry that is misrepresented, lacks quality control, and charges widely varying room rates. With its rigorous inspection program, SELECT REGISTRY has established quality as a hallmark of its member properties.

SELECT REGISTRY doesn't rank its members with diamonds or stars, although many of our members carry the high ratings you'd expect from various groups who evaluate inns and B&Bs. If you're a member of SELECT REGISTRY, you're the cream of the crop. All of our inns are "the best" —and our inspections prove it!

SelectRegistry.com

Social Media

We love to talk about our member inns and B&Bs and we encourage our guests to as well. By sharing experiences, comments and pictures online you can help other travelers discover the SELECT REGISTRY difference. It's the modern way of paying it forward and your innkeepers will be forever grateful.

And don't forget to "Like" us on Facebook: **www.facebook.com/selectregistry** and follow us on Twitter: **@SelectRegistry** and hashtag **#stayselect**.

Visiting one of our inns? Many of them are online as well. Check with your innkeeper or on our website for a complete listing of social media usernames and share your SELECT REGISTRY experience with the world.

U.S. map

SelectRegistry.com

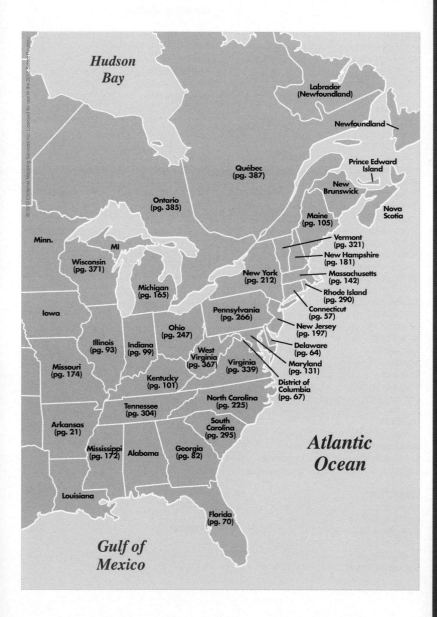

Hudson
Bay

Labrador
(Newfoundland)

Newfoundland

Québec
(pg. 387)

Prince Edward
Island

New
Brunswick

Nova
Scotia

Ontario
(pg. 385)

Maine
(pg. 105)

Minn.

MI

Vermont
(pg. 321)

New Hampshire
(pg. 181)

Wisconsin
(pg. 371)

Michigan
(pg. 165)

New York
(pg. 212)

Massachusetts
(pg. 142)

Rhode Island
(pg. 290)

Iowa

Pennsylvania
(pg. 266)

Connecticut
(pg. 57)

New Jersey
(pg. 197)

Ohio
(pg. 247)

Illinois
(pg. 93)

Indiana
(pg. 99)

West
Virginia
(pg. 367)

Virginia
(pg. 339)

Delaware
(pg. 64)

Maryland
(pg. 131)

Missouri
(pg. 174)

Kentucky
(pg. 101)

District of
Columbia
(pg. 67)

Tennessee
(pg. 304)

North Carolina
(pg. 225)

Arkansas
(pg. 21)

South
Carolina
(pg. 295)

Mississippi
(pg. 172)

Alabama

Georgia
(pg. 82)

Atlantic
Ocean

Louisiana

Florida
(pg. 70)

Gulf of
Mexico

Index by State or Province

SelectRegistry.com

Index by State or Province

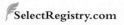

Index by State or Province

Index by State or Province

Arizona

Famous for: Grand Canyon, Painted Desert, Petrified Forest, Copper Mines, Gila Monster, Lake Mead (largest man-made lake in the world), Tombstone (Wyatt Earp's fight at the OK Corral), Cliff Dwellings.

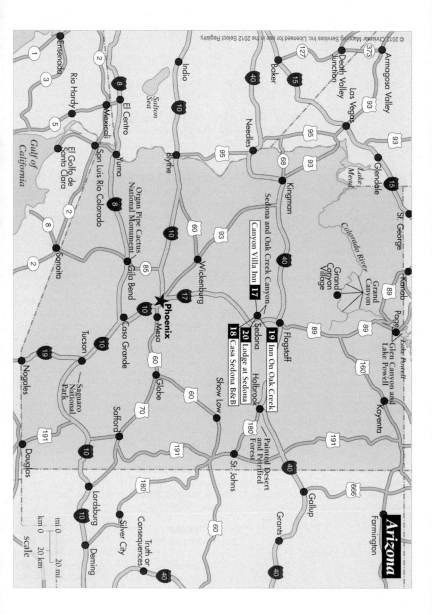

© 2012 Christian Mapping Services Inc. Licensed for use in the 2012 Select Registry.

17 Canyon Villa Inn — Sedona and Oak Creek Canyon

18 Casa Sedona B&B

19 Inn On Oak Creek

20 Lodge at Sedona

Canyon Villa Bed & Breakfast Inn 🍽️

www.canyonvilla.com
40 Canyon Circle Drive, Sedona, AZ 86351
800-453-1166 • 928-284-1226
canvilla@sedona.net

Member Since 1995

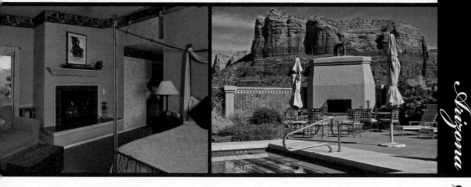

Arizona

Sedona

Owners/Innkeepers
Les & Peg Belch

Canyon Villa Inn is uniquely located and designed to capture a visual experience of Sedona's world famous Bell Rock & Courthouse Butte. Large common areas and themed intimate guestrooms open from arched French doors onto private balconies or lush garden patios. Guestrooms include cable TV, free Wi-Fi, phone, I-Pod clock radios, irons, hair dryers, and 4 with gas-log fireplaces. Private ceramic bathrooms include jetted tubs, personal amenities, irons, hair dryers, makeup mirrors, and bath & pool robes. Three course breakfast, appetizer hour, and fresh cookies & tea each evening. 1000 volume library with over 100 DVDs, guest computer, and printer. Guests relax daily under the warm Arizona sun by a glass tiled swimming pool, hike desert trails from the premises, & stargaze cool evenings outdoors by fireside. Ranked #3 in the 2012 TripAdvisor Traveler's Choice 2012 Award for "Best U.S. Inns and B&Bs." Past recipient of "Best U.S. Bed and Breakfast" award from Harper's "Hideaway Report". Recommended by Frommers and admitted to Diamond Collection status by BedandBreakfast.com.

Rates
10 Red Rock View Rooms $189-349. 1 LIMITED View Room $159-199. Discounts for AAA, AARP, Military. Promotional discounts often include Multi-Night stay discounts as high as 20%. Fares vary by season. Number of Rooms: 11

Cuisine
Three course served breakfast includes our award winning Cinnamon Rolls. Afternoon refreshments and appetizers. Guests welcome to bring their own spirits. Harney & Son teas served with original light deserts throughout the entire evening.

Nearest Airport
Phoenix Sky Harbor (PHX)

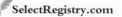

Casa Sedona Inn

www.casasedona.com
55 Hozoni Drive, Sedona, AZ 86336
800-525-3756 • 928-282-2938 • Fax 928-282-2259
casa@sedona.net

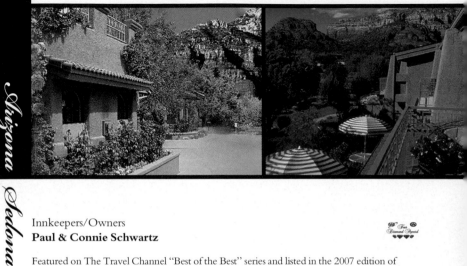

Arizona Sedona

Innkeepers/Owners
Paul & Connie Schwartz

Featured on The Travel Channel "Best of the Best" series and listed in the 2007 edition of "1000 Places to See Before You Die", Casa Sedona is a world-renowned 16-room bed & breakfast inn. Located 6 minutes away from the bustling "uptown" in a quiet area just off the Highway 89A. Relax in our serene landscaped gardens, or on your private patio or balcony, and enjoy inspiring red rock views of Thunder Mountain, Chimney Rock, and "Baby Bell" Rock. Breakfast is served outside – with red rock views – and features mild Southwest Favorites and award-winning French Toast bakes. Afternoon appetizers in the Juniper Garden offer an opportunity for guests to relax, refuel, and share the day's experiences. Guest rooms are up-to-date and well-appointed with AAA ◆◆◆◆ amenties.

Rates
Low Season: $159 - $229 High Season: $179 - $329 Number of Rooms: 16

Cuisine
Two course breakfast. Late afternoon appetizers, beverages, and homemade Coyote cookies. Guests are welcome to bring their own spirits.

Nearest Airport
Phoenix Sky Harbor

 SelectRegistry.com

The Inn on Oak Creek

www.innonoakcreek.com
556 State Route 179, Sedona, AZ 86336
800-499-7896 • 928-282-7896 • Fax 928-282-0696
theinn@sedona.net

Member Since 2001

Owner/ Manager
James Matykiewicz

Initially built in 1972 as an art gallery, then totally refurbished and transformed in 1995, the Inn perches on a bluff overlooking Oak Creek, Arizona's premier year-round spring-fed stream. Within easy walking distance are Sedona's best art galleries, boutique shops, several fine restaurants, and Tlaquepaque shopping village. Almost as close are National Forest trails that will take you to the heart of Red Rock country. So, while guests are constantly surprised that an Inn so centrally located in Sedona can offer such privacy and relaxation, the luxurious AAA Four Diamond accommodations, professional staff, and culinary delights (Five Star Food!) are what really please them. Additionally, located in the Inn's private owner's quarters is The Art Of Cooking, where professional chefs conduct cooking cooking classes several nights a week. The classes are based on a four course dinner menu, are hands on, and participating guests then partake of their handiwork. Contact the innkeeper for dates, time and price.

Rates
11 Rooms, $200/$295 DBL; 1 Suite, $350. Creekside rooms have decks w/dramatic views. All rooms include gas fireplaces and private baths with whirlpool tubs. Number of Rooms: 11

Cuisine
Full four-course gourmet breakfast, afternoon beverages, cookies & hors d'oeuvres included. Guests are welcome to bring their own adult beverages. Cooking classes are conducted on Tuesday and Thursday evenings in the owner's quarters.

Nearest Airport
Flagstaff (40 minutes), Phoenix (2 hours)

The Lodge at Sedona

www.LODGEatSEDONA.com
125 Kallof Place, Sedona, AZ 86336
800-619-4467 • 928-204-1942 • Fax 928-204-2128
Info@LODGEatSEDONA.com

Member Since 2003

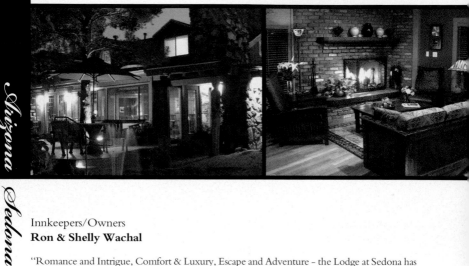

Innkeepers/Owners
Ron & Shelly Wachal

"Romance and Intrigue, Comfort & Luxury, Escape and Adventure – the Lodge at Sedona has it all."-AZ News. Elegant & Secluded Mission/Arts & Craft Estate set on two acres of grand seclusion in the very Heart of Sedona, Arizona. Awarded Top 10 Inns in US by Forbes.com, Best B&Bs by Phoenix Magazine. Recommended by Small Elegant Hotels, Historic Lodging Directory, Bon Appetit, Mobil Three Star, Fodors.com, and Frommer's. Close to hiking trails,biking, golf, tennis, art galleries and shopping. Spectacular Red Rock views, sculpture gardens, fitness center privileges and pools adjacent, fountains and a magical labyrinth. King suites with fireplaces, jet tubs, spa robes, large decks, stereo TV. Massage Services, complete concierge service and full gourmet breakfast and snacks included daily. Check our Seasonal Specials and Hot Deals. "The Lodge at Sedona is one of the most romantic Inns in Arizona." -AZ Foothills Magazine.

Rates
14 Rooms & King Suites: $189/$349 B&B; Kings w/ fireplaces, jet tubs, view decks, stereo TV. Number of Rooms: 14

Cuisine
Professionally prepared and served gourmet breakfast including Sedona Gold coffee, Lodge Granola and yogurt. Sunset appetizers, Spring water & Snacks included daily. Guest beverages welcome!

Nearest Airport
Phoenix (PHX), Flagstaff (FLG), Sedona (KSEZ)

Arkansas

Famous for: Natural Hot Springs, The Ozarks, Waterfalls, Diamonds, Oil, Aluminum.

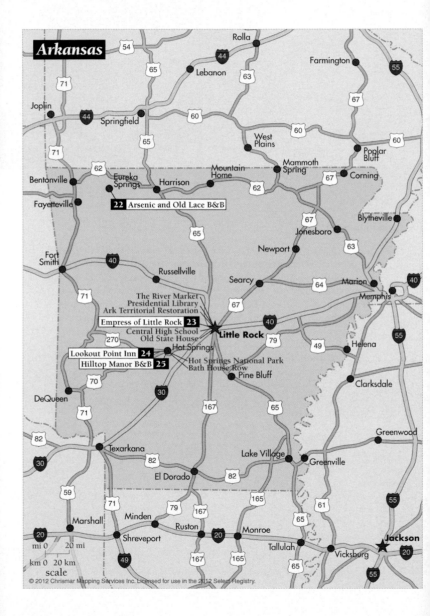

Arkansas

- **22** Arsenic and Old Lace B&B
- The River Market
- Presidential Library
- Ark Territorial Restoration
- **Empress of Little Rock 23**
- Central High School
- Old State House
- **Lookout Point Inn 24**
- **Hilltop Manor B&B 25**
- Hot Springs National Park
- Bath House Row

© 2012 Chrismar Mapping Services Inc. Licensed for use in the 2012 Select Registry.

Arsenic and Old Lace B&B

www.eurekaspringsromancebb.com
60 Hillside Avenue, Eureka Springs, AR 72632
866-350-5454 • 479-253-5454 • Fax 479-253-2246
info@eurekaspringsromancebb.com

Member Since 2006

Arkansas

Eureka Springs

Innkeepers/Owners
Beverly and Doug Breitling

Arsenic and Old Lace is located on a heavily wooded hillside in the Historic District of Eureka Springs. The beautiful Ozark Mountains surround the Inn that is a step back to a quieter, more relaxed time. From our Morning Room, or the Chantilly Rose room balcony, guests enjoy the mixed white squirrels, birds, chipmunks and sometimes even deer. A short walk through a wooded area will bring guests to the shops, historic homes and buildings of the Historic Loop. The mood of the Inn is relaxed luxury, as your hosts strive to make each guest feel as if they are at home. The relaxed feel continues into your room, where you will find comfortable furnishings, jetted tubs, Comphy micro-fiber sheets, luxury showers, televisions, VCR/DVD players, CD players and Wireless Internet access. Enjoy the video library to watch a movie, curl-up with a good book or your loved one. Rest, Relax and Recreate! You've stepped back in time without leaving modern necessities. Excite all of your senses with an unforgettable experience!

Rates
$115/$299. Rates vary seasonally and midweek. Number of Rooms: 5

Cuisine
Enjoy custom blended coffee, tea or hot chocolate; our full gourmet breakfast starts with a delicious fruit course, breakfast breads or scones, and a unique main course. Enjoy homemade snacks all day and a well stocked refrigerator.

Nearest Airport
NW Arkansas Regional (XNA)

The Empress of Little Rock

www.theempress.com
2120 Louisiana Street, Little Rock, AR 72206
501-374-7966 • 501-374-7966 • Fax 501-375-4537
Email: hostess@theempress.com

Member Since 2001

Innkeepers/Owners
Robert Blair and Sharon Welch-Blair

Stay a century away in the award winning small luxury hotel, THE EMPRESS OF LITTLE ROCK. The historic boutique hotel, ranked as a top ten in the US, was built in 1888 as the largest most opulent mansion in Arkansas. Let your senses be lavished with the most modern spa amenities: hydro-massage therapy, steam, aromatherapy, antique Jacuzzi soaking tubs. Work a 1000 piece puzzle by the warmth of firelight in the parlor. Enjoy an elegant two course gourmet breakfast by candlelight in a dinning room fit for Her Majesty, the Queen. Ascend a magnificent double stairwell as Scarlett to the Chatelaine Suite where a night in a canopied featherbed will have you begging for more. If something slightly more daring piques your interest, retire to the Hemingway Spa Suite with a 1940's "Mogambo" touch, a romantic escape to contemplate the next chapter in your life. Stroll through the Secret Garden where the fountain drums and a romantic hammock beckons. Ah!!! The Empress, where unrushed conversation abounds, along with true Southern Hospitality.

Rates
9 Rooms, 5 Spa Suites, 3 Mini-Suites, $139/$329 Featherbeds/Cable/DSL/Jacuzzi/Fireplaces. Number of Rooms: 9

Cuisine
Elegant two-course gourmet breakfast by candlelight served 'Before the Queen' w/ Victorian pomp and circumstance and a "bow-tied butler." Gourmet coffee, snacks and mineral water available 24/7. Wine social hour and in room complimentary liqueur.

Nearest Airport
Little Rock

🍴🍴🍴 ❢

Lookout Point Lakeside Inn

www.LookoutPointInn.com
104 Lookout Circle, Hot Springs, AR 71913
866-525-6155 • 501-525-6155 • Fax 501-525-5850
info@LookoutPointInn.com

Member Since 2005

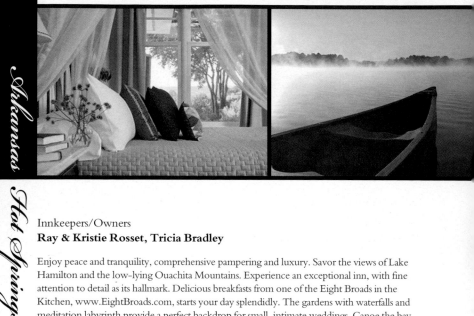

Hot Springs

Innkeepers/Owners
Ray & Kristie Rosset, Tricia Bradley

Enjoy peace and tranquility, comprehensive pampering and luxury. Savor the views of Lake Hamilton and the low-lying Ouachita Mountains. Experience an exceptional inn, with fine attention to detail as its hallmark. Delicious breakfasts from one of the Eight Broads in the Kitchen, www.EightBroads.com, starts your day splendidly. The gardens with waterfalls and meditation labyrinth provide a perfect backdrop for small, intimate weddings. Canoe the bay, watch the birds, nap in the hammock, or soak in the nearby historic Hot Springs bathhouses. A barefoot walk in the gardens or a challenging board game enhances the experience of simplifying life. A one or two bedroom lakeside condominium, called Lakeview Terrace, invites guests to enjoy the 36 ft. deck right at water's edge. Great for a family to enjoy all of Hot Springs fun. Chosen Top Ten B&B/Inn in the U.S. by Trip Advisor Travelers Choice Awards, 2012.

Rates
$147/$369 for rooms and suites. $297-499 for 1 or 2 bedroom condo. Rates based upon type of room and season. Corporate weekday rates available. Wedding, romance and family fun packages available. Number of Rooms: 13

Cuisine
Fresh and hearty breakfast plus innkeeper's reception features dessert, appetizers, wine and tea. Complimentary snack bar. Soups, salads and hot/cold sandwiches available. Gourmet dinner for two by private chef, with dining by the waterfalls.

Nearest Airport
Little Rock, 60 miles. Air service to Hot Springs airport available from Memphis & Dallas.

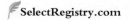 SelectRegistry.com

Hilltop Manor Bed & Breakfast

www.hilltopmanorhotsprings.com
2009 Park Avenue, Hot Springs, AR 71901
(501) 625-7829
info@hilltopmanorhotsprings.com

Member Since 2010

Innkeepers/Owners
Bob & Faith Kraemer

Legends such as Jessie James and Al Capone have spent time on the Hilltop Manor estate. Is it your turn now? Come visit this award winning 1890 craftsman manor which has been restored to classic elegance. Take refuge from life's stress on this five acre estate which borders the National Park forest and was awarded a "Beauty Spot". Gaze at the waterfall from the expansive front porch. Wander the grounds and explore rock walls and buildings from the past. Meander through the grove of Magnolia trees and stop to smell a rosebud. Whatever you choose to do, we are here so that you can relax. We offer five unique, well-appointed suites most with king-sized bed, whirlpool tub, fireplace, refrigerator and microwave. All with decadent linens, robes and a fully plated breakfast each morning. Relish the morning meal which is served in your private suite, the front porch or the dining room with antique lighting overhead. We also serve an afternoon snack each day with beverages in the common area. Named "Top 10 Inns in US" by BedandBreakfast.com. Located 5 min. from Historic Downtown.

Rates
Standard Suites $170-$275 - Perfect for an anytime escape!Deluxe Suites $250-$400 (2 Person Jacuzzi Tub, Historic Fireplace, King Bed, 40" Flat Screen TV, Spa Therapy Sound Machine and More) Perfect for a Special Romantic Escape! Number of Rooms: 5

Cuisine
Hilltop Manor is known for its delicious breakfast that is unique each day. There is always a bread item, fruit dish, egg dish and sweet. We promise you won't go away hungry. Happy to accommodate dietary needs; let us know when making your reservation.

Nearest Airport
Hot Springs Memorial Field Airport - 6 Miles and Little Rock Adams Field Intl Airport - 55 Miles

Northern California   "The Golden State"

Famous for: Spanish Missions, Gold Rush, Golden Gate Bridge, Wine Country, Citrus, Sequoia Redwoods, Hollywood, Disneyland, Lake Tahoe, Sierra Nevada, Yosemite National Park, Big Sur, Earthquakes and Death Valley.

Southern California

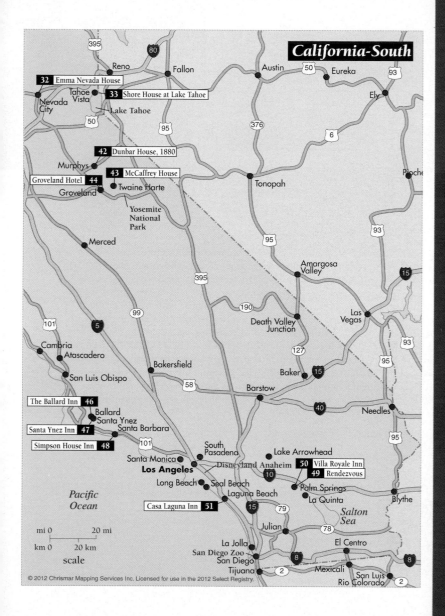

California-South

Location/Inn	
32 Emma Nevada House	
33 Shore House at Lake Tahoe	
42 Dunbar House, 1880	
43 McCaffrey House	
Groveland Hotel **44**	
The Ballard Inn **46**	
Santa Ynez Inn **47**	
Simpson House Inn **48**	
50 Villa Royale Inn	
49 Rendezvous	
Casa Laguna Inn **51**	

395 · Reno · 80 · Fallon · Austin · 50 · Eureka · 93

Tahoe Vista · Nevada City · Lake Tahoe · Ely

50 · 95 · 376 · 6

Murphys · Groveland · Twaine Harte · Tonopah · Pioche

Yosemite National Park · 93

Merced · 95 · 93

395 · Amargosa Valley · 15

99 · 190 · Las Vegas

101 · 5 · Death Valley Junction · 93

Cambria · Atascadero · San Luis Obispo · Bakersfield · 127 · 95

58 · Barstow · Baker · 15

Ballard · Santa Ynez · Santa Barbara · 40 · Needles

101 · 95

South Pasadena · Lake Arrowhead

Santa Monica · Los Angeles · Disneyland Anaheim · 10

Long Beach · Seal Beach · Laguna Beach · Palm Springs · La Quinta · Blythe

Pacific Ocean · 15 · 79 · Salton Sea

Julian · 78

mi 0 · 20 mi
km 0 · 20 km
scale

La Jolla · El Centro

San Diego Zoo · San Diego · Tijuana · 2 · Mexicali · 8

San Luis Rio Colorado · 2

© 2012 Chrismar Mapping Services Inc. Licensed for use in the 2012 Select Registry.

Carter House Inns

www.carterhouse.com
301 L Street, Eureka, CA 95501
800-404-1390 • 707-444-8062 • Fax 707-444-8067
reserve@carterhouse.com

Member Since 2003

California

Eureka

Innkeepers/Owners
Mark and Christi Carter

Northern California's premier inn is an enclave of 3 magnificent Victorians perched alongside Humboldt Bay in Old Town Eureka. The luxurious accommodations at Carter House Inns and the sumptuous dining at its Restaurant 301 (considered among Northern California's best restaurants) set an indulgent tone for a marvelous visit to the giant redwood forests, rugged Pacific beaches and the other wonders of Northern California's Redwood Coast. Our accommodations and service are unparalleled; our award-winning cuisine is prepared w/local organic products and fresh herbs, greens, and vegetables harvested daily from the inn's extensive gardens. The inn also produces its own wine under the label Carter Cellars (WS 96 pts.) and Envy Wines, specializing in limited production of cabs & merlots from some of the finest vineyards in Napa. Check out our incredible food and wine lovers' packages, featuring romantic dining and accommodations in the heart of the Redwood Empire! We offer Humboldt County's finest accommodations, an outstanding full-service restaurant, full bar, and an e-wine shop.

Rates
9 Rooms, $197/$380 B&B, 2 Suites, $304/$612 B&B. Open year-round. Number of Rooms: 11

Cuisine
Full service award-winning restaurant open nightly, full breakfast, full bar, Wine Shop with 3,880 wine selections. With a recent 96-point rating from James Laube, Carter Cellars wine is quickly becoming a cult classic.

Nearest Airport
Eureka-Arcata Airport is 16 miles north of Eureka.

Glendeven Inn

www.glendeven.com
8205 North Highway One, P.O. Box 914, Mendocino, CA 95460
800-822-4536 • 707-937-0083 • Fax 707-937-6108
innkeeper@glendeven.com

Member Since 2002

California

Mendocino

Proprietor
John Dixon

As seen in The New York Times, Vogue, Travel+Leisure, and Sunset Magazine, this well appointed, unfussy, 8-acre, ocean-view, farmstead B&B offers wood-burning fireplaces, full in-room farm-fresh-egg gourmet breakfasts, secluded patios and decks, featherbeds, outstanding gardens, 45+ local wines in its Wine Bar[n] and a complimentary wine and hors d'oeuvres hour. Glendeven is a multi-building 1867 country farmstead situated on a headland meadow with grazing llamas, roaming chickens, manicured gardens, & an organic edible garden. Located 2 minutes south of the historic Mendocino village, Glendeven offers trails to the Pacific headland cliffs, to the beach at its surrounding state park & to its own Forest Trail connecting to Fern Canyon trail along Little River. Its Wine Bar[n] features flight tastings of local Mendocino county varietals in its garden and watertower-view lounge. There is a 2,000 sq ft vacation rental onsite, perfect for couples traveling together. A four-course wine paired ocean-view dinner is available at Glendeven's farmhouse "host table."

Rates
10 rooms & suites plus four (4) vacation rental houses on and off site. $120 to $380. King & Queen beds. 2-6 people per unit. Open year-round. Number of Rooms: 10

Cuisine
A 3-course, hot, in-room breakfast begins the day. 4-course wine pairing dinners available twice weekly. Complimentary wine & hors d'oeuvres in the inn's Wine Bar[n] nightly. Coffee, teas & homemade baked goods always available in the farmhouse lounge.

Nearest Airport
San Francisco, Oakland, and Sacramento

Joshua Grindle Inn

www.joshgrin.com
P.O. Box 647, 44800 Little Lake Road, Mendocino, CA 95460
800-474-6353 • 707-937-4143
stay@joshgrin.com

Member Since 1996

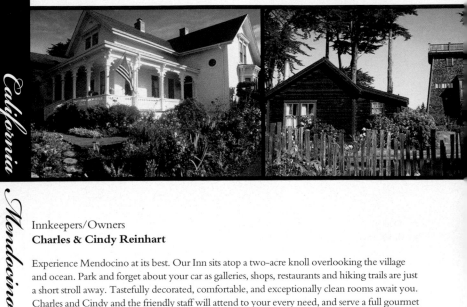

Mendocino

Innkeepers/Owners
Charles & Cindy Reinhart

Experience Mendocino at its best. Our Inn sits atop a two-acre knoll overlooking the village and ocean. Park and forget about your car as galleries, shops, restaurants and hiking trails are just a short stroll away. Tastefully decorated, comfortable, and exceptionally clean rooms await you. Charles and Cindy and the friendly staff will attend to your every need, and serve a full gourmet breakfast. Enjoy chatting with fellow guests over evening refreshments in our parlor, or escape to a private, quiet nook in the gardens. Relax on the front veranda and watch the whales spout in the distance. Mobil Three Star rated.

Rates
10 Rooms Main House, Cottage, Water Tower, $150-$279 B&B. 2 Ocean View, 2 bdrm, Guest Houses $400/+ Number of Rooms: 10

Cuisine
Full gourmet breakfast served to guests using fresh local ingredients. The highly regarded Cafe Beaujolais is a two-block stroll. Wineshop on premises with selection of premium Mendocino wines. Complimentary wine in room & Cream Sherry in Parlor.

Nearest Airport
Little River Airport, Oakland International, San Francisco International, Sonoma

SelectRegistry.com

Sea Rock Inn

www.searock.com

11101 Lansing Street, P.O. Box 906, Mendocino, CA 95460

800-906-0926 • 707-937-0926 • Fax 707-676-9008

innkeeper@searock.com

Member Since 2005

California

Mendocino

Innkeepers/Owners
Andy & Susie Plocher

One of the few inns in Mendocino with ocean views from every hillside accommodation. The Sea Rock Inn beckons with crashing surf and inviting firelight rooms. From your suite or cottage you will experience the true beauty of the Mendocino Coast with spectacular panoramic views of the ocean and dramatic rocky cliffs of the Mendocino Headlands State Park. The setting is perfect for a memorable getaway. Hand-hewn wood treatments accent luxuriously comfortable coastal contemporary design and appointments of virtually every amenity imaginable. Stroll through colorful gardens, curl up by the fire or relax on your deck and watch the sunset from your private ocean view cottage or suite. Hiking trails abound nearby, as does ocean and river kayaking, canoeing and many other outdoor activities. Gourmet dining is a short walk or minute's drive away, and the charming village of Mendocino is a National Historic Register community laden with special shops and attractions. Great rooms, stunning views and nice people...The Sea Rock Inn.

Rates
6 Cottages, 4 Jr.Suites, 4 Suites. $179/$395. Number of Rooms: 14

Cuisine
Guests enjoy an attractive breakfast buffet with daily changing quiche, hard boiled eggs, yogurt, fresh pastries, juices, fruit and more. Upon check in to the room, guests may relax with a complimentary split of fine local wine.

Nearest Airport
SFO or Oakland, 3 1/2 hrs

Emma Nevada House

www.emmanevadahouse.com
528 East Broad Street, Nevada City, CA 95959
800-916-3662 • 530-265-4415 • Fax none
mail@emmanevadahouse.com

Member Since 2006

Innkeepers/Owners
Andrew & Susan Howard

Enjoy Nevada City's four seasons of food, wine and art in California's best-preserved gold country town. Our welcoming home sits in a quiet enclave of unique and elegant Victorians, just on the edge of the most beautiful town in the Sierra Foothills. Park and forget your car, as the historic allure of Nevada City is just a short stroll away. Beyond the fascinating shops, galleries and history, there are also trails alongside boiling river rapids, and seventeen unique and interesting wineries to visit. All this is capped by a proliferation of exceptional restaurants that will delight even the most cosmopolitan of travelers. It is not uncommon to hear favorable comparisons to the most notable restaurants of San Francisco and the Napa Valley. At the Emma Nevada House, you will find large and comfortable rooms characterized by their fine linens, exceptional cleanliness and thoughtful touches. Wrap around porches, beautiful gardens, and a babbling brook invite guests to linger and unwind in this graceful retreat.

Rates
$179/$249. Number of Rooms: 6

Cuisine
Guests enjoy a sit down three course breakfast that many guests say is worth the trip by itself. Menus are seasonal, with variations on fluffy souffles and fruit or berry stuffed French toast as frequent choices.

Nearest Airport
Sacramento, Reno, San Francisco & Oakland

SelectRegistry.com

Shore House at Lake Tahoe

www.shorehouselaketahoe.com
7170 North Lake Blvd., P.O. Box 499, Tahoe Vista, CA 96148
800-207-5160 • 530-546-7270 • Fax 530-546-7130
innkeeper@shorehouselaketahoe.com

Member Since 2000

California

Tahoe Vista

Innkeepers/Owners
Marty & Barb Cohen

The Shore House is the ultimate romantic getaway at the water's edge of spectacular Lake Tahoe. Balconies surrounding each room offer fabulous views of the pristine lake and mountains. Relax in the large outdoor lakefront hot tub. Enjoy fine lakefront restaurants, art galleries, and casinos close by. This winter wonderland offers world class downhill and x-c skiing at 29 resorts, ice skating, snowmobiling, and sleigh rides. Summer activities include spectacular hiking, biking, golf, tennis, rafting, para-sailing, and lunch cruises on the Shore House 36' yacht, Lady of the Lake. Kayak right from the Shore House. Enjoy a romantic couples' massage in the on site massage studio overlooking the Lake and Mountains. The Shore House specializes in intimate lakefront weddings with marriage license and Minister on site. Wedding, Honeymoon, Anniversary and Birthday Packages are also offered.

Rates
All King or Queen Rooms, $190-$325. Each room has a gas log fireplace, custom-built log furnishings, TV, Coffee Maker, Hair Dryer, Robes, Beach Towels and Refrigerator. Number of Rooms: 9

Cuisine
Award-winning gourmet breakfasts, wine and appetizers served daily in lakefront dining room or in lakeside gardens. Fresh Baked Treats in room each day. Walk to extraordinary lakefront restaurants.

Nearest Airport
Reno Tahoe International

The Honor Mansion

www.honormansion.com
891 Grove Street, Healdsburg, CA 95448
800-554-4667 • 707-433-4277 • Fax 707-431-7173
innkeeper@honormansion.com

Member Since 1998

California

Healdsburg

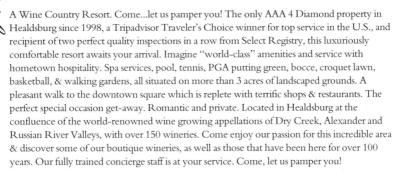

Owners
Steve & Cathi Fowler

A Wine Country Resort. Come...let us pamper you! The only AAA 4 Diamond property in Healdsburg since 1998, a Tripadvisor Traveler's Choice winner for top service in the U.S., and recipient of two perfect quality inspections in a row from Select Registry, this luxuriously comfortable resort awaits your arrival. Imagine "world-class" amenities and service with hometown hospitality. Spa services, pool, tennis, PGA putting green, bocce, croquet lawn, basketball, & walking gardens, all situated on more than 3 acres of landscaped grounds. A pleasant walk to the downtown square which is replete with terrific shops & restaurants. The perfect special occasion get-away. Romantic and private. Located in Healdsburg at the confluence of the world-renowned wine growing appellations of Dry Creek, Alexander and Russian River Valleys, with over 150 wineries. Come enjoy our passion for this incredible area & discover some of our boutique wineries, as well as those that have been here for over 100 years. Our fully trained concierge staff is at your service. Come, let us pamper you!

Rates
13 Rooms, $240/$600, 2 guests per room. K & Q beds, fireplaces, soaking tubs, private decks, spa tubs, wifi and more. Number of Rooms: 13

Cuisine
Full gourmet breakfast buffet, as well as room service menu, complimentary evening wine and appetizers, sherry, cappuccino machine, and bottomless cookie jar. Complimentary soda, water, coffee & tea always available.

Nearest Airport
Oakland and San Francisco

Applewood Inn

www.applewoodinn.com
13555 Hwy 116, Guerneville, CA 95446
800-555-8509 • Fax 707-869-9170
relax@applewoodinn.com

Member Since 2004

Owners
Carlos Pippa and Sylvia Ranyak

A lovely and verdant meadow guarded by towering Redwoods in the heart of Sonoma's Russian River Valley (one of the world's premier growing regions for Pinot Noir & Chardonnay grapes) is home to Applewood Inn and its acclaimed restaurant which is recommended by Zagat and has earned a Michelin star for 2011. Splashing fountains and whimsical statues add texture and interest to the terraced courtyard and gardens that separate the tile roofed and stuccoed villas of this gracious Mediterranean complex. The old-world atmosphere of a "Gentleman's Farm" is evoked in lovingly maintained orchards and kitchen gardens that supply the restaurant through the Summer and early Fall. Gourmet picnic baskets provided by Applewood's kitchen help make a day of exploring the wine country and dramatic Sonoma Coast all the more enjoyable while Day Spa services add a touch of indulgent pampering. Located within a short drive of wineries in both the Napa and Sonoma Valleys, the Sonoma coast and Armstrong State Redwood Reserve.

Rates
$165/$375. Number of Rooms: 19

Cuisine
The Michelin stared restaurant at Applewood offers Mediterranean inspired wine country fare paired with a Sonoma wine list. The inn's romantic dining room features lovely views over a garden courtyard & towering redwoods. Adv reservations suggested.

Nearest Airport
San Francisco/Oakland/Sonoma County

Inn at Occidental

www.innatoccidental.com
3657 Church Street, P.O. Box 857, Occidental, CA 95465-0857
800-522-6324 • 707-874-1047 • Fax 707-874-1078
innkeeper@innatoccidental.com

Member Since 1995

California

Occidental

Innkeepers/Owners
Jerry & Tina Wolsborn

Inn at Occidental of Sonoma Wine Country–according to The Wine Spectator, "One of the Top Five Wine Country Destinations." The antiques, original art and decor provide charm, warmth and elegance exceeded only by the hospitality you experience."Tops our List as the Most Romantic Place to Stay" is what Bride and Groom said of the featherbeds, down comforters, spa tubs for two, fireplaces and private decks. The gourmet breakfast and evening wine and cheese reception add to a memorable experience. Excellent boutique wineries, Armstrong Redwoods State Reserve, Russian River, the dramatic coast and scenic drives along country backroads make for a great destination and the perfect hub for exploring the pristine area. Hiking, biking, horseback riding and golfing nearby. Concierge service. All reasons why AAA VIA says of The Inn "The Best Bed and Breakfast in the West." An Andrew Harper Recommendation.

Rates
3 Suites, 13 Rooms: Fireplaces, Spa Tubs, Decks $199/$379, 2 BR Vacation House $689. Number of Rooms: 18

Cuisine
Full gourmet breakfast. Local wines and cheeses and freshly-baked cookies provided nightly. Wonderful dining nearby. Special Functions: Wedding, Corporate Retreat, Celebrations.

Nearest Airport
San Francisco (SFO), Oakland (OAK), Santa Rosa (limited service)

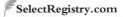

The Inn on First

www.theinnonfirst.com
1938 1st Street, Napa, CA 94559
707-253-1331
innkeeper@theinnonfirst.com

Member Since 2008

California *Napa*

Innkeepers/Owners
Jim Gunther and Jamie Cherry

This is an inn for Foodies. Breakfast is a centerpiece at the inn, with a unique and creative approach, offering whimsical dishes such as breakfast lasagna, omelet corn dogs, and handcrafted noodles with poached eggs in savory broth with prosciutto and onion steamed buns. No matter how often you visit, your breakfast experience will not be repeated. Chef Jim Gunther has created more than 100 breakfast recipes to serve to his guests, with more waiting to be created! The Inn boasts 10 comfortable, elegant rooms, each uniquely appointed, a long list of amenities, including free internet access. Fireplaces, whirlpool tubs and private baths in every room accompanied by complimentary sparkling wine, specialty refreshments, house-made confections and snacks. A romantic getaway located in historic downtown Napa, within walking distance of shops, restaurants, and wine tasting rooms. Close to wineries, easy access to both Napa and Sonoma Valleys.

Rates
10 rooms, 5 Mansion and 5 Garden Suites. Rates vary by season. Winter (November through February): $150-$250; Spring (March through May): $200-$300; Summer (May through July): $275-$325; Peak (August through October): $295-$400. Number of Rooms: 10

Cuisine
Exciting, California Contemporary Comfort food. Guests are served in two courses. The first consists of house-made granola and pastry, fresh fruit salad, and yogurt. The second is a unique and whimsical creation that keeps guests returning.

Nearest Airport
1-Sacramento. 2-Oakland. 3-San Francisco. Although SFO and OAK are closer than SAC, there is less traffic to SAC.

The Wine Country Inn

www.winecountryinn.com
1152 Lodi Lane, St. Helena, CA 94574
888-465-4608 • 707-963-7077 • Fax 707-963-9018
romance@winecountryinn.com

Member Since 1978

California

St. Helena

Innkeeper
Jim Smith

For over 30 years, 3 generations of the Smith's family have been welcoming guests to this slice of Heaven. The stone and wood Wine Country Inn is a tranquil and hidden oasis in the heart of the Napa, America's center for fine wine and eclectic dining. The tree-lined drive, welcoming common room and friendly greeting set the mood for a memorable experience. Smells of freshly baked granola or evening cookies raise expectations of meals to come. Then with the antique-filled guest rooms, panoramic vineyard views, lush gardens, sun-drenched pool with warming hot tub and massage tent almost in the vineyards, guests find it hard to leave the property. But for those who do, the staff are eager to help map out truly memorable days of sampling the finest the area has to offer. At the end of the day guests gather with the innkeepers to compare experiences over more great wine and tables laden with homemade appetizers. To increase enjoyment the inn offers a free evening restaurant shuttle servicing 12 of the finest area restaurants as well as guided day-tours they call Inn-Cursions.

Rates
20 Rooms 4 Suites 5 luxury cottages. Rates are $220/$610 Off-season and $285/$680 Harvest Season. All rates include a full buffet breakfast,wine social in the afternoon and evening restaurant shuttle. Call for seasonal special packages. Number of Rooms: 29

Cuisine
Innovative egg dishes, fresh fruit, juices, home-made granola and nut-breads as well as a fun bagel/waffle bar. Family-recipe appetizers with great local wines in afternoon.

Nearest Airport
Sacramento or San Fran

*SelectRegistry.com

Gerstle Park Inn

www.gerstleparkinn.com
34 Grove St., San Rafael, CA 94901
800-726-7611 • 415-721-7611 • Fax 415-721-7600
innkeeper@gerstleparkinn.com

Member Since 1998

California

San Rafael

Owners
Jim & Judy Dowling

Located 15 minutes from the Golden Gate Bridge and 30 minutes from the wine country, the Inn is in the heart of beautiful Marin County. It is the perfect location from which to explore all of the points of interest in the San Francisco Bay area. The Inn has a country setting on several acres with an orchard, Redwood trees, giant Valley Oaks, Cedar trees and green lawns. Being located at the end of a quiet residential street and backing up to the county's open spaces, it creates a secluded, restful environment as if being in the wine country. The historic estate offers a breathtaking example of comfortable elegance and refinement. In the evening, relax on the veranda during wine hour, play croquet, hike in the woods that border the estate, or pick fruit from the orchard. In the morning, enjoy a full hot breakfast to order at your leisure on the veranda or in the breakfast room. Spacious guest rooms are plush in comfort and color, with fine fabrics, antiques, parlor areas and private decks or patios with beautiful views. There is nothing like this in Marin County!

Rates
12 Rooms, 4 with Jacuzzi tubs; Cottages and Carriage House Suites with kitchens $189/ $275. Number of Rooms: 12

Cuisine
Accommodations include & extensive breakfast menu offering a full hot breakfast cooked to your order during a two hour period. Self service wine hours in the evening & 24 hour kitchen privileges which include a variety of beverages & snacks.

Nearest Airport
SFO-San Francisco and OAK-Oakland A.P., 45 min.

Washington Square Inn

www.wsisf.com
1660 Stockton Street, San Francisco, CA 94133
800-388-0220 • 415-981-4220 • Fax 415-397-7242
info@wsisf.com

Member Since 2006

California

San Francisco

Proprietors
Daniel & Maria Levin

Situated in the very heart of San Francisco's legendary North Beach, the Washington Square Inn welcomes guests with the charm and comfort of a small European hotel. Whether traveling for business or recreation, some of the amenities offered include free wireless Internet access, complimentary breakfast, afternoon tea, evening wine and hors d'oeuvres, and full office services. Rooms feature European antiques, cable TV, soft robes and private baths. Some rooms have sitting areas in bay windows, others offer a cozy atmosphere with fireplaces. Located in the vibrant neighborhood of North Beach, just voted one of the top ten neighborhoods in the US. Our historic hotel boasts beautiful views of Coit Tower, Russian Hill, Washington Square Park and the Cathedral of Saint Peter & Paul. The Inn is one of the best San Francisco hotel deals, offering exemplary lodging and service. You'll have a great location from which to explore this beautiful and exciting city! It's just a short cable car ride or comfortable walk to some of the most famous San Francisco landmarks.

Rates
There are 15 guest accommodations (15 with private baths). Double occupancy rate is between $191 and $341. Telegraph Hill Vacation rental $415 Number of Rooms: 16

Cuisine
Breakfast served in your room or our lobby, includes fresh juices, tea assortment, muffins, croissants, pasteries, fresh fruit, yogurt or toast. Bagels and smoked salmon on the weekends. Fresh coffee every morning and afternoon wine and hors d'oeuvres.

Nearest Airport
San Francisco, Oakland, and San Jose

Mill Rose Inn

www.millroseinn.com

615 Mill Street, Half Moon Bay, CA 94019

800-900-7673 • 650-726-8750 • Fax 650-726-3031

info@millroseinn.com

Member Since 2008

Innkeepers/Owners
Terry & Eve Baldwin

For guests who expect extraordinary personal service, warm hospitality and meticulous attention to detail, the Mill Rose Inn of Half Moon Bay is a destination not to be missed. This award-winning boutique Inn is renowned for an exuberant garden of year round color, sinfully comfortable rooms and suites, decadent culinary treats and an easy five-minute walk to beaches, numerous shops, galleries and restaurants of vibrant Half Moon Bay. The Mill Rose Inn invites you to relax and be pampered in the comfortable luxury of an English country garden by the sea. The innkeepers and their staff welcome you into a world of tranquility and romance. Ideally located 30 minutes south of San Francisco and 45 minutes north of the heart of Silicon Valley on the breathtakingly beautiful California coast, the Inn is the perfect venue for a special celebration, a reunion, or a business meeting, as well as an elegant garden wedding and reception. A Mill Rose Inn massage treatment coupled with our spa enhances your total escape. Owned and operated since 1982. Four-diamond AAA rating since 1992.

Rates
Baroque Rose Room $175 - $230, Burgundy and Briar Rose Rooms $235 - $280, Botticelli Rose Room $265 - $310, Renaissance and Bordeaux Rose Suites $295 - $360 Number of Rooms: 6

Cuisine
Our Lavish gourmet champagne or breakfast with vegan options served to you in your room or dining room gets rave reviews from all our guests. Fresh and homemade emphasized!

Nearest Airport
We are 30 mins. from San Francisco Intl. & 45 mins. from Oakland Intl. & San Jose Intl.

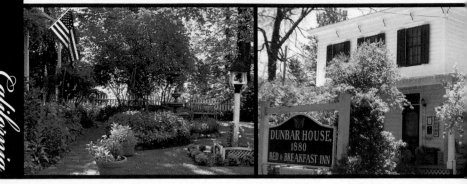

Dunbar House, 1880

www.dunbarhouse.com
271 Jones Street, Murphys, CA 95247
209-728-2897
innkeep@dunbarhouse.com

Member Since 2001

California

Murphys

Innkeepers/Owners
Richard & Arline Taborek

Step into Dunbar House, 1880 and step back into a piece of history, where homes were beautifully decorated with a casual elegance. This AAA ◆◆◆◆ Italianate home is filled with Old World Charm, and offers guests a private haven of relaxation, comfort and ease. Located two hours east of San Francisco, nestled between Lake Tahoe and Yosemite in the Sierra foothills, Murphys has not changed much since the Great Gold Rush. Just steps across the bridge over Murphys Creek, are restaurants, galleries, wineries, seasonal events, and live theatre. Our lovingly tended historic rose garden and surrounding floral gardens are the jewels of our property. Water fountains and lush greenery abound, surrounded by a white picket fence with many private sitting areas. Get a good book, or take a long nap in our hammock for that ultimate, lazy afternoon. An appetizer plate and local bottle of wine await guests in their rooms each day. Grab a fresh baked cookie, a cup of hot chocolate, or a glass of Rosemary Lemonade or Iced Tea, and just sit on our veranda and watch the world go by.

Rates
$199-$275 TV/DVD, wifi, refrigerator, fireplace & AC. Private porches & 2 person Jacuzzi available. Number of Rooms: 5

Cuisine
Enjoy your gourmet breakfast, and our own special roasted coffee blend, served in our cozy dining room by the fire, or in our beautiful century-old garden. Our specialty is our own homemade Mustard Sage Country Sausage, and daily fresh baked goods.

Nearest Airport
SFO-San Francisco, SAC-Sacramento, SJC-San Jose

SelectRegistry.com

McCaffrey House

www.mccaffreyhouse.com
23251 Highway 108, P.O. Box 67, Twain Harte, CA 95383
888-586-0757 • 209-586-0757
innkeeper@mccaffreyhouse.com

Member Since 2004

California

Twain Harte

Innkeepers/Proprietors
Michael & Stephanie McCaffrey

Pure elegance...in a wilderness setting. This AAA Four Diamond Inn is a delightfully warm and enchanting mountain lodge nestled in the quiet forest hollow of the High Sierras – near Yosemite National Park. Guestrooms are artfully decorated and feature handmade Amish quilts, fire stoves, private bath, TV/VCR, CD players, free wifi, iPod Docks and parking, plus exquisite views of the forest that envelops the Inn. McCaffrey House was designed and built by your hosts, Michael and Stephanie. They had one essential theme in mind: refined luxury blended with comfort and modern convenience. General gathering areas are spacious and beautifully decorated, with a fascinating collection of furniture and art which they acquired during their extensive travels. All appointments have such a welcoming touch that they extend an invitation to come often and stay awhile. In summer, breakfast is served on the decks which surround the inn. Enjoy the romance of this mountain lodge, the pleasure of a family vacation, take over the inn for a reunion, a business meeting, or schedule a small wedding.

Rates
$145/$200. Number of Rooms: 8

Cuisine
Awaken to the aroma of fresh coffee. Relax in the dining room for a full country breakfast, prepared by Stephanie McCaffrey. Enjoy fresh fruits & juices, hot entrees, potatoes, muffins, scones, Decadent French Toast, delicious egg casseroles & quiches.

Nearest Airport
Approximately 2.5 hours from SAC, SFO, SJC, OAK Check website under location for directions to the inn.

🍽️ 🍽️ 🍽️ 🍷

Groveland Hotel

www.groveland.com
18767 Main Street, P.O. Box 289, Groveland, CA 95321
800-273-3314 • 209-962-4000 • Fax 209-962-6674
guestservices@groveland.com

Member Since 2005

Innkeepers/Owners
Grover & Peggy Mosley

Drive to Yosemite 24/7 with a picnic and bottle of wine from Cellar Door Restaurant/Saloon. Tuolumne Rafting, US #1 whitewater river, 100+ species of wildflowers, hiking, golf, tennis, stables, swim at Rainbow Pool or discover God's Bath on the Clavey River. Four seasons – Spring, with songbirds, wildflowers and N. America's tallest waterfall. Summer's roses, hydrangeas, lavender and balmy evenings to herald Fall's brilliant color and crispness in the air. Winter temps suggest hot cider, cozy fireplaces, toboggans, snowshoes and skis. Lots of wildlife – deer, squirrel, bear, etc. Feathered species are varied, including an occasional eagle. Country Inns Magazine named it one of the US Top 10 Inns, and Sunset Magazine called it "A West's Best Inn.' Romantic parlour dining with fireplace, music, fresh flowers and candlelight. Upscale linens surround your warm, snuggly bed. We provide the ambiance – you create the memories! Weddings, receptions, family reunions, company parties, etc. Our Conference Room seats 15 people. Full service business center and FREE Wi-Fi.◆◆◆

Rates
Suites: $235 - $349. Rooms: $145 - $249, seasonal pricing. Rates are for 2 guests. Add'l guests: $25. Pets Welcome - $20/pet /night includes treats and use of bowls. $4.50 Energy Surcharge Number of Rooms: 17

Cuisine
Gourmet Breakfast, Lunch for Groups and Full Service Dining, open to the public. Full Service Saloon and Wine Spectator Best of Award of Excellence Wine List. Happy Hour with special Bar Menu and Cocktails

Nearest Airport
Approximately 2.5 hours from Sacramento (SAC), Oakland (OAK), or San Francisco (SFO).

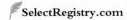

Old Monterey Inn

www.oldmontereyinn.com
500 Martin Street, Monterey, CA 93940
800-350-2344 • 831-375-8284 • Fax 831-375-6730
omi@oldmontereyinn.com

Member Since 1993

California

Monterey

Innkeepers/Owners
Lawrence and Katy Havlick

'The level of service and accommodations here would rival most any inn or hotel we've visited,' says The San Francisco Chronicle. Set amidst an acre of spectacular gardens on a quiet, oak-studded Monterey hillside, the Old Monterey Inn exudes romance and warmth. The 1929 half-timbered English Tudor Inn's rooms all overlook the uniquely beautiful gardens. Inside, guests find the attention to detail, which is the hallmark of the Inn–memorably fluffy featherbeds and 24-hour access to mineral waters, juices, tea and coffee. A full gourmet breakfast is served bedside or in our Heritage dining room, or, weather permitting, in our gardens. The owner imbues every element with the extra touches that help the Inn achieve near perfection. Recommended by prestigious Harper's Hideaway Report, Conde Nast Gold List, and Travel & Leisure (as seen on a recent Today Show Dream Getaway Segment).

Rates
Cottage, 3 Suites & 6 Rooms w/sitting areas - fireplaces, spa tubs, private baths, air conditioning $199-$499. Number of Rooms: 10

Cuisine
Gourmet breakfast. Evening wine and hors d'oeuvres. Extaordinary restaurants nearby. Port and fresh fruit.

Nearest Airport
Monterey Airport - 10 min. San Jose Airport - 1 hr. 15 mins. SFO - 2 hrs. 30 mins.

The Ballard Inn

www.ballardinn.com
2436 Baseline Ave., Ballard, CA 93463
800-638-2466 • 805-688-7770 • Fax 805-688-9560
innkeeper@ballardinn.com

Member Since 1993

California

Ballard

General Manager
Christine Forsyth

Voted one of America's Top Ten Most Romantic Inns, our comfortably elegant 4 diamond Country Inn is nestled among vineyards and orchards in the charming, historic township of Ballard. Each of the fifteen rooms possesses its own special charm and character reflecting local history. Many of our rooms have fireplaces, creating an especially romantic retreat. Borrow a bicycle and take a picnic lunch for an adventurous tour of the Santa Barbara wine country. A tasting of local wine & hors d'oeuvres, bed turn down service with home-made cookies, and a full breakfast are included in your stay. The acclaimed Ballard Inn Restaurant features French-Asian cuisine in an intimate 12 table dining room complete with a magnificent marble fireplace. Our Restaurant is open to the public Wednesday-Sunday. AAA ◆◆◆◆.

Rates
$245-$315 not including tax or service charge. Closed Christmas Eve & Christmas Day.
Number of Rooms: 15

Cuisine
Breakfast: A delicious full breakfast, included with your stay, is served in our dining room each morning. The Restaurant: The Chef's award winning French Asian fare melds the flavors of eastern & western cuisines to create mouthwatering dishes.

Nearest Airport
Santa Barbara

SelectRegistry.com

Santa Ynez Inn

🍽 🍷

www.santaynezinn.com
3627 Sagunto St., Santa Ynez, CA 93460
800.643.5774 • 805.688.5588 • Fax 805.686.4294
info@santaynezinn.com

Member Since 2004

California

Santa Ynez

Innkeeper/Owner - **Douglas Ziegler**
General Manager/Innkeeper - **Rick Segovia**

Our Wine Country Getaway awaits in 14 individually decorated luxury guest rooms. Accommodations feature unique antique furnishings, queen or king-sized beds with Frette linens, remote-controlled gas fireplaces, steam showers and whirlpool tubs in deluxe marble baths. Most rooms offer a semi-private balcony or patio to savor the beauty and serenity of the Santa Ynez Valley. Take advantage of all that Santa Barbara County has to offer, from wine tasting and antique shopping, to Glider rides and Jeep tours. There's something for everyone in Santa Ynez. After a day of Southern California sightseeing adventures, you may wish to unwind in the heated outdoor whirlpool, lounge on the sundeck, or take a leisurely stroll through the gardens of the Inn. Whatever your needs–whether you wish to arrange for wine tasting tours, shopping, dining, glider rides, bicycle rentals or spa treatment–our concierge service is eager to assist you.

Rates
$245/$445 Number of Rooms: 14

Cuisine
Full Gourmet breakfast, Evening Wine & Hors d'oeuvres and Nightly Desserts.

Nearest Airport
Santa Barbara Airport

Simpson House Inn

www.simpsonhouseinn.com
121 East Arrellaga Street, Santa Barbara, CA 93101
800-676-1280 • 805-963-7067 • Fax 805-564-4811
reservations@simpsonhouseinn.com

Member Since 1993

California

Santa Barbara

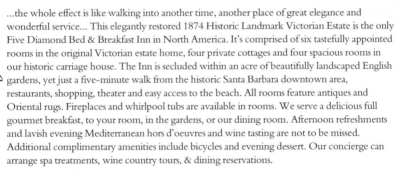

Owners
Glyn & Linda Davies

...the whole effect is like walking into another time, another place of great elegance and wonderful service... This elegantly restored 1874 Historic Landmark Victorian Estate is the only Five Diamond Bed & Breakfast Inn in North America. It's comprised of six tastefully appointed rooms in the original Victorian estate home, four private cottages and four spacious rooms in our historic carriage house. The Inn is secluded within an acre of beautifully landscaped English gardens, yet just a five-minute walk from the historic Santa Barbara downtown area, restaurants, shopping, theater and easy access to the beach. All rooms feature antiques and Oriental rugs. Fireplaces and whirlpool tubs are available in rooms. We serve a delicious full gourmet breakfast, to your room, in the gardens, or our dining room. Afternoon refreshments and lavish evening Mediterranean hors d'oeuvres and wine tasting are not to be missed. Additional complimentary amenities include bicycles and evening dessert. Our concierge can arrange spa treatments, wine country tours, & dining reservations.

Rates
Victorian Estate Home & the Garden Room $230-$475. Carriage House Rooms with wood burning fireplace & king beds. Garden Cottages with fireplace & some whirlpool tubs $535-$610. Sun-Thurs and seasonal rates available. Number of Rooms: 15

Cuisine
Full vegetarian gourmet breakfast delivered to your room or served at individual tables on the veranda or in the dining room. Afternoon refreshments on arrival. Mediterranean hors d'oeuvres buffet with local wine tasting & evening dessert.

Nearest Airport
Santa Barbara Municipal Airport. Flights from Denver, Los Angeles, Phoenix & San Francisco. www.flysba.com.

Rendezvous

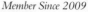

www.palmspringsrendezvous.com
1420 North Indian Canyon Drive, Palm Springs, CA 92262
800-485-2808 • 760-320-1178 • Fax 760-320-5308
info@palmspringsrendezvous.com

Member Since 2009

California

Palm Springs

Innkeepers/Owners
Marty, Barb, & Jake Cohen

Awarded TripAdvisor Travelers' Choice Award for Top 10 Romance & Bargain plus Top 25 Relaxation & Spa by TripAdvisor Users! Your Rendezvous experience starts as you walk through our frosted glass doors and hear our nostalgic 50's music wafting through the air. You then pass into our gorgeous courtyard with pristine pool, hot tub, and blue AstroTurf sun deck. You will want to settle yourself in a lounge chair and wrap yourself in a plush towel and bake in the beautiful desert sun. Our rooms are individually decorated each with great 1950's style. Each room has a California King Bed, 32" Flat Panel TVs, DVD & MP3 Players, a sitting area, refrigerator, microwave, coffee maker, plush robes, and organic bathroom amenities. Most rooms have 2 person whirlpool tubs for added romance. Make sure to schedule a couples massage in our Massage Studio! While the property has all the amenities you could want, the real value comes from the amazing staff. They will make you feel at home, take care of reservations at local restaurants, and pamper you from the moment you step through the door!

Rates
$139-$269 depending on room and season. Number of Rooms: 10

Cuisine
Rendezvous' full gourmet breakfast starts with gourmet coffees and fruit smoothies followed by a fruit dish and fantastic main course. In the evening enjoy our RendezBlue martinis and appetizers. We are happy to cater to individual dietary needs.

Nearest Airport
Palm Springs International airport is 5 miles away. Ontario, Los Angeles & San Diego airports 50-110 miles away.

Villa Royale Inn

www.villaroyale.com
1620 S. Indian Trail, Palm Springs, CA 92264
800-245-2314 • 760-327-2314 • Fax 760-322-3794
info@villaroyale.com

Member Since 2006

California

Palm Springs

Innkeeper/Owner
David Shahriari

Framed by breathtaking mountain views, the Villa Royale's intimate three acres echo an ancient Tuscan estate. Wander through tranquil courtyards overflowing with fragrant citrus, jasmine and lavender, gently cascading fountains, two heated pools and a large jacuzzi. AAA's Westways magazine calls the Villa Royale's AAA Four Diamond Europa Restaurant "a charming hideaway where you'll feel as if you have been transported to an intimate castle in Europe." Europa's bar, with its pool and mountain views, prides itself on its extensive offerings awarded by Wine Spectator Magazine. Luxurious full-service amenities, including full complimentary breakfast and fine dining, a daily newspaper, in-room spa services, and an attentive and caring staff make the Villa Royale Inn your ultimate Palm Springs romantic getaway.

Rates
Four room styles from $99 to $450(Seasonal). Pool Side, Private Patios, & Fire Places are available. Number of Rooms: 30

Cuisine
Cook to Order Complimentary Breakfast.Dinner with Four Diamond cuisine served fireside or by trickling fountains. Small private dinning room for up to 12 ideal for a special occasion or intimate wedding celebration.

Nearest Airport
Five minutes from downtown Palm Springs and the Palm Springs International Airport.

Casa Laguna Inn & Spa

www.casalaguna.com
2510 South Coast Highway, Laguna Beach, CA 92651
800-233-0449 • 949-494-2996 • Fax 949-494-5009
innkeeper@casalaguna.com

Member Since 2004

Proprietor: **Francois Leclair**
General Manager: **Kathryn Mace**

Casa Laguna's 1920s mission-style architecture and terraced gardens exemplify a time when Laguna Beach was known as both an artist colony and a hideaway for famous film stars. Expansive views of the blue Pacific are framed by red tile roofs & towering palms. Relax on a secluded patio or lounge on our sunny pool deck. Take a dip in our heated pool or picnic at nearby Victoria Beach. Schedule a massage or toast the sunset with champagne in our by-reservation-only gazebo soak tub. Dream of our acclaimed gourmet breakfast as you slumber in an antique bed with a cloudlike pillow-top cover & luxurious eco-friendly linens. Our inn is just 1.5 miles from downtown Laguna Beach with its many shops, art galleries, & summer festivals. We are within walking distance of beautiful beaches and tidal pools. We work hard to maintain a relaxing, romantic ambiance. Room occupancy is limited to one or two guests only and our inn is not considered appropriate for children or groups. No smoking is allowed anywhere on the property. Well behaved clean & healthy dogs are welcome with restrictions.

Rates
Rooms, suites & a cottage: $149 to $649 subject to weekend/seasonal adjustments. All rooms have luxurious bedding, AC, flat-panel HDTV, DVD player, & free WiFi. Some rooms have jetted tubs. Most have ambiance or gas fireplaces. Number of Rooms: 22

Cuisine
Our inn has become a well-known "foodie" destination. Guests choose from a menu of 7 to 9 gourmet breakfast entrees & sides. A selection of wine & gourmet hors d'oeuvres is served at our evening reception. A hot/cold beverage bar is open all day long.

Nearest Airport
Orange County, John Wayne - SNA Los Angeles - LAX San Diego - SAN Ontario - ONT

Famous for: Gold Rush, Mile-High City, Mesa Verde, Cliff Dwellings, Rocky Mountains, Skiing, and Hiking.

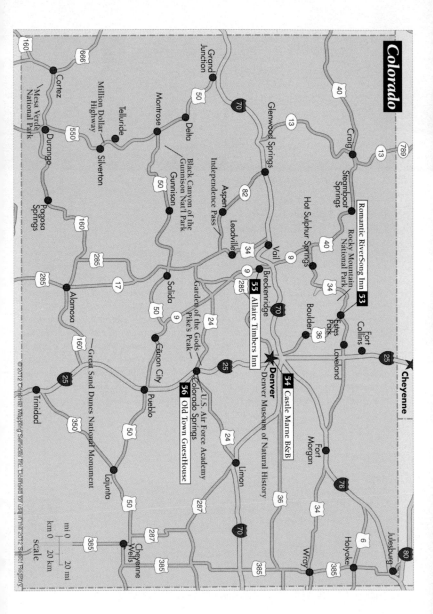

Romantic RiverSong Inn

🍽 🍽 🍽

www.romanticriversong.com

P.O. Box 1910, 1766 Lower Broadview Road, Estes Park, CO 80517-1910

970-586-4666 • 970-586-3223 • Fax 970-577-1336

info@romanticriversong.com

Member Since 1987

Innkeepers/Owners
Sue & Gary Mansfield

Romantic RiverSong represents the classic country inn rarely found in Colorado. Located on a quiet backroad, we were personally chosen by Select Registry's founder Norman Simpson... his choice for a unique place that offered "exceptional hospitality" and "good honest lodging." Secluded on 27 wooded acres with towering Blue Spruce and Ponderosa Pines, the inn offers quiet ponds, hiking trails and tree swings. Romantic RiverSong is a refuge for guests, as well as for wildlife. With only ten guest rooms, the inn has achieved a marvelous balance with its luxurious rooms (radiant-heated floors, jetted tubs for two, crackling fireplaces) and surrounding nature with the melodies of songbirds and a rushing stream. After exploring nearby Rocky Mountain National Park and the variety of quaint shops in town, come home to a relaxing "streamside massage." Then, later that evening enjoy our own chef-prepared candlelight gourmet dinner. Our warm hospitality will make your memories of Romantic RiverSong linger long after you've gone from this little bit of heaven in the Colorado.

Rates
5 Rooms from $165-$195 junior suites; 5 Suites, $225-$350 with Jetted tubs for 2; real wood burning fireplaces, private decks or flowered patios. Free Wifi on property. Hiking sticks and packs available without charge. Guided hikes. Number of Rooms: 10

Cuisine
Mountain morning chill is lifted by a crackling fire and fresh brewed coffee followed by John Wayne Casserole and Happy Trail muffins. Dinner is served on fine china enhanced by soft jazz a glass of wine ..the perfect end to a day of adventure and fun.

Nearest Airport
Denver International (DIA) only 1 hour 45 minutes away , no mtn passes to cross !!
Open year round to Estes Park.

|O| |O| |O|

The Historic Castle Marne Inn

www.castlemarne.com
1572 Race Street, Denver, CO 80206
800-92-MARNE • 303-331-0621 • Fax 303-331-0623
Member Since 1991   info@castlemarne.com

Innkeepers/Owners
The Peiker Family: Diane, Jim, Melissa, and Louie, Louie J, Charlie & Liz

Denver's grandest historic mansion, listed on both National & Local Historic Registers. Built in 1889, features hand-hewn lavastone exterior, hand-rubbed woods, balconies, four-story tower and original stained glass Peacock Window. Beautifully blending antiques and heirlooms to create a charming Victorian atmosphere. Featuring Denver's finest examples of Victorian ceiling art, hand painted from original photos. Relax beside the bubbling fountain. Full gourmet breakfast served in the original Dining Room. Afternoon Tea served in the Parlour. Whirlpool spas and private outdoor hot tubs. Lunch & Private candlelight dinners by reservation. Wedding and Honeymoon packages available. Small weddings and elopements a specialty. The AIA says, "Castle Marne is one of Denver's great architectural legacies."

Rates
9 Rooms, $115/$270. 2 Suites with Jacuzzi tubs. 3 Rooms with private outdoor hot tubs.
Number of Rooms: 9

Cuisine
Full gourmet breakfast featuring home made muffins and breads. Artistically presented fresh fruit, Elegant Private 6 course Dinners served in the original formal dining room. Afternoon Tea and Luncheons. Evening Sleepy Time Tea and fresh baked cookies

Nearest Airport
Denver International

Allaire Timbers Inn

www.allairetimbers.com
9511 Hwy. 9, South Main Street, P.O. Box 4653, Breckenridge, CO 80424
800-624-4904 Outside CO • 970-453-7530 • Fax 970-453-8699
info@allairetimbers.com *Member Since 1995*

Innkeepers
Sue Carlson and Kendra Hall

This contemporary log B&B is the perfect Rocky Mountain getaway. Wonderfully located at the south end of historic Main Street and nestled in the trees. Allaire Timbers offers 10 guest rooms, each with private bath and deck. Two suites offer a special touch of romance with private hot tub and fireplace. Relax by the fire in the Great Room or enjoy the serenity of the sunroom. Retreat to the reading loft, or unwind in the outdoor hot tub with spectacular mountain views. Just steps from downtown Victorian Breckenridge with its many and varied restaurants and shops. Access to the ski area and Breckenridge Riverwalk arts/music amphitheatre via the Free Ride town bus system. Featured in Arrington's Inn Traveler and CNN's Travel Guide.

Rates
8 Lodge Rooms, 2 Suites $129/$400. Number of Rooms: 10

Cuisine
Full breakfast including homemade breads and sweets, fresh juices and fruits, the Inn's special recipe granola and changing menu of hot entrees. Evenings enjoy fresh baked cookies.

Nearest Airport
Denver International

Old Town GuestHouse

www.oldtown-guesthouse.com
115 South 26th Street, Colorado Springs, CO 80904
888-375-4210 • 719-632-9194 • Fax 719-632-9026
Luxury@OldTown-GuestHouse.com

Member Since 2001

Innkeepers/Owners
Don & Shirley Wick

The three-story brick guesthouse is in perfect harmony with the 1859 period of the surrounding historic Old Colorado City. The contemporary Inn offers upscale amenities for discerning adult leisure and business travelers. Our elevator allows the entire inn to be accessible and the African Orchid room exceeds ADA specifications. The soundproof, uniquely decorated guestrooms have private baths and 7 rooms have fireplaces and/or porches overlooking Pikes Peak. Relax in the library or out on the umbrella-covered patio for afternoon wine, beer and snacks, then walk to some of Old Town's many fine restaurants, boutiques and galleries. End your evening with a soak in your own private two-person Hot Tub or your relaxing ensuite Steam Shower. Your morning starts with a gourmet 3 course breakfast served in our dining area. And then it's off to one of the many attractions and activities that the area has to offer (Pikes Peak, Garden of the Gods, Cave of the Winds). Member Pikes Peak Lodging Association, Bed & Breakfast Innkeepers of Colorado and other local community organizations.

Rates
$99/$235 Corporate and military rates available, Private baths, hot tubs, steam showers, fireplaces. Even lower Winter rates November and April with few seasonal blackout dates. Check our website for periodic discounts and packages. Number of Rooms: 8

Cuisine
Full 3 course sit-down breakfast. Hot entree, fruit in season, muffin or sweet bread and a cereal buffet. Evening with wine, beer and light snacks. Dine on our veranda (weather permitting) or in front of the fireplace with semi-private seating.

Nearest Airport
Colorado Springs Airport (20 min. away) Denver International Airport (1hr 30 min.) Call for directions.

SelectRegistry.com

Connecticut

"The Constitution State"

Famous for: Inventors (Charles Goodyear, Elias Howe, Eli Whitney, Eli Terry), Inventions, Watchmaking, Typewriters, Insurance, Submarines.

Manor House

www.manorhouse-norfolk.com
69 Maple Avenue, Norfolk, CT 06058
860-542-5690
innkeeper@manorhouse-norfolk.com

Member Since 2000

Innkeepers/Owners
Karl Vess & L. Keith Mullins

Surround yourself with Victorian Elegance in this 1898 Tudor Estate described by Gourmet Magazine as "Quite Grand," and designated "Connecticut's Most Romantic Hideaway" by the Discerning Traveler. Featured in National Geographic Traveler, Good Housekeeping's "Best Weekend Getaways," and listed as one of the top 25 Inns by American Historic Inns. All rooms offer views of the spacious grounds and perennial gardens, are furnished with period antiques, and luxurious comforters. Savor a full breakfast made with local ingredients in the elegant dining room, relax by the baronial fireplace in the living room, or read a book in the library, all adorned with Tiffany windows and architectural detail. The Manor House is located at the foot of the Berkshires, and travelers can enjoy an array of outdoor activities, shopping, summer theater, and music festivals. A short walk to Infinity Music Hall and Yale School of Music Summer Chamber Festival. Rejuvenate with a treatment in the Spa Room, massage, facials, body wraps, reflexology or hot stones.

Rates
7 Rooms, 1 Suite, $180-$255. Four rooms offer wood or gas fireplaces, 3 with whirlpools, and two with private balconies offering sweeping views of our grounds. All rooms air conditioned. Number of Rooms: 8

Cuisine
Two course country breakfast. All baked goods made in-house. Afternoon Tea and cookies. Complimentary snacks, boscotti, coffee, tea, hot chocolate and spring water available all day in our bar area, which has a refrigerator, ice and all stemware.

Nearest Airport
Bradley International

SelectRegistry.com

The Copper Beech Inn

www.CopperBeechInn.com
Ivoryton, 46 Main Street, Essex, CT 06442
888-809-2056 • 860-767-0330 • Fax 860-767-7840
info@CopperBeechInn.com

Member Since 2003

Innkeepers/Owners
Ian S. Phillips & Barbara C. Phillips

Named 2011's "Best Country Inn" by the readers of Connecticut Magazine, and one of "America's Top 100 Hotel Restaurants" by the ZAGAT Survey and USA Today, The Copper Beech Inn in Essex, is minutes from the Connecticut River and Long Island Sound. Just a 2-hour drive from either New York or Boston, the elegant guest rooms and suites with oversize beds feature Italian marble bathrooms and air-jet tubs. The Inn's award-winning AAA Four-Diamond restaurant features extraordinary food and a Wine Spectator award-winning wine list. The menu, created by Executive Chef Tyler Anderson, features sustainable seafood and high quality, locally-raised ingredients from local farms and artisan producers. Andrew Harper's Hideaway Report named the inn as one of the "The Ten Best in New England" and, The New York Times said "The Copper Beech Inn is a lovely example of what Americans look for in a four-star country inn ... the dining experience always marvelous."

Rates
$219-$379. Rates vary seasonally and on weekdays and weekends. Open Year-Round.
All rooms with Private Bath, some with Mini-Bars. Number of Rooms: 22

Cuisine
Four-Star French and Modern American featuring an extraordinary menu and 2000 plus selection award-winning wine list. "Crystal sparkles, silver shines, ... masses of fresh flowers set the scence for the flawlessly elegant dining" Connecticut Magazine.

Nearest Airport
Hartford 45 mins., Boston 2 hours, New York 2 hours

Stonecroft Country Inn

www.stonecroft.com
515 Pumpkin Hill Road , Ledyard, CT 06339
800-772-0774 • 860-572-0771
stonecroftinn@comcast.net

Member Since 2002

Innkeeper
Jason Crandall

Relax in quiet country elegance on an 1807 sea captain's six-acre estate, less than 10 minutes from Mystic Seaport, Foxwoods and Mohegan Sun casinos. Ancient stone walls and lush green lawns surround the Inn, consisting of The 1807 House, a sunny Georgian colonial, and The Grange, our converted 19th century post & beam barn. Romantic guestrooms feature French, English and American country decor, with fireplaces, whirlpools and heated towel bars, wide-screen TV/DVDs (Grange only) and free Internet access. Savor an exquisite country breakfast, fireside dinner in our elegant granite-walled restaurant or the outside garden terrace. One Inn . . Two Styles . . Endless Charm.

Rates
Please check our website for current rates, specials and packages (including our popular Hide n'Sleep Packages) at www.stonecroft.com. ($99 - $299) Number of Rooms: 10

Cuisine
Full country breakfast in Grange Dining Room or on the stone terrace. Fine, yet affordable dining in the Stonecroft Dining Room or out in our Summer Gardens. Share after dinner drinks & dessert out around our fire pits on warm summer nights.

Nearest Airport
TF Green (Providence) - 45 minutes Bradley (Hartford) - 60 minutes

Inn at Stonington

www.innatstonington.com

60 Water Street, Stonington, CT 06378

860-535-2000 • Fax 860-535-8193

innkeeper@innatstonington.com

Member Since 2005

Innkeeper/Owner
William Griffin

Named by Travel + Leisure as Inn of the Month, this 18 room waterfront inn is located in the heart of Stonington Borough, one of the last untouched and 'historic' villages in New England. The inn offers individually decorated guest rooms with gas fireplaces, baths with oversized soaking Jacuzzi tubs and separate walk in showers. Seaside rooms have private balconies with views of Stonington Harbor and beyond. Common areas include a top floor sitting room with breathtaking views, an intimate bar with adjoining breakfast room, the cozy living room, and a well equipped gym. During your stay, stop by one of the local wineries, visit downtown Mystic or simply take a stroll down Water Street and enjoy the specialty shops and some of the finest antique shops in the area. Enjoy our complimentary wine and cheese before walking to dinner at one of five fabulous restaurants in the village. Area attractions: small beach within walking distance, Stonington area vineyards, Mystic Seaport, Mystic Aquarium, Mohegan Sun and Foxwood Casinos, Watch Hill beaches.

Rates
18 Guest rooms. Seasonal rates $160/$445. Open Year Round. Number of Rooms: 18

Cuisine
Continental breakfast of fresh baked treats, fruit & locally roasted coffee. Complimentary wine and cheese hour nightly.

Nearest Airport
T.F. Green- Providence, RI or Bradley Internation Airport- Windsor Locks, CT

Steamboat Inn

www.steamboatinnmystic.com
73 Steamboat Wharf, Mystic, CT 06355
860-536-8300 • Fax 860-536-9528
info@steamboatinnmystic.com

Member Since 2009

Connecticut

Mystic

Owners - **John McGee & Paul Connor/**
Innkeeper - **Kate Abel**

The Steamboat Inn, offers eleven elegant rooms overlooking the beautiful Mystic River. Located in the heart of Historic Downtown Mystic, Steamboat Inn is just steps from fabulous shopping and fine dining; and just minutes away are The Mystic Seaport, Mystic Aquarium, Foxwoods Resort, Mohegan Sun plus four wineries within 15 minutes of the Inn. Each of our rooms are uniquely decorated with antiques and individually climate controlled. The rooms have private baths with single or double whirlpool tubs. Six of our rooms have wood burning fireplaces. Enjoy breathtaking river views from ten of our rooms. Complimentary wireless internet is offered throughout the Inn. Enjoy a full breakfast each morning in our common room or stop by in the evening for our delicious cookies and sherry! Awarded "most unique setting" two years in a row by Llannier Bed and Breakfast - chosen by the guests of over 8,500 B&B's worldwide. Be among the guests who visit Steamboat year after year, what are you waiting for come explore Steamboat Inn today!

Rates
11 Guest Rooms. Seasonal Rates $150 - $325. Open Year Round. Number of Rooms: 11

Cuisine
Buffet Breakfast includes scrambled eggs, bacon, turkey sausage, fresh fruit, yogurt, cereal, granola, cheeses, fresh bagels, oatmeal, homemade muffins, coffee, tea, and juices. Complimentary sherry and fresh baked cookies nightly.

Nearest Airport
T.F. Green Airport, Providence, RI Bradley Int. Airport, Windsor Locks, CT

SelectRegistry.com

Saybrook Point Inn

www.saybrook.com
2 Bridge Street, Old Saybrook, CT 06475
800-243-0212 • 860-395-2000 • Fax 860-388-1504
info@saybrook.com

Member Since 2010

Innkeeper/Managing Owner
Stephen Tagliatela

Authentic hospitality proudly delivered is the hallmark of this family owned, AAA Four Diamond Inn, Spa & Marina. Located where the Connecticut River meets the Long Island Sound, breathtaking views, elegant spacious accommodations, unique amenities and our New England Main Street town provide the ideal backdrop for the perfect getaway. Newly renovated Spa 'Sanno,' delivers customized well-being experiences 'your way.' In- and outdoor salt water pools overlook the water. Our Health Club has up-to-date equipment and fitness classes. Fresh Salt, a fresh food experience, features modern American seafood, farm to table cuisine, a wonderful oyster bar, outdoor dining, and seasonal entertainment. Our Marina, like the Inn, is recognized for sustainable environmental leadership and is designated an Atlantic Cruising Guide perennial 5 Bell Marina. The Saybrook Point Inn has awards for not only being the first hotel in Connecticut to be certified a Green Hotel by the state, but for continued leadership as a Green Lodging property. Available by Amtrack with courtesy shuttle.

Rates
$229 to $629, vary seasonally and on weekday and weekends. Number of Rooms: 80 Rooms

Cuisine
Modern American seafood. A proud founding member of the Connecticut Farm to Chef Program.

Nearest Airport
Bradley, Hartford and T.F. Green, Providence. Both about one hour away.

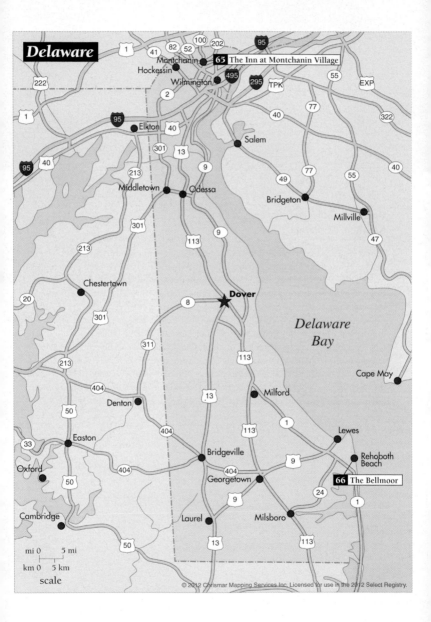

Delaware

"The First State"

Famous for: Historic Brandywine Valley—Museums and Gardens, Du Pont Family Mansions, Beaches, Fishing, Wildlife, Farmland, Bird-watching, Nascar Races, and No-sales-tax Shopping.

Delaware

65 The Inn at Montchanin Village

Montchanin
Hockessin
Wilmington
Elkton
Salem
Middletown
Odessa
Bridgeton
Millville
Chestertown
Dover

Delaware Bay

Cape May
Milford
Denton
Lewes
Easton
Rehoboth Beach
Oxford
Bridgeville
66 The Bellmoor
Georgetown
Cambridge
Laurel
Milsboro

mi 0   5 mi
km 0   5 km
scale

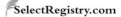
© 2012 Chrismar Mapping Services Inc. Licensed for use in the 2012 Select Registry.

The Inn at Montchanin Village & Spa

🍴🍴🍴 ⏐

www.montchanin.com

Route 100 & Kirk Road, P.O. Box 130, [GPS: 528 Montchanin Rd. Wilmington, DE],
Montchanin, DE 19710, **800-269-2473** • 302-888-2133 • Fax 302-888-0389
inn@montchanin.com

Member Since 2002

General Manager
Vera C. Palmatary

Listed on the National Historic Register, The Inn at Montchanin Village was once a part of the
Winterthur Estate and was named for Alexandria de Montchanin, grandmother of the founder
of the DuPont Company. One of the few remaining villages of its kind, the settlement was
home to laborers who worked at the nearby DuPont powder mills. In eleven carefully restored
buildings dating from 1799 to 1910, there are 28 richly furnished guest rooms/suites appointed
with period and reproduction furniture, marble baths with all the amenities for the demanding
and sophisticated traveler. Most rooms have beautifully manicured private courtyards and
several have cozy fireplaces. The Spa at Montchanin is an innovative facility that offers facials,
body treatments, and massages in a luxurious and peaceful environment. Nestled in the
Brandywine Valley, 10 minutes NW of Wilmington and 25 minutes South of Philadelphia.
Centrally located to all major museums - Winterthur, Longwood Gardens, Hagley Museum,
Nemours Mansion, Brandywine River Museum, and Delaware Museum of Natural History.

Rates
Rooms: $192-$244; Suites: $290-$399. Free parking on site, European turndown, coffee
maker, microwave, beverage area with icemaker, daily paper, free wireless internet, and
fitness room. Please see website for package information. Number of Rooms: 28

Cuisine
Once the village blacksmith's shop, Krazy Kat's Restaurant is famous for it's fresh
nouvelle cuisine and whimsical decor. They serve breakfast, lunch, Sunday brunch, and
dinner. Our private dining room, The Crow's Nest, may accommodate up to 40 guests.

Nearest Airport
Philadelphia International (PHL) Airport: 20 miles New Castle Airport: 10 miles Baltimore
(BWI) Airport: 82.8 miles

Delaware

Montchanin

The Bellmoor

www.thebellmoor.com
6 Christian Street, Rehoboth Beach, DE 19971
800-425-2355 • 302-227-5800 • Fax 302-227-0323
info@thebellmoor.com

Member Since 2004

Proprietors
The Moore Family

Quiet moments in the garden...sunrise on the beach...the crackle of the fire in the Jefferson Library...a leisurely walk to unique boutique shopping and fine dining restaurants...a favorite book in the Sunroom. Our Day Spa offers over 30 services to restore and rejuvenate body and spirit. Whether you choose a seaweed wrap, hot stone pedicure or a soothing springtime facial, you can leave the world behind and experience refined relaxation and well-being. Additional complimentary services: concierge, bellman, high speed Internet access, wireless access, guest computer room, two pools, hot tub, and a fitness room. Enjoy complete relaxation in our beautifully appointed accommodations of unsurpassed comfort combining the warm, residential feel of a B&B with the efficient, professional service of a small European hotel. Enjoy the privacy and comfort of our newly renovated 4th floor Club Suites.

Rates
55 rooms, $125/$465 B&B. 23 suites, $150/$695 B&B; suites include marble bath, fireplace, whirlpool, wet bar. Number of Rooms: 78

Cuisine
Full American breakfast served in the Garden Room or in the garden. Afternoon refreshments. 24 hour coffee service. Rehoboth Beach offers many fine dining options within walking distance of the Inn. Entire property non-smoking.

Nearest Airport
Philadelphia and Baltimore are both within a 2 hour drive.

Washington, DC

Famous for: The White House, the Capitol, Arlington Cemetery, Cherry Festival, the Smithsonian, Washington Monument.

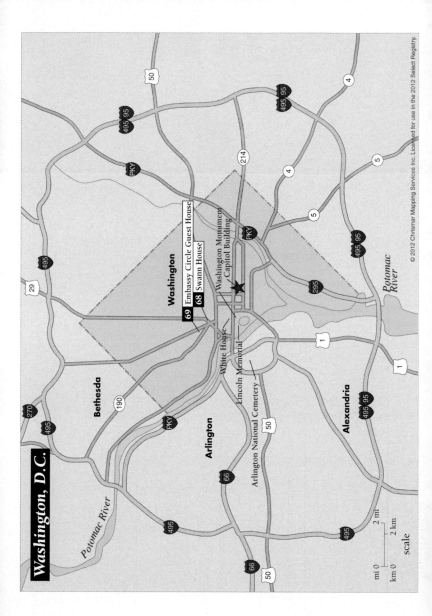

© 2012 Chrismar Mapping Services Inc. Licensed for use in the 2012 Select Registry.

Swann House

www.swannhouse.com
1808 New Hampshire Ave. N.W., Washington, DC 20009
202-265-4414 • Fax 202-265-6755
stay@swannhouse.com

Member Since 2002

Innkeepers/Owners
Richard & Mary Ross

Located on a tree-lined avenue in the heart of the Dupont Circle Historic District, Swann House welcomes you to the Nation's Capital and our 1883 Richardson Romanesque gem. Crystal chandeliers, elaborately carved fireplaces and original plaster moldings reflect just a portion of the nineteenth century craftsmanship that can be seen throughout our inn. Each individually decorated guestroom comes well appointed with sumptuous bathrobes, sateen sheets, down featherbeds and luxurious bath amenities. Select rooms include whirlpool baths, fireplaces and private decks for added luxury. Dozens of restaurants and cafes are just steps away allowing our guests to experience one of Washington's most vibrant and beautiful neighborhoods. Just 12 blocks from the White House and close proximity to several universities, galleries and conference venues, Swann House makes for a wonderful respite whether here for a romantic escape, business meeting or well-deserved getaway. "the Inn that launched 1,000 marriages" Frommer's "Fodor's Choice Gold Award" Fodor's Guide

Rates
8 Rooms $169/$369; 4 Suites $269/$369. 6 w/ fireplace, 4 w/whirlpool. Swimming pool, WiFi, computer. Number of Rooms: 12

Cuisine
2008 Silver Medalist Inn-Credible Breakfast Cookoff. Deluxe continental breakfast with home made granola and baked goods, seasonal fruit plus daily hot entree. Afternoon refreshments, evening sherry. Dozens of fine restaurants within walking distance.

Nearest Airport
Reagan National (DCA) 6 miles, Dulles International (IAD) 26 miles

Embassy Circle Guest House

www.dcinns.com/embassy.html
2224 R ST NW, Washington, DC 20008
202-232-7744 • 877-232-7744
embassy@dcinns.com

Member Since 2011

Innkeepers
Laura & Raymond Saba

Embassy Circle Guest House is a lovingly restored former embassy, renowned for elegance and warm, personal hospitality. Located on a quiet residential street in Dupont Circle, the Guest House is a peaceful haven, surrounded by embassies, art galleries and grand private homes. The vibrant Dupont Circle neighborhood is home to dozens of restaurants and sidewalk cafes, fabulous bookstores and coffee shops. A 5-minute walk to the Dupont Circle Metro, the Guest House is convenient to all of DC s museums, monuments, memorials and universities. Our gracious guest rooms are individually decorated with beautiful antiques, stunning Persian carpets and original artwork. Our sumptuous breakfast buffet offers you a wide range of breakfast choices, including a delicious hot entrée daily – and Innkeepers Laura and Raymond Saba are always available to introduce guests around the breakfast table. Relax in the evening with owners and fellow guests and enjoy a glass of wine while trading stories and restaurant recommendations. Fodor s Choice. Diamond Collection. Top 10 Urban B&B s.

Rates
11 Rooms. $245-$295 in season. $180-$240 off season. Rate includes double occupancy, buffet breakfast, afternoon snacks, evening wine, and free high-speed internet access. Limited parking is available for an additional fee. Number of Rooms: 11

Cuisine
Sumptuous breakfast buffet featuring a daily hot entree, fresh-cut fruit salad and organic honey yogurt, smoked salmon with creamed cheese and capers, organic breads, and great coffee. World's best brownies every afternoon! Evening wine and snacks.

Nearest Airport
Ronald Reagan National Airport (DCA) - 5 milesDulles International Airport (IAD) - 26 miles

Florida

Famous for: Disney World, Busch Gardens, St. Augustine (the oldest city in the U.S., founded 50 years before Plymouth), Florida Keys, Everglades, Space Shuttles, Beaches, Alligators, Oranges, Grapefruit, Wildlife.

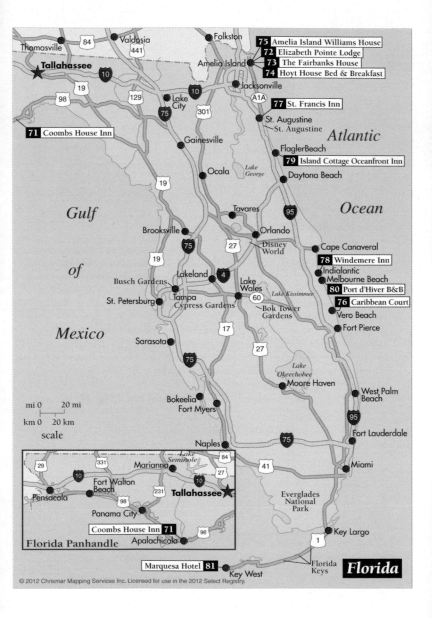

75 Amelia Island Williams House
72 Elizabeth Pointe Lodge
73 The Fairbanks House
74 Hoyt House Bed & Breakfast
77 St. Francis Inn
71 Coombs House Inn
79 Island Cottage Oceanfront Inn
78 Windemere Inn
80 Port d'Hiver B&B
76 Caribbean Court
Coombs House Inn **71**
Marquesa Hotel **81**

Florida

© 2012 Chrismar Mapping Services Inc. Licensed for use in the 2012 Select Registry.

SelectRegistry.com

Coombs Inn

www.coombshouseinn.com
80 Sixth Street and Ave E, Apalachicola, FL 32320
888-244-8320 • 850-653-9199 • Fax 850-653-2785
info@coombshouseinn.com

Member Since 2006

Florida

Apalachicola

Owners
Lady Lynn Wilson and
Sir William Spohrer

Featured in Sports Illustrated Swimsuit Edition The Coombs Inn represents the best of both old Florida and new. Located on Florida's "Forgotten" Gulf Coast, the Inn consists of 3 elegant Victorian mansions in the historic district of this quaint seaside fishing village, adjacent to St. George Island with its white pristine beaches. Each of the 23 distinctive rooms feature antique furniture and paintings, has its own full bath, cable TV, telephone and wireless internet. Our 7 luxury suites have romantic Jacuzzi tubs. Guests enjoy complimentary full breakfasts, Afternoon Tea with cookies and weekend wine receptions. Camellia Hall, a spacious meeting room enhanced by gardens and a classic gazebo, provides the ideal setting for weddings and family reunions. Travel+Leisure Magazine recognized us as one of the "30 Great Inns." Discover this enchanting town, established in 1831 and rich with maritime history. Relax on our many verandas, enjoy a walk to charming restaurants, taste our delicious oysters, visit our museums and theatre, or go fishing or to the beach.

Rates
23 luxury rooms: $109 to $299. 7 jacuzzi suites: Special "Wedding Romance Package" $999 includes: Ceremony, Bouquet and boutonniére, Wedding Cake, Champagne toast, Romantic Jacuzzi Suite, and Breakfast in Bed. Number of Rooms: 23

Cuisine
A complementary elegant breakfast of culinary delights and Starbucks' coffee, afternoon fresh baked cookies and teas, weekend wine receptions.

Nearest Airport
Tallahassee & Panama City or private planes at Apalachicola Regional Airport and St. George Island

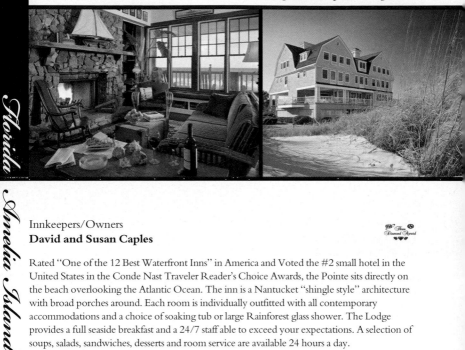

Elizabeth Pointe Lodge

www.elizabethpointelodge.com
98 South Fletcher Avenue, Amelia Island, FL 32034
888-757-1910 • 904-277-4851 • Fax 904-277-6500
info@elizabethpointelodge.com

Member Since 1998

Florida

Amelia Island

Innkeepers/Owners
David and Susan Caples

Rated "One of the 12 Best Waterfront Inns" in America and Voted the #2 small hotel in the
United States in the Conde Nast Traveler Reader's Choice Awards, the Pointe sits directly on
the beach overlooking the Atlantic Ocean. The inn is a Nantucket "shingle style" architecture
with broad porches around. Each room is individually outfitted with all contemporary
accommodations and a choice of soaking tub or large Rainforest glass shower. The Lodge
provides a full seaside breakfast and a 24/7 staff able to exceed your expectations. A selection of
soups, salads, sandwiches, desserts and room service are available 24 hours a day.
Complimentary WiFi DSL Internet service encompasses the property, USA Today and
NYTimes Digest is delivered to your room daily. Beach umbrellas, loungers and towels are set
each day for your enjoyment. Bicycles are housed on site. Parking is complimentary. Elevator
to all floors. Focusing on individualized attention, Concierge assistance is available for day trips,
bicycle touring and other Island experiences. AAA Three Diamond.

Rates
20 Rooms, $230/$375; 4 Oceanhouse deluxe rooms $285/$490; 1 Cottage, $485/$535
B&B. Open year-round. Number of Rooms: 25

Cuisine
A complete and tended buffet breakfast in the Sunrise Room or outside on the deck
overlooking the ocean. A light fare menu available 24 hours. Complimentary social hour
each evening at 6 p.m. Our culinary staff welcomes special dietary requests.

Nearest Airport
Jacksonville International approximately 35 minutes away.

Fairbanks House

www.fairbankshouse.com
227 South 7th Street, Amelia Island, FL 32034
888-891-9880 • 904-277-0500
email@fairbankshouse.com

Member Since 1998

Innkeepers/Owners
Bill & Theresa Hamilton

Featured in The Best Romantic Escapes in Florida and built in 1885, Fairbanks House is an 8000 sq. ft. Italianate villa rising above a quiet Victorian village on Amelia Island. Surrounded by soaring magnolias and live oaks with dripping Spanish moss, the mansion, its cottages and pool rest on a strikingly landscaped acre where guests enjoy a serene, smoke-free stay. Rooms are casually elegant with period antiques, romantic reproductions and comfortable seating. Numerous upscale amenities are designed for a carefree getaway, honeymoon or vacation. King beds, Jacuzzis, robes, bikes, beach gear and full concierge service are but a few examples of our attention to detail. Many of our rooms are quite spacious and give honeymooners and vacationers plenty of room to spread out. Walk to shops, restaurants, carriage and boat tours; bike to secluded beaches and a state park. Ask for details on seasonal specials, Romance Packages, Elopements, Major Holiday packages and Girls Just Wanna Have Fun Getaways. If you don't see it on the website, just ask. We're happy to accommodate.

Rates
6 Rooms $185/$240, 3 Cottages $240/$365, 3 Suites, $275/$395 B&B. Open year-round. Number of Rooms: 12

Cuisine
Sumptuous gourmet breakfast served in our formal dining room, or on piazzas and patios amid our hidden gardens by the pool. Lively daily social hour with beverages, hot/cold hors d'oeuvres. 3 minute walk to cafes, taverns and fine-dining restaurants.

Nearest Airport
Jacksonville, FL

Hoyt House Bed & Breakfast

www.hoythouse.com
804 Atlantic Avenue, Amelia Island, FL 32034
1-904-277-4300 • 1-800-432-2085 • Fax 1-904-277-4305
innkeeper@hoythouse.com

Member Since 2012

Florida

Amelia Island

Myrta Defendini, Innkeeper
Deborah Gold, Innkeeper

A luxurious Bed & Breakfast that has it all under one roof in beautiful Amelia Island. The Hoyt House offers 10 spacious guest rooms, luxuriously appointed king & queen guest chambers all with private baths & some with jetted tubs, flat screen DVD TV & WiFi throughout. A heated swimming pool and hot tub, 3 public salons with original hand-tiled fireplaces & The Amelia Lounge complete with English Pub and full liquor license to service all of your libations poolside or in-room. Tucked under 500 year old oak trees and located in the Historic District where you can find shopping, antiquing, food & drink galore of our 47 restaurants all within a few blocks of the Inn. Enjoy our complimentary cocktail hour, new bikes, DVD library & secure off street parking. Gilchrist & Soames complete your bathroom amenities. If your breakfast is just as important as your bed having 600 count Egyptian cotton linen, then you are in for a treat. Our breakfast serves up our signature warm sticky buns with warm pecans & raisins in a caramel butter bath. We will exceed your expectations.

Rates
Our rates for the mansion are $195 to $310 per night weekday and $205 to $350 per night on the weekend. Our private yacht is available for over night accommodations from $395 per night weekday & $495 on the weekends. Number of Rooms: 10

Cuisine
The Hoyt House offers a true culinary experience that will stimulate your pallet as well as your eyes. Our three course breakfast gives you a choice of 6 appetizers & 7 entrees to choose from. French Press Coffee table side. Daily afternoon English Tea

Nearest Airport
Jacksonville International Airport 35 minutes. Fernandina Beach Airport 3 miles for private planes & small jets.

Amelia Island Williams House

www.williamshouse.com
103 South Ninth Street, Amelia Island, FL 32034
800-414-9258 • 904-277-2328
info@williamshouse.com

Member Since 2007

Innkeepers/Owners
Byron & Deborah McCutchen

Come fall under the spell of this beautiful antebellum mansion, circa 1856 where romance, relaxation, and history combine to whisk you away to another place and time. Choose from ten elegantly decorated guest rooms with private baths and antique furnishings, some feature original working fireplaces w/hand carved mantels, whirlpool tubs, and a private hot tub. Sweeping verandas invite you to come and relax. Enjoy a delicious gourmet breakfast served in our beautiful dining room on antique china, crystal, and silver. Sip wine beneath our 500 year-old live oak tree in our flower lined courtyard. We are located in the historic seaside village of Fernandina Beach on Amelia Island, FL., just one block from downtown boutiques, bistros, antiques, art galleries,and world class restaurants. We offer complimentary bikes for exploring the island, beach equipment, wi-fi, and all the comforts of home. We offer packages for romance, birthdays, girls getaways, Christmas and other holidays. We are the perfect venue for weddings, family gatherings, or business retreats.

Rates
10 rooms $175-$265 weekend rates. Romantic getaway and spa packages available. Midweek discounts. Christmas and other hodliay packages. We are open year round. Number of Rooms: 10

Cuisine
Breakfast is served each morning in our dining room and consist of a fruit course followed by a savory or sweet dish with fresh ground coffee and juice. Each evening during our social hour we offer complimentary choice of wine and cheese.

Nearest Airport
Jacksonville, Florida -20 min drive from the Inn. Take I-95 N to exit 373. east on AIA to rt. on Beech, left on 9th

Caribbean Court Boutique Hotel

www.thecaribbeancourt.com
1601 S. Ocean Drive, Vero Beach, FL 32963
772-231-7211 • 772-231-7299 • Fax 772-231-4220
info@thecaribbeancourt.com

Member Since 2012

Florida

Vero Beach

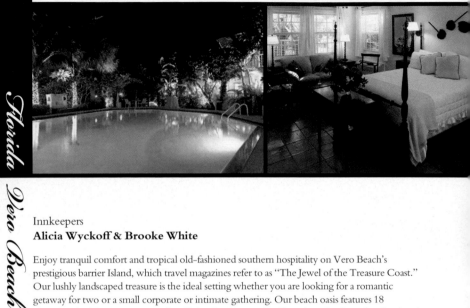

Innkeepers
Alicia Wyckoff & Brooke White

Enjoy tranquil comfort and tropical old-fashioned southern hospitality on Vero Beach's prestigious barrier Island, which travel magazines refer to as "The Jewel of the Treasure Coast." Our lushly landscaped treasure is the ideal setting whether you are looking for a romantic getaway for two or a small corporate or intimate gathering. Our beach oasis features 18 charming double occupancy studio efficiencies, decorated with antique furniture, hand-painted tiles, and original artwork. Rooms feature all modern conveniences: television, VCR/DVD, refrigerator/freezer, Direct TV, microwave, coffee maker, safe and hair dryer. Embroidered waffle robes, cotton sheets, fluffy towels, pillow top mattresses, honor mini bar, and even four pet friendly rooms are provided for your comfort as well. You will also enjoy complimentary off street parking, gourmet coffee, designer toiletries, high speed wireless internet and local and long distance calling within the continental United States. The Boutique Hotel offers beach access, a heated pool, 24 hour concierge and front desk service.

Rates
Rates $100-$279, are subject to seasonal demand and occupancy. High season is February-April. Year round, we are especially popular for special occasions, small conferences, weddings, family reunions and other intimate functions. Number of Rooms: 18

Cuisine
Savor Maison Martinique Restaurant's award winning French cuisine, extensive wine list, full bar, elegant indoor or casual "al-fresco" dining and Romantic Havana Nights Piano Bar's nightly live entertainment, tropical lite menu and plentiful spirits.

Nearest Airport
Accessibility: Orlando (MCO) is best; West Palm Beach (PBI) a close second. Proximity: Melbourne (MLB) is closest.

SelectRegistry.com

St. Francis Inn

www.stfrancisinn.com
279 St. George Street, St. Augustine, FL 32084
800-824-6062 • 904-824-6068 • Fax 904-810-5525
info@stfrancisinn.com

Member Since 2002

Innkeepers/Owners
Joe & Margaret Finnegan

Guestrooms and suites with antiques, balconies with rocking chairs and swings, fireplaces and whirlpools add to the tranquil ambiance. Walk to everything from the Inn's Old City location. This historic inn overflows with hospitality, set in a lush tropical courtyard on brick paved streets with horse-drawn buggies passing by. A historic treasure, but modern comforts abound! Great value, with many guest amenities: swimming pool, gourmet Southern breakfasts, brunch on weekends and holidays, bicycles, social hour, evening sweets, DVD, wi-fi, health club privileges, private parking, free and discounted attractions tickets, coffee and inn-baked cookies, sherry and flowers in your room. Add in-room massages, gift baskets, inroom breakfasts, picnic baskets, flowers, champagne and other ala carte extras. Tropical setting provides endless outdoor activities, plus sightseeing, historic landmarks, cultural events and celebrations steps away. Many packages available to enhance your stay with added value and savings, themed for romance, history, and more.

Rates
12 Rooms $139/$309; 4 Suites $199/$299; 2-BR Cottage $279/$359 for 4. Each with queen or king bed, private bath, central heat/air, wifi, cable tv, mp3/iPod connection. Several with fireplaces, whirlpool, fridge. Great amenities! Number of Rooms: 17

Cuisine
Homemade breakfast entrees, in our dining room, your room, on a private balcony or in the courtyard. Mimosas, Bloody Mary's at weekend/holiday breakfast. Social hour appetizers; evening sweets; cookies all day. Specialty lattes, cappuccinos, espressos.

Nearest Airport
St. Johns County (SGJ); Jacksonville International (JAX)

Florida

St. Augustine

Windemere Inn By The Sea

www.windemereinn.com
815 S. Miramar Avenue (A1A), Indialantic, FL 32903
800-224-6853 • 321-728-9334
stay@windemereinn.com

Member Since 2005

Florida

Indialantic

Innkeeper/Owner
Elizabeth G. Fisher

Imagine ..a luxury, oceanfront bed and breakfast, only an hour east of Orlando. Guest rooms and suites are furnished with antiques and fine linens, most with ocean views, some with balconies, porches, whirlpool tubs or TVs. Start each morning with a full, gourmet breakfast, enjoy pastries and sherry at "tea time." Windemere is the ideal spot for your small wedding, honeymoon or special getaway, corporate retreat, for watching a rocket launch form Kennedy Space Center, or witnessing sea turtles nest and hatch. The grounds have several gardens, including herbs for cooking. The central point is a koi pond alive with marine plants and animals. Sit on our Beach-side Pergola and watch dolphins and surfers play in the waves, or the sun or moon rise. The Inn has private beach access and provides beach gear. We are able to cater to most dietary needs upon request. Windemere is 45 minutes south of Kennedy Space Center, an hour east of Orlando and 10 minutes from Historic Downtown Melbourne with shopping, arts and entertainment and casual and fine dining. Visit www.windemereinn.com.

Rates
Guest rooms-7 $170 to $300. Two bedroom suites -2 $390 and $440. Weekly, AAA, & corporate discounts. Number of Rooms: 9

Cuisine
Start each day with sunrise over the Atlantic, and a full gourmet breakfast. A fruit course is followed by alternating daily sweet and savory dishes and freshly baked breads and muffins. Home made pastries and desserts are served at "tea time" daily.

Nearest Airport
Melbourne International Airport 15 minutes west, Orlando International Airport 1 hour west

Island Cottage Oceanfront Inn, Café & Spa

🍽️ 🍽️   🍷

www.islandcottagevillas.com
2316 S. Oceanshore Blvd., Flagler Beach, FL 32136
87-ROMANCE-2 • 877-662-6232
Romance@IslandCottageVillas.com

Member Since 2007

Florida

Flagler Beach

Innkeepers/Owners
Mark & Toni Treworgy

Tucked away in a tiny beach community along the Atlantic shoreline rests this quaint "Key West" styled jewel appreciated for its warmth, tranquility, spectacular ocean views, romantic ambiance & pampering. ...... Plan to indulge in a couples massage or facial at the Inn's exclusive Spa or just sit back in barefoot comfort & enjoy the sparkling pool, the sounds of the surf & the scent of fresh sea air. ...... Rooms feature dramatic ocean vistas, private decks, fireplaces & Jacuzzis for two, ... & the on-site gift shop showcases original art of the innkeeper, scented soaps, candles & exquisite hand made jewelry. ...... Guests are treated to "Afternoon Tea" with home baked cookies each day plus a delicious & beautifully presented gourmet breakfast each morning served on elegantly set tables with pressed linens, shimmering silver, sparkling crystal & soft candlelight. Dining is offered beside a flickering indoor fireplace or out-of-doors under a lovely covered pavilion. ...... Room service menu features fine wines, lighter fare salads & picnic baskets.

Rates
3 rooms- $259 to $329/night .... 3 Suites- $349 to 389/night. ... Reservations of 3 or more nights are discounted. Romance Packages & Indulgence items available. Inn does not accept drive-ups. Advanced Reservations are Required. Number of Rooms: 6

Cuisine
Gourmet hot breakfast includes fresh locally grown fruits, home grown herbs, coffee, tea, chilled juice & mimosas served by candlelight on individual tables w/ Patio or Cafe dining. Afternoon Tea includes home baked cookies, fresh fruit & chocolates.

Nearest Airport
Daytona - 22 miles / Jacksonville & Sanford - 90 miles / Orlando - 100 miles

Port d'Hiver Bed & Breakfast

www.portdhiver.com
201 Ocean Avenue, Melbourne Beach, FL 32951
866-621-7678 • 321-722-2727 • Fax 321-723-3221

Member Since 2008

info@portdhiver.com

Florida

Melbourne Beach

Innkeepers/Owners
Mike and Linda Rydson, Valerie Garofalo

Port d'Hiver Bed and Breakfast is old Florida luxury at its finest. A comfortable yet elegant retreat just 200 feet from the Atlantic Ocean, Port d'Hiver has ocean views, private porches, a bubbling spa pool & winding brick paths through a private compound of Island style buildings surrounded by lush tropical landscaping. Soak away the world in a large spa tub in one of our spacious new cabana rooms or watch the sunrise over the ocean from the deck of your beautifully restored historic room. Enjoy breakfast either on your porch or in our cheerfully inviting dining room. We also offer wine and refreshments at 5 o'clock in the main house, complimentary concierge services, wireless high speed internet inside and out, flat screen TVs, evening turn down service & the finest amenities. Fish, surf, dine, or watch the sea turtles... Melbourne Beach is a barrier island only .7 miles across from the ocean to the Indian River Lagoon. Port d'Hiver is a 2010 AAA ◆◆◆◆ property & in 2009 received TOP 10 MOST ROMANTIC INNS OF THE YEAR by American Historic Inns and iLoveInns.com.

Rates
$200/$525. Number of Rooms: 11

Cuisine
Casually elegant 3 course breakfast w/choice of entrees served individually in our dining room or on your private deck. Special vegetarian, lactose and gluten free diets are no problem. Wine & appetizers at 5 PM, cookies, coffee & snack room 24 hours.

Nearest Airport
Melbourne International - 7 miles, Orlando International - 69 miles

The Marquesa Hotel

www.marquesa.com
600 Fleming St., Key West, FL 33040
800–869–4631 Reservations Only • 305-292-1919 • Fax 305-294-2121
info@marquesa.com

Member Since 1991

Innkeeper/Owner
Carol Wightman

In the heart of Key West's Historic District, The Marquesa Hotel and Cafe is a landmark 127-year-old home. Floor-to-ceiling windows, exotic orchids, two shimmering pools and lush gardens are Marquesa trademarks. Rooms and suites are luxurious with private marble baths, bathrobes, flat screen televisions and fine furnishings. Located one block from Duval Street for shops, galleries, restaurants and nightlife. The Miami Herald rated it as one of Florida's top 10 Inns. Travel & Leisure Magazine's Reader Poll ranked The Marquesa in the "500 World's Best Hotels" and Conde Nast Traveller on their "Gold List." Zagat Survey members rated Cafe Marquesa as the highest rated restaurant in Key West. Explore nearby North-America's only living coral reef, go flats fishing, kayak, snorkel, deep sea fishing, para-sailing or relax by one of our two pools and do nothing! Our staff will help make the most of your stay.

Rates
14 Rooms, $190/$395; 13 Suites, $300/$520. Open year-round. Special event minimum night stays apply. Number of Rooms: 27

Cuisine
Poolside or room service dining for breakfast; fine dining in Cafe Marquesa w/an innovative & delicious menu. Excellent wine list & full bar. Fresh local seafood, quality grilled meats. Named one of Key West's Top Five Romantic Restaurants by Key TV.

Nearest Airport
Key West International Airport - 3 miles

Georgia

Famous for: Stone Mountain, Okefenokee Swamp, Live Oak Trees, Islands, Beaches, Peaches, Historic Savannah.

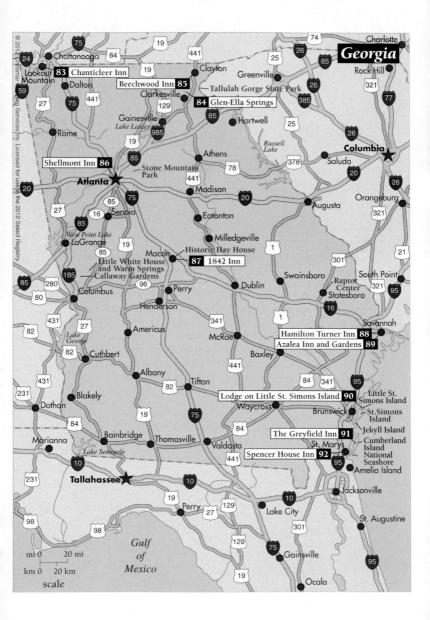

Chanticleer Inn Bed & Breakfast

www.stayatchanticleer.com

1300 Mockingbird Lane, Lookout Mountain, GA 30750

866-999-1015 • 706-820-2002 • Fax 706-820-7976

info@stayatchanticleer.com

Member Since 2003

Georgia

Lookout Mountain

Innkeepers/Owners
Robert & Audrey Hart

The Chanticleer Inn combines the ambiance of yesteryear with the comfort and amenities of today. Built in 1927, the Inn and the 17 English Cottage style guest rooms are nestled around the inn's courtyard and swimming pool. While the Mountain stone exterior retains it's original charm, the interior spaces have been completely renovated. Antique furnishings create a unique and inviting atmosphere in each guest room. Amenities include a patio, private bath, individual central heat and air, DVD player and flat screen TV with cable. Some rooms feature private patio, fireplace and/or whirlpool or steam shower. Located high atop historic Lookout Mountain & only 10 minutes from downtown Chattanooga, TN. The Inn is directly across the street from Rock City Gardens & two Banquet facilities all with spectacular views of the Chattanooga Valley. Nearby are hiking trails with waterfalls, golf courses, restaurants, shopping, and many other attractions. Family owned and operated, the Inn serves a full home-made breakfast each morning. We'll make sure your stay is comfortable and memorable.

Rates
$135-$245/night rate includes full breakfast, evening cookies/desserts, bottled water, Coffee & Tea; Some rooms and suites offer Whirlpool, Steam Shower or Fireplace. All rooms have private baths, telephones and TV. WIFI Number of Rooms: 17

Cuisine
A complimentary breakfast is prepared by our chef each morning along with homemade cookies/desserts each evening. Made to order boxed lunches, cheese platters, antipasto, chocolate covered strawberries and more are available for an extra charge.

Nearest Airport
Chattanooga, 25 Minutes; Atlanta, 2 hours; Nashville, 2 hours; Birmingham, 2 hours

ᵀᴼᴵ ᵀᴼᴵ ᵀᴼᴵ ♀

Glen-Ella Springs Inn

www.glenella.com
1789 Bear Gap Rd, Clarkesville, GA 30523
888-455-8786 • 706-754-7295 • Fax 706-754-1560
info@glenella.com

Member Since 1990

Innkeepers/Owners
Ed and Luci Kivett

RELAX...RESTORE...REJUVENATE! This historic Inn is located in the foothills of the Blue Ridge Mountains. Over a century old, Glen-Ella Springs Inn & Meeting Place features 16 rustic yet elegant rooms all with private baths and complete with amenities expected by today's discriminating traveler. The Inn's fine dining restaurant is open most evenings by reservation and has been named one of Georgia's Top Dining Destinations since 2004. Located on 17 acres, the property has a 12 acre meadow with extensive perennial herb and flower gardens, as well as, an open air swimming pool. If outdoor adventure peaks your interest, you will find numerous hiking trails and waterfalls close by. Tallulah Falls State Park and Black Rock Mountain State Park are within 30 minutes of the Inn offering some of the area's most beautiful vistas. Shopping enthusiasts will find original art, hand thrown pottery and antique galleries all around the region and guests can also plan to visit one of the many north Georgia wineries all within a short drive of the Inn.

Rates
16 Rooms, $150/$275 B&B. Open year-round. Number of Rooms: 16

Cuisine
A freshly prepared full breakfast is included with your room. The Inn's fine dining restaurant features American Continental cuisine prepared with a Southern flare. Guests enjoy the ambiance of the original heart pine paneled dining room and terrace.

Nearest Airport
Greenville, SC or Atlanta, GA

ℱSelectRegistry.com

Beechwood Inn

www.beechwoodinn.ws
220 Beechwood Dr, P.O. Box 429, Clayton, GA 30525
706-782-5485 • Fax 706-782-5485
info@beechwoodinn.ws

Member Since 2005

Innkeepers/Owners
David & Gayle Darugh

Relax- Renew - Restore: Award winning Georgia Mountain hospitality and gourmet dining. Wine Enthusiast Magazine places Beechwood Inn in the Top 5 Destinations "for your next wine and food-focused escape," Dec 2011. Travel writer Becky Lamb says, "The Beechwood Inn is the closest thing to a Napa Valley Bed and Breakfast we have here in Georgia." Nestled among 100 year-old terraced gardens overlooking Black Rock Mountain, it is a place where all elements add up to a culinary and wine-oriented journey. Come relax your mind, refresh your body, and rejuvenate your soul as we pamper you with affordable elegance. Each of our 8 guest room suites is individually decorated, most have fireplaces, private porches, mountain views and all have private baths. The Inn's restaurant features a Wine Spectator Award of Excellence selection of vintages. The beautifully landscaped 5 acre property is also perfect for weddings, receptions, and group functions. The Inn is Eco-Friendly: Recycling Center, Non-Toxic Cleaning Agents, Low Carbon Footprint, Many Organic Local Foods and Native Plantings.

Rates
7 guest suites, 1 garden cabin $159/$239. Private baths, fireplaces, porches, views, free WIFI, 600 thread count sheets, hair-dryers, complimentary soft drinks and itinerary planning. Complimentary wine-thirty daily. Number of Rooms: 8

Cuisine
Gourmet Breakfast served daily. Chef's Table dinners featuring local and organic foods on Saturdays. Extensive wine list. Visit our website for information on gourmet wine events, cooking classes, wine tastings & special packages.

Nearest Airport
Atlanta, GA and Asheville, NC each 90 minutes;Greenville SC 90 minutes

Shellmont Inn

www.shellmont.com
821 Piedmont Ave. N.E., Atlanta, GA 30308
404-872-9290 • Fax 404-872-5379
innkeeper@shellmont.com

Member Since 1994

Innkeepers/Owners
Ed and Debbie McCord

The Shellmont Inn is an award-winning premier Urban Inn offering all the luxurious amenities found in an upscale boutique hotel. Located in Atlanta's theater, restaurant and cultural district, this crowning jewel is an urban oasis just steps from Atlanta's Midtown Mile and bustling Peachtree Street. Business travelers find us technologically savvy, while leisure travelers find our Inn romantic and tranquil. Whether here on business or pleasure, Shellmont Inn offers outstanding personal service in a sophisticated, elegant atmosphere. Indulge in a sumptuous breakfast. Relax in a spa tub. Unwind on a wicker-laden veranda. When your travels bring you to Atlanta, Shellmont Inn will always exceed your expectations. THE EXPERIENCE IS UNFORGETTABLE!

Rates
Rooms $175/$215; Deluxe Whirlpool Suites $225/$285;Carriage House Cottage $250/$365. Elegant Atlanta Elopement Package $1750/$1850. Open year-round. Number of Rooms: 5

Cuisine
A Southern Regional inspired full gourmet breakfast features fresh local ingredients and herbs grown in our garden. Complimentary beverages and delicious afternoon refreshments served daily. Evening turn-down service with treats, fresh fruit basket.

Nearest Airport
Hartsfield-Jackson Int'l - 8 miles South of Inn Location

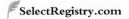

SelectRegistry.com

1842 Inn

www.the1842inn.com
353 College Street, Macon, GA 31201
800-336-1842 • 478-741-1842 • Fax 478-741-1842
management@1842inn.com

Member Since 1994

Georgia

Macon

Owner
Edmund E. Olson

The 1842 Inn boasts 19 luxurious rooms and public areas tastefully designed with fine English antiques, tapestries and paintings. A quaint garden courtyard and garden pool greet guests for cocktails or breakfast. Nightly turndowns and fresh flowers enhance many other gracious grand hotel amenities. Rooms available with whirlpool tubs and fireplaces. High level of service. Considered 'One of America's Top 100 Inns in the 20th Century' by the International Restaurant and Hospitality Rating Bureau.

Rates
19 Guest Rooms, $189/$240 B&B. (Rates subject to change without notice.) Open year-round. Number of Rooms: 19

Cuisine
Full breakfast and hors d'oeuvres included. Full service attended cash bar.

Nearest Airport
Macon, Atlanta

Hamilton Turner

www.hamilton-turnerinn.com
330 Abercorn Street, Savannah, GA 31401
888-448-8849 • 912-233-1833 • Fax 912-233-0291
innkeeper@hamilton-turnerinn.com

Member Since 2003

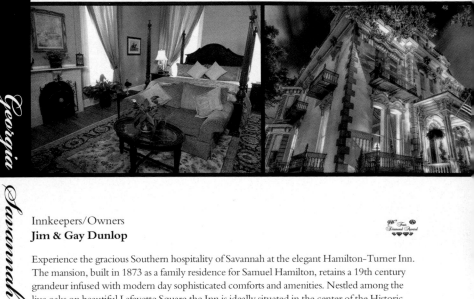

Innkeepers/Owners
Jim & Gay Dunlop

Experience the gracious Southern hospitality of Savannah at the elegant Hamilton-Turner Inn. The mansion, built in 1873 as a family residence for Samuel Hamilton, retains a 19th century grandeur infused with modern day sophisticated comforts and amenities. Nestled among the live oaks on beautiful Lafayette Square the Inn is ideally situated in the center of the Historic District. Fine cuisine and other points of interest are within a short stroll. Our concierge staff is poised to offer recommendations and secure reservations for touring, restaurants and leisure activities. Choose from grand suites overlooking the moss-draped oaks in the park; luxuriously appointed rooms; garden-view courtyard rooms with private entrances; and three carriage house rooms with shared parlor. Some accommodations offer fireplace, whirlpool spa bath, and bay windows. Whether you are looking for a reunion with longtime friends, romantic honeymoon getaway, business travel retreat or golf vacation, the Inn has a package to exceed your desires. Featured in Southern Living and Conde Nast Traveler.

Rates
11 bedrooms, 6 suites from $189 to $369 per night, double occupancy. King, 2 queen, queen, and 2 twin beds available. Carriage house offers 3 guestrooms and parlor. ADA room and pet friendly rooms. Number of Rooms: 17

Cuisine
Complimentary cuisine features full southern mansion breakfast, afternoon iced-tea and sweets, evening wine and hors d'oeuvres, late evening port, turndown sweet.

Nearest Airport
Savannah/Hilton Head International SAV, 8 miles.

Azalea Inn and Gardens

www.azaleainn.com

217 East Huntingdon Street, Savannah, GA 31401

912-236-6080 • 800-582-3823 • Fax 912-236-0127

Info@AzaleaInn.com

Member Since 2012

Georgia *Savannah*

Innkeepers/Owners

Teresa and Micheal Jacobson

Savannah visitors are fascinated with the easy-going appeal found at our romantic Inn located in the Landmark Savannah Historic District – within two walking blocks of Forsyth Park, the city's infamously verdant and captivating "Central Park". Proving you can 'travel well on little' in historic Savannah, or indulge to your heart's content, Innkeepers Teresa and Micheal Jacobson spoil their guests with casual dining, nightly wine socials, and tips on where to go to personally experience historic Savannah character. The Inn's gardens feature indigenous plants and trees, plus low volume irrigation for earth-friendly, water conservation. We also take fresh, seasonal and local seriously. Our produce and herb garden was expanded in early 2011 with the addition of nine raised beds (featured in the NOGS Tour of Hidden Gardens 2011) which produced more tomatoes than we had canning jars along with a plethora of other vegetables and herbs. If we were not able to use in the Inn, we donated to the local SAFE Shelter for battered women and children.

Rates

$199-$429. Many rooms have working fireplaces and private balconies while others may have jet-air tubs and private decks. Our Cottage Garden house is ideal for longer stays. Number of Rooms: Ten

Cuisine

Bountiful hot Southern breakfast - Sweet Georgia Shrimp served over Georgia Grits, Spiced Apple and Pear French Toast with local fruits. Evening wine and house-made appetizers. At the end of the day, evening sherry and a fresh-made dessert await you.

Nearest Airport

Savannah-Hilton Head International Airport; Jacksonville International Airport, Jacksonville, FL is 2 hours by car

Lodge on Little St. Simons Island

www.LittleSSI.com

P.O. Box 21078, 1000 Hampton Point Drive, Little St. Simons Island, GA 31522-0578

888-733-5774 • 912-638-7472 • Fax 912-634-1811

Member Since 1993   Lodge@LittleStSimonsIsland.com

Georgia

Little St. Simons Island

General Manager
Joel Meyer

Nature prevails on this pristine Georgia island where 10,000 acres are shared with no more than 32 overnight guests at a time. Accessible only by boat, Little St. Simons Island unfolds its secrets to those eager to discover a bounty of natural wonders. Seven miles of shell-strewn, private beaches meet acres of legendary moss-draped live oaks, glistening tidal creeks, and shimmering salt marshes to provide an unparalleled setting for a host of activities and total relaxation. Guests enjoy guided interpretive tours, birding, canoeing, kayaking, fishing, hiking, and bicycling. Creature comforts include gracious accommodations, delicious regional cuisine, and warm Southern hospitality. The Lodge on Little St. Simons Island was recently voted #1 Resort in the Mainland US ~ Conde Nast Traveler's Readers' Choice Awards.

Rates
All-inclusive rates range from $450 - $775 per couple, per night. Full house and exclusive full island reservations are available. Visit www.LittleSSI.com to learn about special offers. Number of Rooms: 16

Cuisine
Delicious regional cuisine served family-style. Rate includes three meals daily, beverages, snacks, and a complimentary cocktail hour. Picnics are also available upon request. We gladly accommodate dietary restrictions.

Nearest Airport
Brunswick, GA (BQK), Savannah, GA (SAV), and Jacksonville, FL (JAX).

Greyfield Inn

www.greyfieldinn.com

P.O. Box 900, Fernandina Beach, FL 32035, Cumberland Island, GA 32035

888-243-9238 • 904-261-6408 • Fax 904-321-0666

seashore@greyfieldinn.com

Member Since 1982

Innkeepers/Owners
The Ferguson Family

This turn-of-the-century Carnegie mansion is on Georgia's largest and southernmost coastal island. Miles of trails traverse the island's unique ecosystems along with a beautiful, undeveloped white sand beach for shelling, swimming, sunning and birding. Exceptional food, lovely, original furnishings, and a peaceful, relaxing environment provide guests with a step back into another era. Overnight rate includes an island outing with our naturalist, bicycles and kayaks for exploring the island, round-trip boat passage on our private ferry, all meals and pantry snacks throughout the day and all non-alcoholic beverages.

Rates
16 Rooms, $395/$595 AP. Open year-round. Number of Rooms: 16

Cuisine
Hearty southern breakfast, delightful picnic lunch, gourmet dinner. All meals focus on local southern foods & traditions, including island grown produce & locally caught seafood. Full bar; wine, beer, liquor, cocktail hour with hors d'oeuvres.

Nearest Airport
Jacksonville, Florida

Georgia Cumberland Island

Spencer House Inn

www.spencerhouseinn.com
200 Osborne Street, St. Marys, GA 31558
912-882-1872 • 888-840-1872 • Fax Fax 912-882-9427
info@spencerhouseinn.com

Member Since 2003

Georgia

St. Marys

Innkeepers/Owners
Mike & Mary Neff

Spencer House Inn is located nine miles east of I-95 on the Georgia/Florida border by the St. Marys River. For your convenience, the Inn has an elevator and an outside ramp. Spencer House Inn, built in 1872, is in the heart of the St. Marys Historic District within walking distance to restaurants, shops, museums and the ferry to Cumberland Island National Seashore. We can assist you in making ferry reservations and also pack a picnic lunch for you as you head off for your day of adventure on a beautiful, undeveloped and pristine barrier island – the beach was voted "one of the best wild beaches" by National Geographic Traveler magazine – and we are on the Colonial Coast Birding Trail too. You will enjoy relaxing in the cypress rockers on the Inn's verandas. Take a leisurely stroll around the historic village to the waterfront park, fishing piers, boat ramp and marsh walk. There are golf courses nearby and outfitters available for a kayak trip. Okefenokee Wildlife Refuge is 45 minutes away. The beaches of Jekyll, St. Simons and Amelia Islands are a short drive.

Rates
$135/$245. Rates subject to change. All private baths. Elevator & outside ramp. Complimentary wireless access. Daily paper. HDTV with cable, HBO, ESPN & DVD player. Open year-round. Comp pick up from marina and St. Marys airport. Number of Rooms: 14

Cuisine
Full buffet breakfast with hot entree. Picnic lunches available. Walk to restaurants for lunch and dinner. Guest refrigerator. Afternoon iced tea, coffee and homemade treats.

Nearest Airport
Jacksonville, FL (JAX).

 SelectRegistry.com

Illinois

"The Prairie State"

Famous for: Hogs, Pigs, Cattle, Electronics, Chemicals, Manufacturing, Ancient Burial Mounds, Lake Michigan, Chicago "Windy City," Sears Tower, Wrigley Building.

Harvey House Bed & Breakfast

www.harveyhousebb.com
107 S. Scoville Ave., Oak Park, IL 60302
888-848-6810 • 708-848-6810
harveyhousebb@gmail.com

Member Since 2008

Illinois

Oak Park

Innkeeper/Owner
Beth Harvey

Located in the Historic District of Oak Park, Illinois, Harvey House Bed & Breakfast is just minutes away from downtown Chicago. Visitors from around the world travel to this area to see its famous architecture, such as the Frank Lloyd Wright Home and Studio. The Inn is walking distance to shops, galleries, fine restaurants, and the train station. With its welcoming, informal atmosphere guests can enjoy good company or simply take a break from daily life. Each elegantly appointed suite has individual character; some rooms feature jetted tubs, fireplaces, and kitchenettes. National and local accolades include the New York Times, Midwest and Chicago Magazines, and the Chicago Tribune. Harvey House is an Urban Oasis.

Rates
5 suites all with private baths, 3 with fireplaces and jucuzzi tubs. Off Season: $165 - $325. In Season: $210 - $350. Number of Rooms: 5

Cuisine
Offering a friendly atmosphere in which to enjoy delicious food incorporating the best of what is freshest and in season. A full gourmet breakfast is served daily and we accommodate most dietary requests. Guest can choose what time they want breakfast.

Nearest Airport
Chicago, IL (ORD-O'Hare) 10 miles or Midway Airport also 10 miles.

Copperstone Inn

www.copperstoneinn.com

6702 Yale Bridge Road, Rockton, IL 61072

815-629-9999 • 815-629-9999 • Fax 815-629-4732

sspanton@copperstoneinn.com

Member Since 2011

Illinois

Rockton

Innkeepers
Saundra Spanton & Nicola Weldon

Awarded "Best of the Best" by Lanier B&B, Copperstone Inn is an ultimate blend of luxury and nature set on Orchard Ridge Farms, a 130 acre property just outside of Rockton. The 1858 limestone farmhouse spans a majestic 9,000 sq ft including the 2008 owner-designed addition. Explore the pristine grounds including multiple gardens, 2 ponds, wooded trails, apple orchard, and walking paths dotted with sitting areas perfect for bird-watching. Inside, you will find sophisticated comfort in our guest rooms and common areas, as no detail has been overlooked! All 7 rooms have private baths, 100% natural toiletries and amenities, fine linens, robes, and homemade fresh baked cookies. Awaken each morning to the aroma of a gourmet breakfast prepared with our own seasonal vegetables and herbs. Whether you're catching a movie in the theater room, reading by the fireplace, enjoying the bar, or indulging in our spa, you will experience total relaxation of the mind, body, and spirit. Plan your escape to Copperstone Inn now, our unforgettable surroundings and personalized service await you!

Rates
$159-$379 subject to day-season-room type. Spacious rooms, 3 w/fireplaces, 4 w/ whirlpool tubs, 3 w/private balconies, complimentary beverages, flat screens, Bose systems, satellite TV & radio, free-WIFI. Number of Rooms: 7

Cuisine
Multi-course breakfast featuring fresh fruit, sweet and savory dishes, and fresh baked goods. Menu changes daily. 24 hr coffee, tea, snacks, and fruit. Seasonal afternoon snacks. Excellent restaurants within 10 miles serving lunch and dinner.

Nearest Airport
30 min. to Rockford (RFD), 1 1/2 hours to Milwaukee (MKE), 1 1/2 hours to Chicago (ORD)

Goldmoor Inn

www.goldmoor.com
9001 W. Sand Hill Road, Galena, IL 61036
800-255-3925 • 815-777-3925 • Fax 815-777-3993
goldmoor@galenalink.com

Member Since 2001

Innkeeper/Owner
Patricia Smith

Magnificent country inn overlooks the Mississippi River, 6 miles South of historic Galena. The Goldmoor with it's elite yet tranquil setting is the perfect venue for weddings, honeymoons, romantic getaways, anniversaries, family reunions and business retreats. All luxurious accommodations including suites, cottages and contemporary log cabins feature king size beds, two person whirlpools, fireplaces, galley kitchens, and private baths. Add to that, European terry robes, fine linens, heated towel bars, refrigerators stocked with complimentary beverages, satellite TV, stereo system, free wireless internet, and free long distance are just a few of the many ways you are pampered at the Goldmoor Inn. Runner-up in the 2007 Inn-Credible Egg Breakfast Cook-off and bronze winner in 2008, the Goldmoor provides our guests with a full, gourmet breakfast and free room service. Renew your mind, body and soul with a rejuvenating massage in the comfort of your accommodation, open air pavilion, or our soothing spa. The Goldmoor has been the top-rated ABBA inn in Illinois since 1993.

Rates
Seasonal: 12 Suites $155 - $335, 3 Cottages $185 - $335, 2 Cabins $155 - $275.
Number of Rooms: 17

Cuisine
Breakfast served. Dining available for special occasions.

Nearest Airport
Dubuque, IA, 25 minute; Chicago, 2.45 hours.

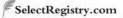

Inn at Irish Hollow

www.irishhollow.com
2800 S. Irish Hollow Road, Galena, IL 61036
(815)777-6000
innkeeper@irishhollow.com

Member Since 2010

Illinois Galena

Owners/Innkeepers
Bill Barrick, Tony Kemp, Matthew Carroll

Irish Hollow is the ultimate romantic, pampering and inspiring Inn, set in the magnificent rolling hills of the Galena countryside. Secluded on an amazing 500-acre Farm Estate, I.H. features Spectacular Cottages, Superb Amenities, Magical Meals, and the perfect background for your personal journey. Located near historic Galena, a stone's throw from the Mississippi River, down the valley from Downhill Skiing and surrounded by thousands of acres of Trail-carved Conservation Land, I.H. offers the ideal setting for everyone. Spend an awesome day on Snowshoes, Bikes, Woods-Wandering or just sitting by the Creek. WI-FI and IPod stations keep you connected.... while the roaring Wood-Burning Fireplaces, Private Candlelit Dinners in the Woods, Double Spa Tubs, Rain Showers for two, Horse-Drawn Buggy Rides and Couples Massage reconnect the two of you! I.H. specializes in All-Natural and Homegrown Cuisine, Outdoor Fitness, Special Diet accommodation, Great Wine and Personalized Service...all in a scrumptious setting. Our "CREATE YOUR OWN STAY" Menu lets you design your ultimate visit!

Rates
5 Private Cottages and 3 Luxury Suites nightly $195-$450. Seasonal Packages (visit IrishHollow.com for details and rates), Full Country Gourmet Breakfast, Farmhouse Dinners, Organic Beds, Spa Tubs, Wood Fires, BodyWorks Treatments. Number of Rooms: 8

Cuisine
Internationally acclaimed All-Natural Cuisine. Country Gourmet Breakfast (with delivery option) 7-course Farmhouse Dinner, Luscious Picnic, Private Campfire in the Woods, Special Diets including Vegan, Gluten-Free, Hand-Crafted Bakery, Great Wine List.

Nearest Airport
Dubuque Regional Airport, 30 minutes. O'Hare International Airport, 2.5 hours.

Market Street Inn

www.marketstreetinn.com
220 E. Market Street, Taylorville, IL 62568-2212
800-500-1466 • 217-824-7220 • Fax 217-824-7229
innkeeper@marketstreetinn.com

Member Since 2002

Illinois

Taylorville

Innkeepers/Owners
Joseph & Myrna Hauser

Rich in architectural detail, this romantic 1892 Queen Anne Victorian jewel boasts six original fireplaces, now with gas logs, and mantels, ornate woodwork, fretwork over pocket doors and beveled glass windows. Sit by the parlor fireplace and feast your eyes upon the antiques, semi-antiques and Oriental rugs to appreciate the blend of history, luxury, charm and hospitality. The grand oak staircase beckons one to unwind in one of the 8 guest rooms—each with delightfully different decor. Modern amenities include central air, private baths–most with double whirlpool tubs/showers, fireplaces, cable TV, and wireless DSL. Our Carriage House has two suites: the Hunt Club with two fireplaces, a wet bar, a double whirlpool and walk-in shower w/ body sprays, also an accessible suite. At day's end stroll through the perennial gardens to view over 200 hostas & then relax in a rocker in the gazebo of the Victorian wrap-around porch. Lincoln's Library, Museum, home & tomb are just 30 minutes away. Lincoln Prairie Bike Trail is six blocks away. FREE golfing–stay & play. Also skydiving.

Rates
10 Rooms, $145-$275 most with double whirlpools & fireplaces. Accessible Suite in Carriage House. Queen Whirlpool Rooms $165, King Whirlpool Rooms $199. Standard Queen Room $145. Packages available on our website. Ask about pets. Number of Rooms: 10

Cuisine
Full hearty candlelight breakfast served daily. Social Hour: complimentary wine served daily and hors d'oeuvres. Complimentary soda & bottled water. Upscale dining 2 blocks away (www.oneeastmarket.com) & several other enjoyable dining choices.

Nearest Airport
Taylorville Municipal(TAZ) Springfield Airport (SPI) Bloomington (BMI) St. Louis International (STL)

Indiana   **"The Hoosier State"**

Famous for: Farmlands, Cornfields, Wildflowers, Indiana Dunes National Lakeshore, Indianapolis 500.

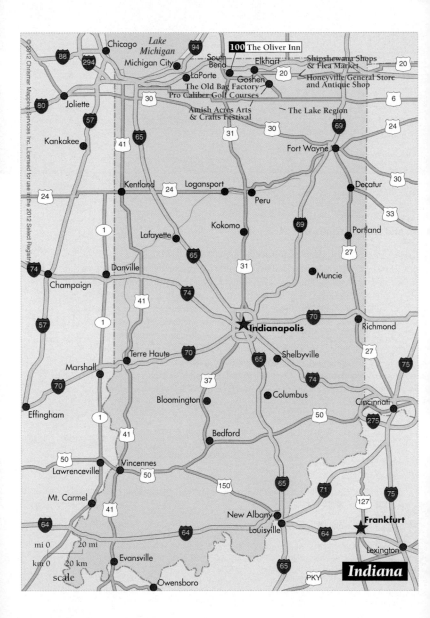

100 The Oliver Inn

Shipshewana Shops & Flea Market

Honeyville General Store and Antique Shop

The Old Bag Factory

Pro Caliber Golf Courses

Amish Acres Arts & Crafts Festival

The Lake Region

Chicago • Lake Michigan • Michigan City • South Bend • Elkhart • LaPorte • Goshen • Joliette • Kankakee • Kentland • Logansport • Peru • Fort Wayne • Decatur • Portland • Lafayette • Kokomo • Danville • Champaign • Muncie • Terre Haute • Indianapolis • Shelbyville • Richmond • Marshall • Bloomington • Columbus • Cincinnati • Effingham • Bedford • Lawrenceville • Vincennes • Mt. Carmel • New Albany • Louisville • Frankfort • Evansville • Owensboro • Lexington

mi 0   20 mi
km 0   20 km
scale

Indiana

The Oliver Inn

www.oliverinn.com
630 W. Washington Street, South Bend, IN 46601
888-697-4466 • 574-232-4545 • Fax 574-288-9788
oliver@michiana.org

Member Since 2000

Indiana

South Bend

Innkeepers/Owners
Tom and Alice Erlandson

Experience turn-of-the-century Victorian elegance at The Oliver Inn Bed & Breakfast. This historic 24 room mansion is surrounded by a lush acre of manicured gardens, with a gazebo, hammock, and lawn swings. The Oliver Inn features large, comfortable common areas, 11 fireplaces, nine beautiful guest rooms in the main house, private baths, two-person whirlpool tubs, A/C, CD players, sound machines, hairdryers, and luxurious robes. Enjoy a candlelit breakfast while listening to live piano music. Complimentary snacks, gourmet coffees and soft drinks available from the Butler's Pantry. Experience the ultimate in relaxation, and serenity in our Carriage House Suite. This second floor suite features two queen bedrooms, two bathrooms, (jetted marble shower, double Jacuzzi tub), a living room with fireplace, a full kitchen and a screened in veranda. For dinner, stroll next door to Tippecanoe Place Restaurant in the Studebaker Mansion. Come discover why The Oliver Inn was voted the Michiana area's 'Best Bed & Breakfast.'

Rates
8 Rooms plus 2, two-bedroom suites, $135/$339 - Rates higher for Special Events.
Number of Rooms: 10

Cuisine
Full candlelight breakfast with live piano music. Complimentary drinks and snacks from Butler's Pantry. Dine at Tippecanoe Place Restaurant in the Studebaker Mansion right next door.Private lunches and dinners for groups of 8 or more.

Nearest Airport
South Bend (SBN) 90 Miles from Chicago, 140 Mi. from Indianapolis, 220 Mi. from Detroit.

Kentucky

"The Bluegrass State"

Famous for: Horses, Kentucky Derby, Tobacco Farms, Fine Bourbon, Lakes, Hardwood Forests, Daniel Boone, Bluegrass music, "My Old Kentucky Home."

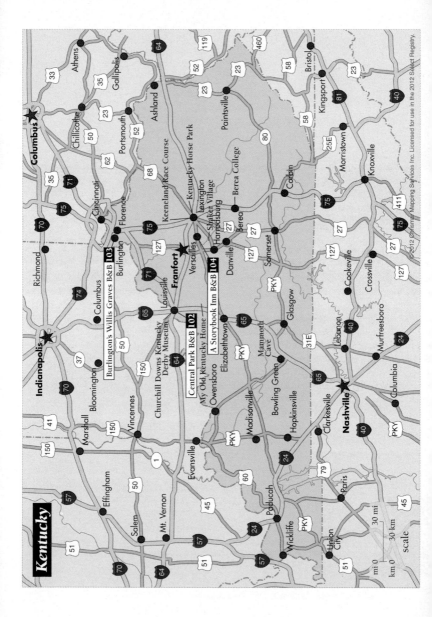

Central Park Bed & Breakfast

www.centralparkbandb.com

1353 South 4th Street, Old Louisville Historic District, Louisville, KY 40208

877-922-1505 • 502-638-1505 • Fax 502-638-1525

Member Since 2006

centralpark@win.net

Kentucky

Louisville

Proprietors
Robert and Eva Wessels

Come and bask in the ambiance of a Gilded Age mansion facing Central Park. We are located in one of the largest Victorian neighborhoods in America. Relax and have a glass of wine on the veranda or sip a cup of tea by the 19th century grand piano in the parlor. We have created a bit of a Victorian dream for a romantic get away for any special couple wanting to soak in a tub for two or lounge in a king size bed dressed in luxury linens by the fireplace. It can be a romantic interlude or a corporate retreat. Whether you are a traveler searching for a luxurious respite or the business traveler looking for more than a hotel, we have the place for you. We prepare a delicious three course breakfast daily. Our coffees are specially blended for the Inn. We always have specialty teas, treats and wine available each evening. We are centrally located close to downtown (1.5mi), the Expo Center, Churchill Downs(1mi), or the airport (10min). All rooms have a private bathroom, a fireplace, television, comfortable sitting area, and internet access. The Inn's antiques are of Victorian period.

Rates
Queens $135/$145, Kings/suites $185/$195, Carriage House (Child & pet friendly) $185.00, Corporate rates for single bus. travelers (Please call for rates). Number of Rooms: 7

Cuisine
Creative 3-course breakfast served in dining room or on the veranda overlooking the courtyard. Fresh roasted coffee, teas, juices, & fresh baked goods. Afternoon beverages & desserts. Fine & casual dining less than 2 blocks from Inn.

Nearest Airport
Louisville International (SDF), 10-min.

Burlington's Willis Graves Bed & Breakfast Inn

www.burligrave.com
5825 North Jefferson Street, Burlington, KY 41005
888-226-5096 • 859-689-5096 • Fax 859-689-0528
inn@burligrave.com

Member Since 2007

Innkeepers/Owners
Bob & Nancy Swartzel

Experience sophisticated charm and relaxed country living at this award-winning inn on the edge of a small town, just twenty minutes from Cincinnati. Choose between two masterfully restored early and mid-1800s buildings, the Willis Graves Federal brick homestead and William Rouse log cabin, furnished with appropriate antiques and reproductions. Attention to detail and luxurious touches are obvious everywhere. For your comfort and relaxation, we offer whirlpool baths, steam showers, plush robes and towels, fireplaces, triple sheeting with fine linens, down comforters, top quality mattresses, and fresh baked cookies. Guests may also enjoy in-room massage, wireless Internet, cable television, DVD and CD players, a comprehensive movie collection, and our inviting porches. Each morning, a full gourmet breakfast is served at individual tables set with white tablecloths, cloth napkins, and fine china. Suites offer in-room dining as an option. Gracious hospitality and beautiful surroundings create the perfect setting for your next romantic getaway, reunion, or business retreat.

Rates
$105-$225, special rates available. Number of Rooms: 5

Cuisine
A full gourmet breakfast is offered daily with a fresh fruit course to start. French roast coffee, assorted teas, juices, breads, and made from scratch entrees are served from our menu. Complimentary water and homemade cookies are in each room.

Nearest Airport
Cincinnati/Northern Kentucky International Airport

A Storybook Inn

www.storybook-inn.com
277 Rose Hill Avenue, Versailles, KY 40383
877-279-2563 • 859-879-9993 • Fax 859-873-0332
stay@storybook-inn.com

Member Since 2007

Kentucky
Versailles

Innkeeper/Owner
C. Elise Buckley

A delight to the senses! "Elegant," "A Real Treasure!" Immaculate! are words that were used by our discerning guests to describe beautiful, historic A Storybook Inn. Your search is over for a storybook destination that skillfully combines elegance with a gracious, welcoming sense of calm. The Innkeeper has succeeded in keeping the historic aspects intact, but has given the lovely old place a fresh feel all round. Serving our guests are why we are here! Every detail for your comfort has been considered; fantastic full breakfasts, freshly made entrees, premium fresh ground coffee/assorted teas. Hand-selected furnishings/quality antiques, FREE WIRELESS, satellite TV hi-thread count hand-pressed bedding, unique accessories and acres of beautifully landscaped grounds. Minutes from Keeneland Race Course, Lexington, Midway fine dining/shops, world class horse farms, Shaker Village, The Kentucky Horse Park, antiquing, and the Airport. Complimentary snacks and a glass of wine when you arrive. Always complimentary bottled water and soft drinks. Close to everything! Worlds apart!

Rates
Low Season Rates are: $233.-$515.High Season rates range from $223 to $515 Ask us about our midweek discount. Discount active military/clergy. Every suite is beautifully appointed year round. Enjoy our guesthouse with fireplace. Number of Rooms: 6

Cuisine
We serve a full breakfast w/fresh fruit, homemade muffins, freshly prepared sweet or savory entree each morning. Fresh ground coffee, juice and filtered water.We serve breakfast in our newly added 50 ft. glass Conservatory overlooking the courtyard.

Nearest Airport
Lexington Bluegrass Field is a very convenient 10 minute from the inn. Louisville Airport is an hour from the inn.

SelectRegistry.com

Maine

"The Pine Tree State"

Famous for: Lobsters, Lighthouses, Rocky Coastlines, Potatoes, Pines, Ports, Paper.

Brewster House Bed & Breakfast

www.BrewsterHouse.com
180 Main Street, Freeport, ME 04032
207-865-4121 • 800-865-0822
info@brewsterhouse.com

Member Since 2010

Maine

Freeport

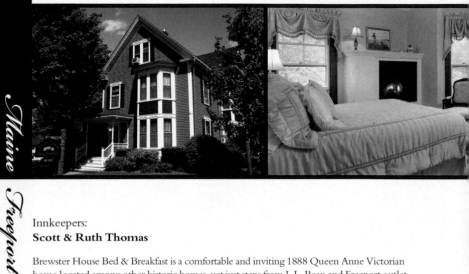

Innkeepers:
Scott & Ruth Thomas

Brewster House Bed & Breakfast is a comfortable and inviting 1888 Queen Anne Victorian home located among other historic homes, yet just steps from L.L. Bean and Freeport outlet shops. Built by a Mayflower descendant, Brewster House offers comfortable rooms with charming decor, gas fireplaces, bay windows and large private baths. Relax in your room or in our cozy parlor and enjoy our afternoon refreshments, after your visit to the Freeport shops and outlets, or your day trips to nearby lighthouses, coastal beaches and state parks, or a sail in Casco Bay on an antique wooden schooner. We'll provide maps, directions, and suggested itineraries to help you explore the Maine coast and find your way to lighthouses and lobster shacks. In addition to our 5 king or queen rooms, we have two 2-room suites for up to 3 or 4 guests. Three of our rooms have gas fireplaces and all have fine linens, luxurious robes and slippers, coffee/tea service, flat screen TVs, clock radios with iPod docks, air conditioning, and individual heat. There is complimentary WiFi throughout the house.

Rates
$179 - 229 king/queen rooms, $249 - 289 suites, seasonal rates, packages and specials. Open all year. Number of Rooms: 7

Cuisine
We serve a full, hot, gourmet breakfast daily. We begin with either a hot or cold fruit course, and alternate between sweet and savory main courses daily. Ruth loves to try new recipes, so you'll rarely have the same meal twice - even on return visits!

Nearest Airport
Portland, Maine (PWM) 25 minutes, Manchester, NH (MHT) 1:45 hours, Boston (BOS) 2 hours

Lodge at Moosehead Lake

www.lodgeatmooseheadlake.com
368 Lily Bay Road, P.O. Box 1167, Greenville, ME 04441
800-825-6977 • 207-695-4400 • Fax 207-695-2281
innkeeper@lodgeatmooseheadlake.com

Member Since 1995

Maine
Greenville

Proprietors
Dennis & Linda Bortis

Only The Lodge at Moosehead Lake captures the essence of the Maine North woods while pampering guests with luxurious amenities. Unspoiled vistas of Moosehead Lake against a mountain background provide the setting for this one of a kind country inn. Guests marvel at incredible sunsets from the dining room, pub, common areas, private decks and eight of the nine lodging rooms. Each room is individually decorated to reflect the natural surroundings of Moosehead Lake while providing the ultimate in luxury in every detail. You will enjoy a stone fireplace, one-of-a-kind hand carved beds, relics from the turn of the century logging era and twig furniture that defines the unique Moosehead Lake Region. A visit to the Lodge need never be the same twice! The travel and leisure industry has recognized the Lodge for its hospitality and uniqueness. This amazing spot is perfect for enjoying nature and incredible wildlife viewing. The goal is to make your visit as pleasant and stress free as possible. There are few places quite like this. Come see for yourself.

Rates
5 Lodge Rooms, 4 Suites, $250 to $695. King or Queen luxurious beds. Open all year but April. Number of Rooms: 9

Cuisine
Hearty North woods breakfast included. Dinner features Up North Cuisine Friday-Sunday from Mid-June through Mid-October. Enjoy dining room with magnificent sunsets over Moosehead Lake. Winter suppers Friday and Saturday from January-March. Full bar.

Nearest Airport
Bangor, Maine; Portland, Maine; Manchester, New Hampshire

Blair Hill Inn

www.blairhill.com
351 Lily Bay Road, Greenville, ME 04441
207-695-0224 • Fax 207-695-4324
info@blairhill.com

Maine
Greenville

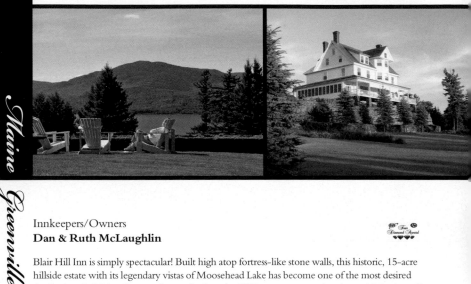

Innkeepers/Owners
Dan & Ruth McLaughlin

Blair Hill Inn is simply spectacular! Built high atop fortress-like stone walls, this historic, 15-acre hillside estate with its legendary vistas of Moosehead Lake has become one of the most desired destinations in Maine. Restored to perfection, the 1891 country manor has the sophistication of a luxury hotel with the casual intimacy of a boutique B&B. Its tasteful blend of traditional and trendy appeals to the young and young at heart. This exceptional inn is also regarded as one of Maine's premiere restaurants, featuring regional ingredients served in refreshingly creative ways. Above all, here you will find the most genuine and warm service of any place you have ever stayed. Everyone who travels up the winding drive to the top of Blair Hill and stays or dines at this special place, speaks of attaining an elusive experience that is both hard to find and to put into words. Come visit beautiful, welcoming Blair Hill Inn.

Rates
8 beautiful, spacious guest rooms @ $350/$495 double occup. True to the century old tradition of the grand hotels of Moosehead Lake, a storied tourist destination, Blair Hill Inn offers an idyllic stay amid the wilds of Maine. Number of Rooms: 8

Cuisine
Creative 5-course menus feature the inn's own gardens, greenhouse and Maine's best farms and fishermen. An Aztec wood-burning grill is a hallmark of the inn's cuisine. Open weekends June-Oct. Full, multi-course breakfasts are worth a visit alone.

Nearest Airport
Bangor International and Portland International

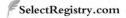

Belfast Bay Inn

www.belfastbayinn.com
72 Main Street, Belfast, ME 04915
207-338-5600 • Fax 207-338-9100
info@belfastbayinn.com

Member Since 2009

Innkeepers/Owners
Ed & Judy Hemmingsen

You are invited to Belfast's only AAA-◆◆◆◆ Award winning Boutique Hotel with upscale accommodations featuring luxuriously appointed 2-person guest suites. We are located in the heart of downtown Belfast, a quaint seaside city declared "Coolest Small Town" by Budget Traveler and ranked one of the top ten art communities in America. We are surrounded by shops, galleries, restaurants, and we are steps to the waterfront at the town pier. We fully restored these mid-1800 Greek Revival row houses to offer refined and sophisticated guest suites for discerning tastes. Each gracefully decorated suite has distinctive features including hardwood and stone floors, crown moldings, granite counter tops, classic original oil paintings, carefully chosen furniture and fine upholstery. Some suites have gas fireplaces, balconies and water views. Treat yourself to our many guest amenities by scheduling an in-suite massage. Enjoy breakfast delivered to your suite each morning. Select a movie from our gallery or browse our wine collection at our Molly Amber gift shop.

Rates
6 Suites and 2 Rooms $198 - $378. Number of Rooms: 8

Cuisine
Hearty breakfast of homemade breads and sweets, fresh juices and fruits, granola and a changing menu of hot entrees. Evenings enjoy fresh baked cookies, coffee and tea.

Nearest Airport
Bangor International Airport

🍽

Inn at Bay Ledge

www.innatbayledge.com
150 Sand Point Road, Bar Harbor, ME 04609
207-288-4204 • Fax 207-288-5573
info@bayledge.com

Member Since 2002

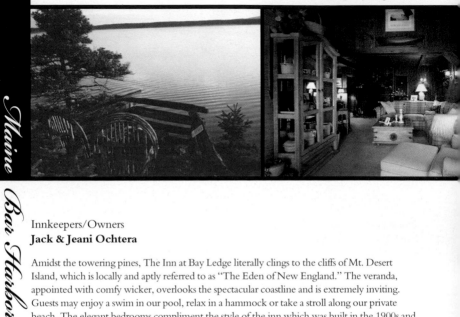

Innkeepers/Owners
Jack & Jeani Ochtera

Amidst the towering pines, The Inn at Bay Ledge literally clings to the cliffs of Mt. Desert Island, which is locally and aptly referred to as "The Eden of New England." The veranda, appointed with comfy wicker, overlooks the spectacular coastline and is extremely inviting. Guests may enjoy a swim in our pool, relax in a hammock or take a stroll along our private beach. The elegant bedrooms compliment the style of the inn which was built in the 1900s and possesses an upscale country ambiance. Beautifully decorated with antiques, all rooms are unique with views of Frenchmen Bay. King and queen beds are covered with designer linens, down quilts and feather beds. The Summer Cottage sits just 25 feet from the cliff's edge, and every room has a bay view! Fireplace flanked by French doors with panaromic views of Frenchmen Bay. Air conditioned for your comfort! For your special holiday, the Summer Cottage will make it perfect.

Rates
8 rooms, $125/$375 low season; high season $165/$475. 4 cottages $125/$375 low season; high season $175/$475. Number of Rooms: 12

Cuisine
Full gourmet breakfast served in the sunroom overlooking the bay. Afternoon tea & refreshments on the porch.

Nearest Airport
Bar Harbor 15 minutes, Bangor 1 hour, Portland 3 hours, Boston 5 hours

Manor House Inn

www.barharbormanorhouse.com
106 West Street, Bar Harbor, ME 04609
800-437-0088 • 207-288-3759 • Fax 207-288-2974
info@barharbormanorhouse.com

Member Since 1998

Innkeepers/Owners
Ken & Stacey Smith

Manor House Inn was built in 1887 as the 22 room Cottage "Boscobel." It has been authentically restored to its original splendor and is listed on the National Historic Register. The Inn now includes the Victorian era Chauffeur's Cottage, 2 airy Garden Cottages and the Acadia Cottage. The moment you step into our front entry a romantic Victorian past becomes your present. Enjoy casual comfort, convenience, and privacy while staying within easy walking distance, on historic West Street, of Bar Harbor's fine shops, restaurants, and ocean activities. Wake each morning to the smell of a delicious home baked breakfast. After a day spent enjoying the natural beauty of Acadia National Park and exploring Mount Desert Island return to the Inn and take tea with us in the gardens and enjoy some sweets from the kitchen. Or simply relax on one of our many wicker filled porches surrounded by cool green ferns and the smell of fresh sea air. We look forward to welcoming you.

Rates
18 Rooms/Suites $160/$275. Off-season $85/$210. We open in mid April and close in late October. Number of Rooms: 18

Cuisine
Each morning a full country breakfast is served buffet style from our Butler's Pantry. Afternoon tea and sweets are served each afternoon.

Nearest Airport
Hancock County Airport~20 minutes; Bangor International~1 Hour; Portland Jetport~3 Hours

Ullikana & A Yellow House

www.ullikana.com
16 The Field, 15 TheField, Bar Harbor, ME 04609
207-288-9552 • Fax 207-288-3682
relax@ullikana.com

Member Since 2000

Innkeepers/Owners
Helene Harton and Roy Kasindorf

Ullikana, a secluded, romantic haven, overlooking the harbor, and our sister inn, A Yellow House, only steps away, are two of the few remaining cottages from the 1800s in Bar Harbor. Only a minute walk from the center of town, our quiet location offers a haven of hospitality. Watch the lobster boats in the harbor from the garden or the patio, where sumptuous breakfasts are served. Relax in the casual elegance of these historic inns, where art is an important part of our decor. "Everything blends perfectly here. Few innkeepers have mastered the art of hospitality as well as Roy and Helene", says Moon Handbooks. We invite you to share the history and hospitality of Ullikana and A Yellow House with us.

Rates
16 Rooms, high season: $185/$355; low season: $160/$285. All our rooms have king or queen beds. All have private baths. Some have porches overlooking the harbor. Some rooms have fireplaces. Number of Rooms: 16

Cuisine
We serve a full breakfast on our patio, looking out on the water where our guests also enjoy afternoon refreshments."The elaborate breakfast is a real treat" says Fodor's.

Nearest Airport
Bangor and Bar Harbor

SelectRegistry.com

Pentagöet Inn

www.pentagoet.com
26 Main Street, Castine, ME 04421
800-845-1701 • 207-326-8616 • Fax 207-326-9382
stay@pentagoet.com

Member Since 2005

Innkeepers/Owners
Jack Burke & Julie Van de Graaf

The Pentagöet has been welcoming guests since it was built as a steamboat era hotel in 1894 and continues a tradition of gracious hospitality. This authentic Queen Anne Victorian has a wraparound porch, three story turret, extensive perennial gardens and renowned window boxes. You will feel at home with the charming mix of antiques and collectibles, fine linens and amenities. Overlooking Penobscot Bay the vintage seaside village of Castine is on the National Historic Register. Our concierge can plan itineraries for kayaking, sailing, hiking, antiques and art galleries, there are guest bikes for a sunset pedal to the lighthouse. We are centrally located for day trips to Camden, Blue Hill, Deer Isle, Stonington, Acadia and Bar Harbor. We invite you to dinner in our nationally recognized restaurant. Enjoy our exceptional home cooking that honors the classics in its soulful simplicity, bowing to the seasons and our local farms. Have a nightcap in our cozy old world bar, the inn's "utterly fascinating Passports Pub," according to Andrew Harper's Hideaway Report.

Rates
16 Rooms, all private baths, $140-$295. Open May-October. Seasonal packages and specials. Number of Rooms: 16

Cuisine
Full country breakfast, afternoon tea, evening hors d'oeuvres, guest coffee/tea bar. Dinner features local, organic produce, lobster, native fish and meats, New England specialties, fine desserts. Full bar and well stocked wine cellar.

Nearest Airport
Bangor (BGR) 1 hr, Bar Harbor (BHB) 50 min, Portland (PWM) 2.5 hrs

The Blue Hill Inn

www.bluehillinn.com
40 Union Street, P.O. Box 403, Blue Hill, ME 04614
800-826-7415 • 207-374-2844
sarah@bluehillinn.com

Member Since 1994

Maine

Blue Hill

Innkeeper/Owner
Sarah Pebworth

The coastal village of Blue Hill wraps around Blue Hill Bay and is centrally located for exploring Acadia National Park, Deer Isle, Castine, and the peninsula. This area offers rugged coastlines, blueberry fields, sea life, lighthouses, fine galleries, and small town charm. Stroll under evening skies brilliant with stars. The 1830 Federal inn, situated in the historic district, is a short walk to the bay, Kneisel Chamber Music Hall, and Blue Hill Mountain. The Blue Hill Inn retains many original features and was recognized as a 2010 Editors' Choice Best Classic B&B in Yankee Magazine's Travel Guide. After a day of hiking, boating, bird-watching, gallery hopping, or reading in the garden, you'll be pampered with afternoon treats, evening hors d'oeuvres, luxurious linens, air conditioned rooms, free wifi, and staff attentive to the every detail of your memorable stay. The inn offers a full bar and fine wines. Reserve a table in our candle-lit dining room for a meal designed with your pleasure in mind. The inn is proud to have been designated a Maine Environmental Leader.

Rates
11 rooms, 2 pet-friendly suites with kitchens, all have private baths. In-season, our rates include our three-course breakfast, which features lots of guest-friendly choices, local products, and organic coffees and teas. Number of Rooms: 13

Cuisine
Enjoy a complimentary three-course breakfast with many choices, served in our sunny dining room. An elegant dinner is served at the inn Monday though Friday. Our varied menus feature locally grown produce and Maine seafood. Full bar and fine wines.

Nearest Airport
Hancock Co.-Bar Harbor (BHB) - 40 min., Bangor (BGR) - 1 hour, Portland (PWM) - 3 hours.

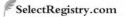
SelectRegistry.com

Pilgrim's Inn

www.pilgrimsinn.com
P.O. Box 69, 20 Main Street, Deer Isle, ME 04627
888-778-7505 • 207-348-6615 • Fax please call
innkeeper@pilgrimsinn.com

🍴 🍴 ♀

Member Since 1980

Maine
Deer Isle

Innkeeper/Owner
Tony Lawless & Tina Oddleifson

Overlooking Northwest Harbor and a tranquil pond, this 1793 colonial is surrounded by the unspoiled beauty of remote Deer Isle in Penobscot Bay. Glowing hearths, colonial colors, pumpkin pine floors and antique furnishings; combined with warm hospitality and flavorful meals in the cozy Whale's Rib Tavern have pleased many contented guests. Day trips to picturesque seaside villages and Acadia National Park make it an ideal location for an extended stay. The area is a kayaking, sailing and hiking paradise and is home to many artists, writers and the world renowned Haystack Mountain School of Crafts. The Inn is listed on the National Register of Historic Places; has been chosen as an Editors' Choice in Yankee Magazine's Travel Guide to New England; and as of one of the Country's Best B&Bs by Forbes.com. It has been designated as an Environmental Leader by the State of Maine and recently featured in the US edition of "1000 Places to See Before you Die." In addition to 12 rooms in the inn, three cottages on the property are perfect for families with children and pets.

Rates
12 Rooms and 3 cottages; $109/$259, B&B. Most rooms have views of the pond or Northwest Harbor. All rooms have private baths. Open Mid-May through Mid-October. Number of Rooms: 15

Cuisine
Full country breakfast; refreshments available all day; and dinner at the Whale's Rib Tavern featuring American heritage cuisine and creative daily specials.

Nearest Airport
Bangor International Airport

Camden Maine Stay Inn

www.camdenmainestay.com
22 High Street (US 1 North), Camden, ME 04843
207-236-9636 • Fax 207-236-0621
innkeeper@camdenmainestay.com

Member Since 1995

Maine

Camden

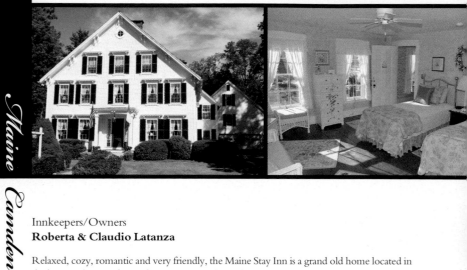

Innkeepers/Owners
Roberta & Claudio Latanza

Relaxed, cozy, romantic and very friendly, the Maine Stay Inn is a grand old home located in the historic district of one of America's most beautiful seaside villages, known as the place "where the mountains meet the sea". It projects the true essence of New England, its history, its tradition. To visit the Maine Stay Inn is to literally step into a venerable piece of history. Built in 1802 by a direct descendant of John Alden, the striking main house, attached carriage house and four-story barn are an outstanding example of the progressive farm buildings common to 19th century Maine. Our three parlors are tastefully decorated with antique Italian furnishings, paintings and ceramics. Winner of Karen Brown Reader's Choice Award 2009 for "Warmest Welcome in New England." Chosen by Frontgate as one of America's Finest Homes. In the words of Vacations Magazine, "Down east hospitality at its very best." Frommer's comments, "Camden's premier Bed and Breakfast", and Fodor's agrees, "Camden's best B&B." Welcome to the History and the Tradition of Maine... with an Italian accent!

Rates
From $115 to $270 per night. Each room has individual style and character. Many of them have original wide plank pine flooring and Vermont Castings stoves. All rooms are very romantic with private baths. Open year-round. Number of Rooms: 8

Cuisine
Gourmet breakfast, which may be enjoyed at our antique harvest table in the dining room or at a table for two on our sun porch overlooking our large beautiful garden. Tea and coffee served in the afternoon. Nearby casual and fine dining restaurants.

Nearest Airport
Rockland (RKD); Bangor (BGR); Portland (PWM); Boston (BOS)

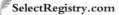

Camden Maine Hartstone Inn

www.hartstoneinn.com
41 Elm Street, Camden, ME 04843
800-788-4823 • 207-236-4259 • Fax 207-236-9575
info@hartstoneinn.com

Member Since 2002

Maine

Camden

Owners
Mary Jo Brink and Michael Salmon

Steps from Camden Harbor! AAA 4 Diamond hideaway in the heart of Camden village that Fodor's considers "An elegant and sophisticated retreat and culinary destination," this Mansard style Victorian built in 1835 offers a unique experience in pampered luxury. "From luscious linens in the guest rooms to the world-class cuisine in the dining room and the collection of 400 orchids, Mary Jo and Michael Salmon get absolutely everything right," says the Maine Explorers Guide. Each air conditioned guestroom combines carefully chosen furnishings to create a mood of lavish comfort and romance. Luxurious amenities include: on site massage room, ipads, WiFi, fireplaces, Jacuzzi Tubs, soft robes, Flat Screen w/ dvd. The Cuisine at the Hartstone has been recognized by The American Culinary Federation with their Achievement of Excellence Award. For your vacation in Camden choose the Hartstone Inn and reward yourself with a sumptuous multi-course breakfast, join the fun at happy hour with specialty cocktails & complimentary hors d'oeuvres. Critics and Repeat Guest say "don't miss dinner!"

Rates
6 rooms, 8 suites, $105/$280 B&B. Gourmet Getaway, Chef for a Day, Cooking Class and Spa packages available. Preview all of our packages www.hartstoneinn.com Number of Rooms: 14

Cuisine
Sumptuous multi-course breakfast, afternoon cookies and tea, happy hour w/specialty cocktails and complimentary hors d'oeuvres. Memorable five-course dinner is available nightly by reservation. Full bar and Wine Spectator award winning wine list.

Nearest Airport
Bangor or Portland

Hawthorn Inn

www.camdenhawthorn.com
9 High Street, Camden, ME 04843
866-381-3647 • 207-236-8842 • Fax N/A
info@camdenhawthorn.com

Member Since 2008

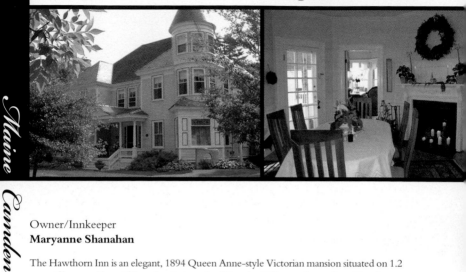

Owner/Innkeeper
Maryanne Shanahan

The Hawthorn Inn is an elegant, 1894 Queen Anne-style Victorian mansion situated on 1.2 acres of lawn and beautiful gardens just north of Camden Village and steps from Camden Harbor. One of 66 homes listed in the National Register of Historical Places in the High Street Historic District, the inn offers spacious accommodations with beautiful decor, Jacuzzis, soaking tubs, gas fireplaces, private decks, seasonal views of the Harbor from most rooms. Guests experience the romance of this elegant retreat in pampered luxury. They love to savor the Inn's renowned gourmet breakfast on the terrace and decks in summer and in the sunny dining room or cozy library in winter. The Hawthorn has a reputation for its warm and welcoming atmosphere, offering the perfect balance in comfort and sophistication. Attention to detail in decor and guests needs is in abundance at the inn. With just a short walk to town and the Harbor steps away from the back gate, the Hawthorn offers a peaceful oasis close to the Village and a beautiful venue for weddings, reunions and retreats.

Rates
Suites and rooms, $100/289. Corporate retreats, weddings, commitment ceremonies. Open year-round. Packages and Specials. Number of Rooms: 10

Cuisine
Full, gourmet breakfast. Local and organic foods. Afternoon refreshments; happy hour with wine bar and complimentary hors d'oeuvres.

Nearest Airport
Knox Municipal (RKD), Bangor (BGR), Portland Jetport (PWM)

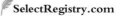 SelectRegistry.com

Inn at Sunrise Point

www.sunrisepoint.com
P.O. Box 1344, Camden, ME 04843
207-236-7716 • Fax 207-236-0820
info@sunrisepoint.com

Member Since 2005

Innkeeper/Owner
Daina H. Hill

A pampering seaside haven, this Andrew Harper's Best Hideaways-recommended bed and breakfast inn offers spectacular ocean views and all the luxuries you can expect from a AAA Four-Diamond property. Set on five secluded acres, this oceanfront hideaway is five minutes from picturesque Camden. Sleep soundly in the wonderful sea air, comforted by the gentle murmur of waves outside your window. Awaken to extraordinary sunrises across Penobscot Bay before enjoying a sumptuous breakfast in the Inn's sunlit conservatory or ocean room. Later, relax in the cherry-paneled library with a glass of fine wine and watch the moonrise over the Bay. Stay in a beautifully furnished room in the main house – a wonderfully restored cedar shingled Maine summer "cottage," or in one of the romantic, luxury cottages at the water's edge.Or choose the spacious loft set high among the trees. A luxurious, romantic and elegant retreat for discerning travelers. Ocean views, private decks, fireplaces, free wireless and more in all accommodations.

Rates
3 rooms $320-$415. 5 cottages $360-$625. Loft 2 rm suite $360-$610. Open Mid-April to Mid-November. Rates vary within range depending on dates. Number of Rooms: 9

Cuisine
Sumptuous three course breakfast in oceanfront conservatory, featuring Maine specialties and local produce; complimentary afternoon refreshments; full bar; fine dining and casual local seafood nearby for dinner.

Nearest Airport
Portland (PWM), Bangor (BGR), Rockland Municipal (RKD)

Maine Camden

Inns at Blackberry Common

www.innsatblackberrycommon.com
82 Elm Street, Camden, ME 04843
800-388-6000 • 207-236-6060 • Fax 207-236-9032
innkeepers@blackberryinn.com

Member Since 2006

Maine

Camden

Innkeepers/Owners
Jim & Cyndi Ostrowski

Just three blocks to the picturesque schooner filled harbor, our Inns are a quiet romantic oasis surrounded by over an acre of Maine gardens. Maine Explorer's Guide says "the prettiest interior in Camden." Three gracious parlors of the 1849 Victorian boast original tin ceilings and ornate moldings. Our extensive gardens, complete with a blackberry patch, are a quiet retreat after a day of sailing, hiking or kayaking. Choose an elegant guestroom in Maine's only recognized "Painted Lady" Victorian. Select a suite room in our restored Carriage House tucked amid the gardens. Or stay in a stately guestroom in our Federal Colonial or in the delightful Tinker's Cottage. Amenities include lavish featherbeds, fine linens, gas fireplaces, cable TV and soaking clawfoot or whirlpool tub for extra pampering. WiFi and A/C throughout. Create a special memory! Seasonal Dinner and Culinary packages. Fine selection of wines and spirits. Featured in "Gourmet Getaways: 50 Top Spots to Cook and Learn" 2009. Lighthouses and bicycling are our specialty.

Rates
$99/$289. Open all year. Fireplaces, whirlpools, WiFi & A/C. Seasonal lighthouse, dining and culinary packages. Number of Rooms: 18

Cuisine
Multi-course breakfast of local Maine specialties and our fresh garden herbs and berries served in our dining room or on the garden patio. Complimentary afternoon refreshments. Gourmet dinner service for guests. Excellent selction of wines daily!

Nearest Airport
Portland Jetport; Bangor International

Berry Manor Inn

www.berrymanorinn.com
81 Talbot Avenue, P.O. Box 1117 , Rockland, ME 04841
800-774-5692 • 207-596-7696 • Fax 207-596-9958
info@berrymanorinn.com

Member Since 2007

Innkeepers/Owners
Cheryl Michaelsen & Michael LaPosta, Jr.

The Berry Manor Inn was built with all the grandeur of the Victorian age and remains one of the most stately homes of the Rockland/Camden area. The spacious guest rooms are uniquely decorated in the colors of the Victorian era with a pleasing balance of elegance and comfort without being pretentious. All guest rooms have private luxury baths, many with whirlpool tubs, a/c, TVs and most rooms have fireplaces. The inn prides itself on providing a range of guest services and amenities to enhance the comfort of our guests including the evening offering of homemade pie made by the MOMs! The inn is located in a quiet, residential neighborhood away from Rt.1, but within walking distance to Rockland's harbor, downtown shops, art galleries, Farnsworth Art Museum, Lighthouse Museum, an array of great restaurants and just 6 miles from Camden. The inn was named by bedandbreakfast.com in 2012 and by TripAdvisor in 2008 as one of the Top 10 Best B&Bs in US. We invite you to enjoy our lobsters, nearby lighthouses, renowned museums and experience the Maine standard for B&B relaxed luxury.

Rates
$175/$290 Late June - Mid October; $115/$235 Late October - Early June. Suite $430-$240. Transition and holiday rates apply. All rooms have private baths, in room heat/AC, TVs and WiFi. Inn is Open Year Round. Packages available. Number of Rooms: 12

Cuisine
Delicious multi-course breakfast featuring sweet or savory entrees that varies daily. Dietary restrictions accommodated with notice. Complimentary Guest Pantry area stocked w/soda, ice and our moms' homemade pies recently featured on the Food Network!

Nearest Airport
Rockland (RKD)5 min srv'd CapeAir/JetBlue @ Boston; Portland (PWM)1.5hrs; Bangor (BGR)2 hr

Newcastle Inn

www.newcastleinn.com
60 River Road, Newcastle, ME 04553
207-563-5685 • 877-376-6111
info@newcastleinn.com

Member Since 1990

Maine

Newcastle

Innkeeper/Owner
Julie Bolthuis

Located in Maine's MidCoast, Newcastle Inn has been welcoming guests since 1911. All guestrooms have a private bath and offer warmth and details such as gas fireplaces or stoves, four poster beds, Jacuzzi tubs or views of the Damariscotta River. There is complimentary WiFi and two rooms are dog friendly. A delicious, made-from-scratch breakfast is served in the dining room, or weather permitting, outside on the deck which overlooks the gardens and the river. The common areas provide opportunity to mix and mingle with other guests, or if you prefer, there are spaces for you to find your own "private corner." Complimentary coffee, tea, cold beverages, snacks, and the "bottomless cookie jar" are available in the Guest Pantry. After a day exploring the area with its beaches, lighthouses, art galleries and antique shops, our pub is the perfect place to relax and enjoy a glass of wine or a Maine micro-brewed beer. Newcastle Inn is centrally located for all you want to see and do on your trip to MidCoast Maine.

Rates
$180/$275 in season; $145/$215 off season. Corporate rates available. One room can accommodate a third guest for additional charge of $40.00/night. The dog fee is $35.00/night, limit one dog in the room. Number of Rooms: 14

Cuisine
A full breakfast is served each morning. You won't leave the table hungry! Dietary restrictions/allergies gladly accommodated.

Nearest Airport
Portland Jetport, Portland, ME - 1 hour

SelectRegistry.com

The Squire Tarbox Inn

www.squiretarboxinn.com
1181 Main Road, Westport Island/Wiscasset, ME 04578
207-882-7693 • Fax 207-882-7107
innkeepers@squiretarboxinn.com

Member Since 1974

Maine

Westport Island/Wiscasset

Innkeepers/Owners
Roni and Mario De Pietro

Once upon a time, there was a Country Inn conspicuous from all others. After a restoration for your comfort, this colonial farm created an alternate luxury, amidst the splendor of nature. Set within fields, stone walls, and woods, and with kindness to all creatures great and small, pristine barns are filled with gentle animals. The Inn offers you peace and tranquility, away from tourist crowds, but convenient to coastal adventures. Relax with a drink on our screened in deck while watching the wild life or the beautiful sunsets. Dine leisurely and enjoy the ambiance in our 1763 dining room or on the deck with meals created by our Swiss/owner chef Mario, using all local organic vegetables from our own farm. Take a row or just daydream in the boat on the salt water marsh. Sleep with the luxury of down duvets and pillows and the comfort of Posturepedic mattresses. On the National Register of Historic Places.

Rates
$115/$199 double occupancy. Open mid April - Dec. 31. $35 for an extra person in a room. Number of Rooms: 11

Cuisine
A mouthwatering hot breakfast with eggs from our own chickens is served. Chocolate chip cookies all day; a full liquor license. Gourmet kitchen with an a la carte dinner menu prepared by Swiss owner/chef Mario, served daily except Tuesdays.

Nearest Airport
Portland Jetport

Inn at English Meadows

www.englishmeadowsinn.com
141 Port Road, Kennebunk, ME 04043
207-967-5766 • 800-272-0698
innkeeper@englishmeadowsinn.com

Member Since 2012

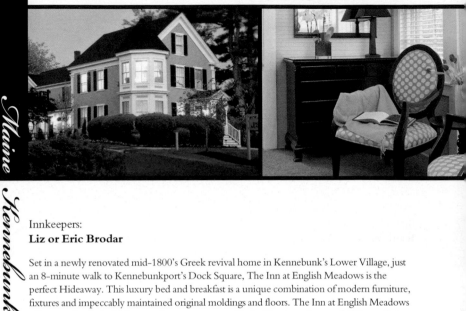

Innkeepers:
Liz or Eric Brodar

Set in a newly renovated mid-1800's Greek revival home in Kennebunk's Lower Village, just an 8-minute walk to Kennebunkport's Dock Square, The Inn at English Meadows is the perfect Hideaway. This luxury bed and breakfast is a unique combination of modern furniture, fixtures and impeccably maintained original moldings and floors. The Inn at English Meadows offers two dramatically decorated common rooms filled with art, art deco, and Chineses from the owner's personal collection that will delight your senses and appeal to your inner self. The five rooms, four suites and bungalow show off the modern style of the Inn. Elegant amenities, including Frette fine linens, bath robes, slippers, towels, and toiletries by Malin & Goetz and beds by Vera Wang, await our guests. A variety of special touches are offered, such as, WiFi Internet access, docking stations, flat-screen TVs, and fireplaces. The highlight of your stay will be the three-course gourmet breakfast and homemade refreshments that are served each morning and afternoon.

Rates
$199 - $389 Number of Rooms: 10

Cuisine
Guests of The Inn have expressed that the freshly prepared, three course gourmet breakfast is nothing short of divine. Menu items prepared by Liz, the culinary creative, are strongly influenced by her time spent traveling abroad.

Nearest Airport
PWM Portland Jetport, MHT Manchester, BOS Boston Logan

 SelectRegistry.com

Captain Jefferds Inn

www.captainjefferdsinn.com
P.O. Box 691, 5 Pearl Street, Kennebunkport, ME 04046
800-839-6844 • 207-967-2311
captjeff@captainjefferdsinn.com

Member Since 2008

Maine

Kennebunkport

Innkeepers/Owners
Erik & Sarah Lindblom

For travelers seeking a unique escape, the Captain Jefferds Inn holds particular appeal. Perhaps it's the historic lines of this 1804 sea captain's home tucked away within the heart of the historic residential district of Kennebunkport. Maybe it's the inn's beautifully manicured gardens, the siren song of ocean waves, or the ease of access to recreational activities. Then again it might be the absolute comfort and attention to detail found in each thoughtfully decorated room. Find yourself selecting from a wonderful assortment of home baked goodies, light hors d'oeuvres and seasonal hot and cold beverages. Find yourself experiencing personalized service and little touches to enhance your stay like wireless internet access throughout the property and beach cruiser bicycles. Find yourself lounging on the Kennebunk Beaches or taking a five minute stroll to explore Dock Square's specialty boutiques, art galleries, antique shops and restaurants ranging from casual to five-diamond rated. Regardless of what leads you to Kennebunkport, find yourself at the Captain Jefferds Inn.

Rates
$149/$389 Seasonally adjusted. Open year-round. Number of Rooms: 15

Cuisine
Full served 3-course gourmet breakfast with fresh flowers, candlelight and fireplace in the cooler months. Afternoon tea with home baked goods and light hors d'oeuvres. Fine wines and champagne are available for purchase.

Nearest Airport
PWM - Portland Jetport, MHT - Manchester Boston Regional Airport, BOS - Boston Logan International Airport

Captain Lord Mansion

www.captainlord.com
6 Pleasant Street, P.O. Box 800, Kennebunkport, ME 04046-0800
800-522-3141 • 207-967-3141 • Fax 207-967-3172
innkeeper@captainlord.com

Member Since 1975

Innkeepers/Owners
Bev Davis and Rick Litchfield

Make enduring memories with us! Your comfort, serenity and relaxation are vitally important to us. We strive to provide warm hospitality and lots of personal service. Our central location, extensively landscaped grounds and large, beautifully-appointed guest rooms are dedicated to your complete satisfaction. Each guest-room offers such amenities as an oversize four-poster bed, cozy gas fireplace, flat screen TV and a heated marble bath floor. Several baths have multiple body-jet showers; 9 have double jacuzzi-style tubs. Find fresh flowers, freshly-prepared, family-style breakfasts, afternoon refreshments and lots of personal attention. New, on-premises romantic spa.The Inn's scenic location is situated at the head of a beautiful sloping green, overlooking the Kennebunk River. Our picturesque, quiet, yet convenient neighborhood affords you a terrific place from which to walk to explore the shops, restaurants and galleries in the historic village of Kennebunkport.

Rates
15 Rooms, $179/$449 B&B; 1 Suite $349/$549 B&B. Open year-round. Number of Rooms: 16

Cuisine
Full 3-course breakfast. Also, casual afternoon tea, with available fresh fruit, cheese and crackers as well as freshly-baked sweets. The Inn also offers a selection of fine wines, chocolate-covered strawberries and fruit platters for purchase.

Nearest Airport
Portland, ME; 35 Miles north of inn.

SelectRegistry.com

Maine Stay Inn & Cottages

www.mainestayinn.com
34 Maine Street, Kennebunkport, ME 04046
800-950-2117 • 207-967-2117
innkeeper@mainestayinn.com

Member Since 1996

Innkeepers/Owners
Judi and Walter Hauer

Experience relaxed sophistication at the Maine Stay Inn, where exceptional warmth and hospitality greet you at our door. Listed on the National Register of Historic Places, the Maine Stay is located steps from the quaint seaside village of Kennebunkport, known for its fine restaurants, shops, and galleries. And don't miss the area's incredible beaches, coves, and nature reserves! Enjoy afternoon tea and freshly baked cookies on our wrap-around porch or before the living room fire – a perfect opportunity to meet fellow guests and innkeepers. Or relax in your luxurious guest room with cable television, complimentary WiFi, fine linens, and many with whirlpool tubs and/or gas fireplaces. Choose a Victorian Inn Room/Suite, the intimacy of a Romantic Cottage Suite, or a stylish Contemporary Cottage Suite. Our Classic Cottage Suites offer spacious accommodations, perfect for families or friends traveling together. Cottage Suite guests often choose to have the gourmet breakfast delivered to their door – the ultimate in luxury! Enjoy classic elegance with modern comforts.

Rates
4 Inn Rooms, $129/$269; 2 Inn Suites, $179/$349; 11 Cottage Rooms/Suites, $149/$359. Open year-round. Number of Rooms: 17

Cuisine
We strive to serve the freshest & most interesting breakfasts possible & offer guests different gourmet entrees daily. Enjoy summer fruit bruschetta w/candied nuts one day and savory french toast with baby greens the next. Afternoon refreshments daily.

Nearest Airport
Portland, ME

Haven By The Sea

www.havenbythesea.com
59 Church Street, Wells Beach, ME 04090
207-646-4194 • Fax 207-646-4194
jarvis@havenbythesea.com

Member Since 2006

Maine

Wells Beach

Innkeepers/Owners
John & Susan Jarvis

Completely renovated and known as Wells Beach oceanside premier Inn. Find yourself just steps back from one of Maine's most beautiful beaches. Haven By The Sea is a place so charming, so welcoming, so relaxing, you will return time and time again. The Inn itself was once a seaside church located in a quiet residential neighborhood and uniquely restored as one of Southern Maine's destination spots. Enjoy breakfast in the multi-level dining room or terrace with its breeze from the ocean and surrounding marshlands. Enjoy a refreshment at "Temptations", the Inn's bar, for your added convenience and pleasure. Some guestrooms-suites have private decks and balcony waterviews. Original hardwood floors give the building a sense of history, warmth and old-world charm. Large common areas, all with fireplaces, offer a comfortable setting to relax and unwind. Historical colors and tasteful decor treat the eye. The Inn is conveniently located between the historic towns of Ogunquit and Kennebunkport with specialty shops and dining experiences .

Rates
Guest Rooms: $209/279 Suites: $309 King and Queen Beds; Private Baths, Cable TV, Wireless Internet and Central Air Conditioning. Number of Rooms: 6

Cuisine
Full breakfast served in the Dining Room or Terrace. Full bar service available select hours (Monday - Saturday). Guest Services area offers a refrigerator, cold Maine Poland Spring water; gourmet coffee/tea available during the day/evening hours.

Nearest Airport
Portland, ME 45 Min. Manchester, NH 1 Hr./15 Min. Logan, MA 1 Hr./30 Min.

SelectRegistry.com

Dockside Guest Quarters

🍽️ 🍽️ 🍽️ 🍷

www.docksidegq.com
22 Harris Island Rd., York, ME 03909
800-270-1977 • 207-363-2868 • Fax 207-363-1977
info@docksidegq.com

Member Since 1975

Maine

York

Innkeepers/Owners
Eric & Carol Lusty

The Dockside is a special place that captures the essence of the Maine seacoast, with its natural beauty, gracious hospitality, abundant sights, recreation and activities. Uniquely situated on a private peninsula overlooking York Harbor and the Atlantic Ocean, each room has a panoramic water view. Accommodations are in the Maine House, a classic New England Cottage, furnished with antiques and marine art. The large wrap around porch, complete with wicker rocking chairs and iced tea, offers great views of the harbor activities. The multi-unit buildings at the water's edge offer several different room types, all with private decks and water views. Each room is tastefully and individually decorated. There is plenty to do on site and close by; pristine beaches, nature walk, golf, boat rentals, art galleries and antique shops. The Dockside Restaurant boasts a water view from every table. Our creatively diverse menu and extensive wine list will ensure a truly memorable dining experience. You can also, dine or enjoy your favorite beverage from the screened porch.

Rates
(19) water-view rooms $135-265, 6 suites $248-325. (1) 3 bedroom unit $2450 weekly. Off season rates & packages. Weekly discounts. Number of Rooms: 25

Cuisine
Our restaurant is a favorite with locals and visitors alike. Lunch or dinner on the porch, overlooking York Harbor is a special experience you are sure to enjoy. Our cozy bar or harbor view deck is great for a lite meal or beverages.

Nearest Airport
Manchester, NH 1 hr.; Boston, MA 1.5 hrs.; Portland, Maine 50 minutes.

The Waterford Inne

www.waterfordinne.com
Box 149, 258 Chadbourne Road, Waterford, ME 04088
207-583-4037 • 207-542-3630 • Fax 207-583-4037
inne@gwi.net

Member Since 1979

Maine

Waterford

Innkeeper/Owner
Barbara Vanderzanden

A 19th century farmhouse on a country lane amidst 25 acres of fields and woods, distinctively different, a true country inn offering special accommodations, a charming blend of three centuries - the warmth of early furnishings combined with contemporary comforts. An air of quiet simple elegance pervades the common rooms rich with antiques and art, pewter and primitives. An intimate library with an eclectic collection to appeal to all tastes–travel, nature, history... Step outside to explore the pleasures of country simplicity, to take a walk, to listen to the songbirds, to smell the freshness of a summer morning or perhaps the winter fragrance of a wood-burning fire. Wander through the gardens which provide a colorful array of flowers and a bounty of fresh fare for your dining table. Return inne-side to pamper your palate with country chic cuisine. The road to the Waterford Inne is traveled by hikers and cyclists, antiquers and skiers, discriminating travelers who seek charm, quiet and personal attention. Re-create your spirit with a peaceful journey back to the country.

Rates
8 uniquely decorated guestrooms. 6 rooms with bath en suite $160-$200. 2 rooms with semi-private bath (excellent for families) $125 each. Open year round (with a few breaks between January and April.) Number of Rooms: 8

Cuisine
Full breakfast included. Fine dinners available with advance reservation. We do not offer a menu, but prepare a fine meal (with attention to guests' preferences and dietary restrictions). $40 fixed price. Guests are invited to bring their own spirits.

Nearest Airport
Portland, ME The inn is approximately 60 miles NW of Portland.

Maryland

"The Old Line State"

Famous for: Maryland Crabs, Chesapeake Bay, Ocean City, Atlantic Coast, River Valleys, Rolling Hills, Forests, Appalachian Mountains, Fort McHenry, Tobacco.

© 2012 Chrismar Mapping Services Inc. Licensed for use in the 2012 Select Registry.

132 Lake Pointe Inn
133 Antietam Overlook Farm
134 Stoney Creek Farm
135 Antrim 1844 Country Inn
136 1840s Carrollton Inn
137 Wayside Inn B&B
138 Brampton B&B Inn
139 Great Oak Manor Inn
140 Sandaway Waterfront Lodging
141 Savage River Lodge

Lake Pointe Inn

www.deepcreekinns.com
174 Lake Pointe Drive, Deep Creek Lake, MD 21541
800-523-LAKE • 301-387-0111 • Fax 301-387-0190
Member Since 2000   relax@deepcreekinns.com

Maryland Deep Creek Lake

Innkeeper
Ed Spak

The Lake Pointe Inn decorated in the Arts & Crafts style, embraces you with an exceptionally warm welcome when you enter the chestnut paneled Great Room with it's Mission Style furnishings. Nestled in the Lake Pointe Community in Western Maryland, the Inn is perched just 13 feet from water's edge. The wraparound porch invites you to relax in a rocking chair, read or watch the waterfowl frolic. It is easy to enjoy Garrett County's 4 season activities while staying at the Inn. Golf, skiing and snowboarding await you at the Wisp Resort, adjacent to the Lake Pointe Community. Tour the area using our complimentary canoes, kayaks and bicycles or hike in the 5 nearby State Parks. The outdoor fireplace, herb garden and hammock provide a perfect haven for private conversation or stargazing. Frank Lloyd Wright's Fallingwater and Kentuck Knob are nearby. Lake Pointe Inn is a perfect getaway in any season for any reason!

Rates
$232/$292; All have gas fireplaces, TV/DVD. Some rooms have:Spa Tub, Steam Shower, Balcony. Number of Rooms: 10

Cuisine
Full breakfast and light hors d'oeuvres included in daily rate; dinners served to Inn guests on 3-day holiday weekends.

Nearest Airport
Pittsburgh International PA Washington DC Baltimore MD

Antietam Overlook Farm

www.antietamoverlook.com
4812 Porterstown Rd., Keedysville, MD 21756
800-878-4241 • 301-432-4200 • Fax 301-432-5230
Reservations@antietamoverlook.com

Member Since 1992

Maryland Keedysville

Owner: **Mark Svrcek**
Innkeeper: **Michelle Krantz**

Experience Antietam Overlook & 95-acres of mountaintop beauty. Elevation: 1000' at the edge of the Battlefield & 40 mile views of four states. The Inn is built of hand crafted timber frame, rough-cut pine and hardwood. Warm fireplaces & comfortable furnishings create an atmosphere that even the men appreciate. In the winter months, guests are invited to relax by the main fireplace where interesting conversation adds to the Antietam experience. The views are spectacular year round, but in the spring, summer & fall, the "Overlook" porch with its Western view for sunsets, is breathtaking. Spacious suites include fireplaces, comfy queen & king beds, soaking tubs, private baths and private screened porches. Enjoy the Hot Tub under the stars. While our seclusion and tranquility are unparalleled, guests also enjoy visiting The Antietam National Battlefield, Harpers Ferry, Shepherdstown WV & Gettysburg. Antiquing? We have the route planned for you. Antietam's 150th Anniv. & special events are planned. Oh, bring your horses and ride the 4200 acres of Battlefield. It is allowed.

Rates
6 Suites, $185/$350 B&B. Generals Quarters $450. Open year-round. Attractions: Antietam National Battlefield, Harpers Ferry, antiquing, Charlestown horse races, Hollywood Casino, hiking, biking, horseback riding and relaxing. Number of Rooms: 6

Cuisine
3 course gourmet breakfast is always included. Many dining experiences are nearby. Our House Chef is usually available to create your dream dining experience. Enjoy a Five Course Dinner with 5 wines for an added fee of $175.00 per person.

Nearest Airport
Reagan National, BWI & Dulles are 1 Hour. Hagerstown airport is 25 minutes away.

Stoney Creek Farm

www.stoneycreekfarm.com

19223 Manor Church Road, Boonsboro, MD 21713

301-432-6272

innkeeper@stoneycreekfarm.com

Member Since 2007

Maryland

Boonsboro

Innkeepers/Owners

Denise Lawhead and David Kempton

Get away from the hustle and bustle, unwind at Stoney Creek Farm! Lovingly restored in 2005, our bed & breakfast spares no comfort and affords every modern amenity to eclectic travelers from near and far. Guests at the Inn enjoy our beautifully accommodated rooms, wonderful gardens and grounds, five miles of wooded trails for hiking or horse back riding as well as our delicious hot breakfast in the mornings and wine and cheese in the evenings. Delicious upscale dining and unique shopping, including many antique shops, are all around. We're just minutes from the beautiful C&O canal, Antietam Battlefield, and a twenty minute drive from historic Shepherdstown and a half hour from historic Gettysburg. Stoney Creek Farm is also a unique location for your special event including wedding ceremonies, receptions, civil unions or even your company retreat. Get away from the hustle and bustle, visit Stoney Creek Farm. Situated in the rolling hills of beautiful Washington County, Maryland, Stoney Creek Farm awaits your arrival and welcomes you home to our historic Inn.

Rates
King Rooms $225 (Sunday through Thursday) $250 (Friday through Saturday) Queen Rooms $195 (Sunday through Thursday) $225 (Friday through Saturday) Number of Rooms: 4

Cuisine
Gourmet breakfast offered. Wine and cheese served nightly.

Nearest Airport
Baltimore, Washington Dulles

Antrim 1844 Country Inn

🍴 🍴 🍷

www.antrim1844.com
30 Trevanion Road, Taneytown, MD 21787
800-858-1844 • 410-756-6812 • Fax 410-756-2744
info@antrim1844.com

Member Since 1993

Maryland

Taneytown

Proprietors
Dorothy and Richard Mollett

You are cordially invited to relive the elegance and hospitality of this National Historic Trust Antebellum Plantation. Antrim 1844 is located amidst 24 manicured acres of countryside accentuated by softly lit romantic walkways, rose gardens and bronze fountains. Embrace the comfort of one of our masterfully restored guestrooms adorned with lavish antique decor, fireplaces, jacuzzis, and WIFI. Savor our Modern French Six Course Pre-fixe fine dining experience in our award winning Smokehouse Restaurant or dine privately in The Wine Cellar which boasts over 20,000 bottles of an extrodinary wine collection. Wine Spectators "Best of Award of Excellence" for over a decade as well as a proud member of DiRoNA.

Rates
40 Guest Rooms and Suites, $160/$400. Open year-round. Number of Rooms: 40

Cuisine
Afternoon tea. Evening hors d'ouevres. Elegant 6-course prix fixe dinner $68.50.
Morning wake up tray at your door & full served breakfast. Enjoy a drink in the Pickwick Pub or privately dine in the wine cellar which boasts over 20,000 bottles of wine.

Nearest Airport
Baltimore Washington International (BWI), Reagan Nationaland Dulles

1840s Carrollton Inn

www.1840scarrolltoninn.com
50 Albemarle Street, Baltimore, MD 21202
410-385-1840 • Fax 410-385-9080
info@1840scarrolltoninn.com

Member Since 2008

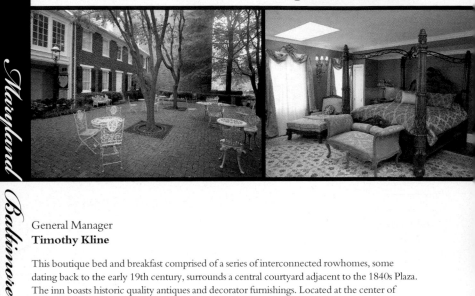

General Manager
Timothy Kline

This boutique bed and breakfast comprised of a series of interconnected rowhomes, some dating back to the early 19th century, surrounds a central courtyard adjacent to the 1840s Plaza. The inn boasts historic quality antiques and decorator furnishings. Located at the center of historic Jonestown, the 1840s Carrollton Inn is within a short walk of Inner Harbor attractions, Little Italy's fine dining and the nightlife at Power Plant Live. The 1840s Carrollton Inn, next door to the historic Carroll Mansion, celebrates the life of Charles Carroll of Carrollton, the longest lived and only Catholic signer of the Declaration of Independence. Guests retreat to the comfort of overnight rooms with beds featuring handcrafted Kingsdown mattresses, large baths with whirlpool tubs and fireplaces topped with mantles of marble and oak. Business and leisure travelers alike enjoy the convenience of complimentary WI-FI access, flat-screen cable television, in-room telephone, refrigerator and microwave. Romance, spa, all-inclusive and elopement packages available as well as monthly specials!

Rates
Room rates range from $150 - $350 per night. Corporate, government and military rates available. Monthly and seasonal special rates, add-on and all-inclusive packages also available. Visit our website for details. Number of Rooms: 13

Cuisine
A full breakfast is served from a menu each morning, prepared to order, and included with overnight accommodations. Guests may enjoy dining in the charming garden courtyard, the historic first floor parlor or in the privacy of their room or suite.

Nearest Airport
Baltimore/Washington International Airport (BWI) is located just 10 miles from the Inn (a 20-minute drive).

Wayside Inn Bed & Breakfast

www.waysideinnmd.com
4344 Columbia Road, Ellicott City, MD 21042-5910
410-461-4636
bnbboy@verizon.net

Member Since 2008

Maryland

Ellicott City

Innkeepers/Owners
David & Susan Balderson

Step back in time to a gentler way of living. Two hundred years of history await you at the Wayside Inn. Conveniently located in historic Ellicott City, Maryland, and within a short drive of either Baltimore or Washington, D.C., the Wayside Inn is the perfect place for you to escape into the past. Guests of the Inn enjoy outstanding, home-away-from-home hospitality. Your Room or Suite is filled with fine antiques or reproductions, the finest linens, and too many ammenities to list here. Your comfortable night's sleep in one of our exquisite rooms is followed by a full, gourmet breakfast, created fresh that morning by the innkeepers. Then spend the day exploring the area: shopping in Historic Ellicott City, antiquing in Frederick, touring our nation's capital, meandering through Annapolis, cruising on the Chesapeake Bay, or experiencing Baltimore's famous Inner Harbor. In the evening, treat yourself to a fabulous dinner at one of our area's many restaurants, wine bars or micro-breweries. Five of Baltimore Magazine's Top 50 restaurants within a five mile radius.

Rates
$159-$219. Number of Rooms: 6

Cuisine
A full, upscale breakfast is served each morning between 7:30 AM and 9:30 AM.

Nearest Airport
Baltimore/Washington International. Travelers also come into National and Dulles Airports.

Brampton Bed and Breakfast Inn

www.bramptoninn.com
25227 Chestertown Road, Chestertown, MD 21620
866-305-1860 • 410-778-1860
innkeeper@bramptoninn.com

Member Since 2001

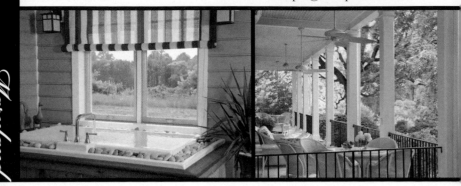

Innkeepers/Owners
Michael & Danielle Hanscom, Rita Scardino

The award-winning Brampton Bed and Breakfast Inn is the Eastern Shore's romantic oasis. Located on 25 wooded and landscaped acres, one mile outside the charming waterfront town of Chestertown, Maryland. Brampton beautifully blends the grand elegance of a historical estate with the comfort and amenities today's travelers deserve. Ignite or rekindle romance in a spacious, private and well-appointed guest room, suite or cottage, offering wood-burning or gas fireplaces, whirlpool soaking tubs and glorious views. Enjoy a full a-la-carte breakfast graciously served at individual tables in Brampton's beautiful dining room or breakfast in bed delivered to the cottages upon request. Afternoon tea features delectable treats. Attention to detail, personal service, and friendly innkeepers will make your visit a memorable one. Chestertown is a colonial village with abundant outdoor activities, unique shops and great restaurants. It serves as a perfect base for exploring all that the Eastern Shore has to offer.

Rates
13 rooms, suites and secluded cottages with private, en-suite bathrooms, featuring whirlpool tubs and/or showers. All our rooms have working wood or gas fireplaces. $219 - $419. Number of Rooms: 13

Cuisine
Our complimentary full breakfast includes: fresh seasonal fruit, just baked muffins or scones, choice of entree using local organic eggs, meat and vegetables. Daily afternoon tea. Beverages and home baked cookies 24/7. Proud member of eightbroads.com

Nearest Airport
Baltimore (BWI), Philadelphia (PHL) 90 min Washington DC (IAD) or (DCA) 2 hrs, NYC (JFK) 3 1/2 hrs from NYC (JFK)

 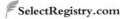

Great Oak Manor

www.greatoak.com
10568 Cliff Road, Chestertown, MD 21620
800-504-3098 • 410-778-5943
innkeeper@greatoak.com

Member Since 2003

Owner
Bernd Duerrmeier

F. Scott Fitzgerald wrote of blue lawns and country houses, such is Great Oak Manor. From the estate's walled garden bordered by 65-year old boxwoods and its circular drive on the estate side, to its magnificent view of the Chesapeake Bay and private beach on the water side, this country estate provides the appropriate setting for a relaxing getaway or a romantic weekend. Our guest and public rooms are spacious and beautifully furnished. Built at a time when grandeur was more important than cost, guests are swept away by the majesty of the house. This is a true Manor House with fine details, beautiful furnishings, Orientals, and an 850 volume library. The Manor has a reflection pool in the glass conservatory and a private beach. The Manor will meet your every need, with 1,200 ft. of waterfront lawn and towering trees on the Chesapeake Bay, and the most beautiful sunsets on the Eastern Shore of Maryland. A perfect place to rejuvenate your soul. Our Conservatory which overlooks the Bay, is popular for small business retreats, weddings or family reunions.

Rates
9 rooms,$159/$315,3 suites,$249/$315.Elegant spacious rooms, fireplaces, massage therapy available. Number of Rooms: 12

Cuisine
Sumptuous Country Breakfast at private tables in the dining room or on the patio overlooking the bay. Fresh baked goods cooked daily, fresh. Afternoon homemade sweets and refreshments, coffee,tea,water,and soda. Complimentary evening Port and Sherry.

Nearest Airport
BWI Baltimore MD.(90 min.), PHL (90 min.)

Sandaway Waterfront Lodging

www.sandaway.com
7 Miles From St. Michaels, 103 W. Strand Rd., Oxford, MD 21654
888-726-3292 • 888-SANDAWAY
info@sandaway.com

Member Since 1970

Maryland

Oxford

Innkeeper – **Ben Gibson**
Active Owners – **Ken & Wendy Gibson**

Sandaway is a Chesapeake Bay getaway with eighteen bed and breakfast style accommodations on 2.5 acres of waterfront property with a private sandy beach. Our waterfront location in the colonial village of Oxford, Maryland makes us a unique destination. Guests can walk to restaurants, marinas, our museum, and some shops along brick sidewalks past charming homes with white picket fences. Overnight guests can choose between suites in the circa 1875 Sandaway Lodge, or Sandaway's more modern Deluxe Waterfront rooms. Most guestrooms on the property have water views or porches, overlooking the Tred Avon River, Choptank River, and Chesapeake Bay beyond. Sandaway guests can take the car ferry across the river for a short-cut to St. Michaels, and also drive to the nearby towns of Easton, Tilghman, and Cambridge. At the end of the day, find yourself a beachfront seat at Sandaway. Sailboats entering the harbor at sunset and osprey flying by will create lasting memories. We are indeed "The Land of Pleasant Living."

Rates
Sandaway's rates range from $169 to $299. Most guestrooms and suites are waterfront with private porches. Wedding and Group Rates Available. Not Recommended for Children. Non-Smoking Accommodations. Number of Rooms: 18

Cuisine
24 hour coffee, tea, and snacks. At breakfast time a "Lite Fare Breakfast" is delivered to your door in a basket. Walk to famous Oxford restaurants, or dine close by in St. Michaels, Trappe, Easton & Cambridge. Enjoy Eastern Shore of Maryland cuisine.

Nearest Airport
BWI & National - 1.5 hours. Dulles - 2 hrs. 15 min. Recommended directions at sandaway.com

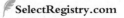

Savage River Lodge

www.savageriverlodge.com
1600 Mt. Aetna Road, Frostburg, MD 21532
(301) 689-3200 • Fax (301) 689-2746
info@savageriverlodge.com

Member Since 2010

Maryland
Frostburg

Innkeepers/Owners
Jan Russell and Mike Dreisbach

The Savage River Lodge is situated on 42 acres in the center of a 750-acre state forest in Western Maryland. We offer 18 individual luxury cabins, a gourmet restaurant, fully-stocked bar and superior hospitality. Our outdoor recreation includes xc skiing, snow shoeing, biking, fly fishing, geo-caching and miles of hiking trails. Other attractions in the area include Frank Lloyd Wright's Falling Water, downhill skiing, golf and more. Our restaurant offers some of the most interesting food in the area such as wild game, vegetarian/vegan and gluten free options. We also specialize in American classics, such as steak, and seafood and have in-cabin dining available for those who want a more private experience. Homemade muffins and juice are delivered to the cabins each morning. We are annually awarded the Wine Spectator Award of Excellence, the Wine Enthusiast Award of Distinction and SRL was a recipient of Travelocity's Local Secret Big Finds. In 2011 we were awarded the Sustainable/Green Award from the Maryland Dept. of Tourism and we're a certified Md. Green Travel Partner.

Rates
Our cabin rates begin at $225 per night for a double occupancy Standard cabin, which includes a complimentary morning muffin basket with freshly made muffins and orange juice. We are also pet friendly! Number of Rooms: 18

Cuisine
The Savage River Lodge is where wild game meets tempeh. Our seasonally changing menus have a variety of American classics and serve all palates, including vegetarian/vegan and gluten free. Open daily for lunch and dinner and breakfast on the weekends.

Nearest Airport
2 1/2 hours from Pittsburgh, Baltimore Washington International, and Dulles Airports.

Massachusetts

Famous for: Pilgrims, Thanksgiving, Salem Witch Trials, Boston Tea Party, Birth of the American Revolution, Minutemen, Freedom Trail, Swan Boats, Cape Cod, The Berkshires, Education, Arts, Technology, and Medicine.

Birchwood Inn

www.birchwood-inn.com
7 Hubbard Street, P.O. Box 2020, Lenox, MA 01240
800-524-1646 • 413-637-2600 • Fax 413-637-4604
innkeeper@birchwood-inn.com

Member Since 2003

Innkeeper/Owner
Ellen Gutman Chenaux

Imagine... a warm welcome to our Colonial Revival 1766 inn in Lenox, MA, in the heart of the Berkshires... the wag of a friendly tail... hot-from-the-oven chocolate chip cookies... awakening to the aroma of freshly baked bread... savoring our sumptuous breakfasts created by one of the "Eight Broads in the Kitchen"... New England stone-fenced gardens... a tranquil front porch, enjoying afternoon tea and the Berkshire breezes... curling up next to a crackling hearth with a good read and a steaming mug of mulled cider... a hammock and spring blossoms... autumn's vibrant foliage... fireflies in the summer twilight... firesides when snowflakes fall... snow angels... hiking, biking or snowshoeing on neighboring Kennedy Park's trails... a short walk to the shops, restaurants, and galleries of historic Lenox... picnicking at Tanglewood... exploring historic homes... indulging your passion for food with a "Fun for Foodies" experience... de-stressing in a yoga class...luxuriating in a spa day... all at our doorstep.

Rates
$195/$350. Rates/minimum stays change seasonally. Comfortably elegant guestrooms, six with fireplaces. Number of Rooms: 11

Cuisine
Fireside award-winning breakfasts feature fruit dishes, local produce, homemade breads, and creative entrees served at individual tables. Afternoon tea offers homemade pastries, ice creams, and sorbets plus freshly baked goodies for "sweet dreams

Nearest Airport
1 hour from Albany and Hartford (Bradley) airports. 2 1/2 hours from Boston (Logan) and 3 hours from NYC airports.

Brook Farm Inn

www.brookfarm.com
15 Hawthorne Street, Lenox, MA 01240
800-285-7638 (POET) • 413-637-3013 • Fax 413-637-4751
Member Since 2001
innkeeper@brookfarm.com

Massachusetts

Lenox

Innkeepers/Owners
Phil & Linda Halpern

There is poetry here... This Victorian Berkshires treasure is nestled in a wooded glen, surrounded by award-winning gardens. Brook Farm Inn is just a short walk to historic Lenox village. Built in 1882, and furnished with antiques, the inn features a library filled with poetry, history and literature, where the sounds of classical music can be heard. The main building has 12 guest rooms, and the carriage house has luxury accommodations, including 2 handicap accessible rooms. Brook Farm Inn is close to Tanglewood and all cultural and outdoor attractions. Your friendly hosts offer gracious hospitality and assistance in planning a memorable Berkshires vacation. The sumptuous buffet breakfasts are unsurpassed. Afternoon tea and scones are served on weekends in the library. Seasonal activities are downhill and xc-skiing, hiking, biking, theater, concerts, antiquing and museum and historic home tours. The foliage season is spectacular, and special packages are offered. Attractions: Tanglewood, Berkshire Theatre Festival, Rockwell Museum, Shakespeare & Co., Hancock Shaker Village.

Rates
$149/$429 depending on season and room choice. Antiques, canopy beds. 9 rooms w/ fireplaces, some w/whirlpool tubs. WIFI. Heated outdoor pool. Gardens with picnic area. Open all year. Seasonal package with restaurant and museum. Number of Rooms: 15

Cuisine
Full buffet breakfast; afternoon tea with homemade scones on weekends. Well-stocked guest pantry with refrigerators, ice, tea, coffee, hot chocolate, and cookies.Breakfast is meatless, with hot entree, our own granola, fresh fruit, homebaked goods.

Nearest Airport
45 min. to Albany, NY. One hour to Hartford, CT. 2 hours to Boston. 3 hours to NYC area.

 SelectRegistry.com

Gateways Inn

www.gatewaysinn.com
51 Walker Street, Lenox, MA 01240
888-492-9466 • 413-637-2532 • Fax 413-637-1432
innkeeper@gatewaysinn.com

Member Since 2001

Innkeepers/Owners
Michele & Eiran Gazit

Gateways Inn is a stately neoclassical mansion, built in 1912 by Harley Procter of Procter & Gamble as a summer home in the picturesqe Berkshire Town of Lenox. The mansion later became an Inn. Today the Innkeepers & staff welcome guests from the world over, providing gracious hospitality in a European Manor Home atmosphere with a Shakespearean theme. The 12 guest rooms are each unique in decor, all with private baths, as well as updated comforts & amenities. The Restaurant showcases a Farm to Table seasonal Mediterranean menu. Our award-winning Piano Bar offers an impressively large collection of Single Malt Scotches and Grappas. Business travelers welcomed. Customized weddings, private parties & meetings are our specialty. Italian Cooking School events are scheduled throughout the year. Shakespeare & Company, The Mount and Tanglewood, the summer home of the Boston Symphony Orchestra, are all nearby. The Inn is a short stroll to Town Center with many fine shops and galleries. The nearby nature parks offer the best in outdoor activities.

Rates
11 Rooms. 1 Suite, $200 - $600, depending on season. Peak season minimum stays apply. Open year-round. Corporate Rates and packages available. Number of Rooms: 12

Cuisine
Full scrumptious breakfast served daily. Full bar service. Extensive wine list. Wine Spectator Award. Special menus for Holidays. Custom menus for weddings and private parties.

Nearest Airport
NYC - 2.5 hour drive; Albany, NY- 1 hour by car; Hartford, CT-1 1/2 hour drive;Boston, MA- 2 hours by car.

The Inn at Richmond

www.innatrichmond.com
802 State Road (Route 41), Richmond, MA 01254
888-968-4748 • 513-698-2566 • Fax 413-698-2100
innkeepers@innatrichmond.com

Member Since 2006

Owner **Carl M. Dunham, Jr.**
Innkeeper **Pam Knisley**

Experience tranquility and comfort at The Inn at Richmond! Let this historic house be your home away from home as you explore all the Berkshires have to offer — spectacular theater, inspiring music and museums, outdoor activities for every interest. Nestled in the countryside near Pittsfield and Lenox, the Inn boasts acres of gardens and pastures; guests can enjoy a stroll through barns, spend quiet time on the terrace, cuddle by a roaring fire or play a game of pool in our game room. Conveniently situated, the Inn is a short drive to Berkshire attractions - Tanglewood, Barrington Stage, Norman Rockwell Museum, Berkshire Theater Group and outdoor adventures - riding lessons at Berkshire Equestrian Center, kayaking, hiking, biking, fishing, snow shoeing and skiing. The casual elegance of this historic home makes a perfect setting for your getaway, family celebration or intimate wedding. A pet-friendly cottage and stalls for guests to board horses during their visit are available. Be a part of the harmonious blend of scenic natural beauty and true New England hospitality.

Rates
6 Rooms/Suites, some with fireplaces; 3 Cottages with kitchens. Rates: Nov - May $160/$270; June - Oct $210/$380. In room amenities include cable TV, air conditioning, robes, premium toileties, WI-FI in Main House. Open year round. Number of Rooms: 9

Cuisine
Guests are treated to a delicious country breakfast - a freshly prepared hot entree featuring locally produced foods; fruits, breads, pastries, cereals, yogurt and the usual selection of breakfast beverages are offered. Special diets accommodated.

Nearest Airport
Albany International Airport, Albany, NY - 50 minutes; Bradley International Airport, Hartford, CT - 1.5 hours

SelectRegistry.com

Applegate Inn

www.applegateinn.com
279 West Park Street, Lee, MA 01238
800-691-9012 • 413-243-4451 • Fax 413-243-9832
info@applegateinn.com

Member Since 2002

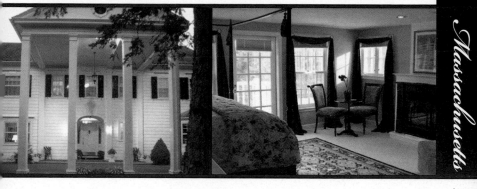

Massachusetts

Lee

Owners/Innkeepers
Len & Gloria Friedman

Once inside the iron gate, the circular drive, lined with lilac bushes reveals this elegant 1920s white-pillared Georgian mansion. It is situated on a 6 acre country estate across the road from a golf and tennis club, half mile from the historic town of Lee and 3 miles from Stockbridge. The 11 upscale guest accommodations are uniquely decorated and luxuriously appointed. For your comfort, the inn is air conditioned and heated with individual room controls and provides wifi internet. From the screened porch look beyond the heated swimming pool to the lawns, towering trees and gardens. This is tranquility itself; a relaxing place to rejuvenate while pampered with attentive service, candlelit breakfasts, and wine and cheese served each afternoon. Explore Tanglewood, theater, dance, Norman Rockwell Museum, golf, tennis, hiking, swimming, boating, skiing, antiquing, shopping and other natural and cultural wonders of the Berkshires, or linger at the inn by a roaring fire, rest in a hammock for two under an old apple tree, or stroll the perennial gardens.

Rates
Rooms $150/$275; Suites $270/$395; Cottage $270/$375. AC, TV, VCR/DVD, CD, wifi, some with fireplace, jacuzzi, mini-fridge, balcony, patio and steam shower for two. All have robes, hair dryer, phone, flowers, brandy & chocolate. Number of Rooms: 11

Cuisine
Multi-course gourmet candlelit breakfast served on china & crystal. Wine & cheese served in the afternoon. Fruit bowl, cookie jar & guest pantry always available.

Nearest Airport
Albany & Bradley Airports

Devonfield Inn B & B

www.devonfield.com
85 Stockbridge Road., Lee, MA 01238
800-664-0880 • 413-243-3298 • Fax 413-243-1360
innkeeper@devonfield.com

Member Since 2003

Innkeepers/Owners
Bruce & Ronnie Singer

Centrally located, yet a world apart, Devonfield Inn is set on a 32 acre pastoral meadow shaded by graceful birch trees, with the rolling tapestry of the Berkshire Hills beyond. This 200 year old historic estate home has been graciously updated and is filled with fine antiques. It is sophisticated, yet comfortable and inviting. Devonfield's upscale suites and bedrooms are all beautifully appointed, spacious and offer modern private baths. Quilts, down comforters, plush sheets, towels, CD players and TV/DVDs enhance every room along with handmade chocolates and bottled water. Many have wood-burning fireplaces, Jacuzzis and fine terry robes. For your comfort, the Inn is completely air conditioned and provides wireless Internet. The guest pantry is always open and stocked with treats. There is a refrigerator and microwave as well. Follow breakfast with a stroll through the flower-filled gardens, play tennis, or take a dip in the heated pool, and then enjoy the best in cultural and recreational activities in all seasons. Or, just relax and enjoy the sights and sounds of nature.

Rates
6 Rooms; 3 Suites; 1 Guest Cottage. Off Season: $180/$325. In Season: $225/$375
Number of Rooms: 10

Cuisine
A fireside (fall and winter) candlelit gourmet breakfast is served on fine china accompanied by classical music. Breakfast includes a buffet of fresh baked goods, fruits, granola, yogurt, juices and more, followed by a specially selected hot entree.

Nearest Airport
Bradley, CT (63 miles); Albany (45 miles)

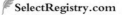

The Inn at Stockbridge

www.stockbridgeinn.com
30 East St, PO Box 618, Stockbridge, MA 01262
888-466-7865 • 413-298-3337 • Fax 413-298-3406
innkeeper@stockbridgeinn.com

Member Since 1986

Innkeepers/Owners
Len & Alice Schiller

Enjoy peaceful charm and elegance in a 1906 Georgian style mansion secluded on 12 acres in Stockbridge, a town described by Norman Rockwell as the best of New England and the best of America. Awaken to the aroma of fresh coffee, stroll the beautiful grounds, take a dip in the heated pool, exercise in the fitness room, relax on the wrap around porch and take time away from the cares of the world. Antiques, collectibles and luxury are very much at home here. Amenities and attention to detail found only in upscale properties for the discriminating traveler await you here. Fireplace and double whirlpool rooms with a private deck are available. Voted by the Discerning Traveler as one of the Most Romantic Inns. Centrally located to all Berkshire cultural attractions including the Norman Rockwell Museum and Tanglewood, theatre, dance, golf, hiking, boating, skiing, antiquing, shopping. Enjoy the culture and the outdoors or just relax. The Schiller's have been inviting guests to enjoy the Berkshires for over 18 years.

Rates
Main house rooms $170/$360. Cottage house suites 275-360. Barn suites 290-395. Barn & cottage house suites feature a fireplace and whirlpool and come equipped with an individual refrigerator and coffee maker. Number of Rooms: 16

Cuisine
Multi-course bountiful candlelit breakfast featuring local products. Breakfast includes a buffet of freshly baked goods, fruit, granola, yogurt, and a specially selected entree. Wine and cheese hour Guest pantry with snacks and beverages always available.

Nearest Airport
Albany, NY - Hartford, CT

Hawthorne Inn

www.concordmass.com
462 Lexington Road, , Concord, MA 01742-3729
978-369-5610 • Fax 978-287-4949
Inn@ConcordMass.com

Member Since 1980

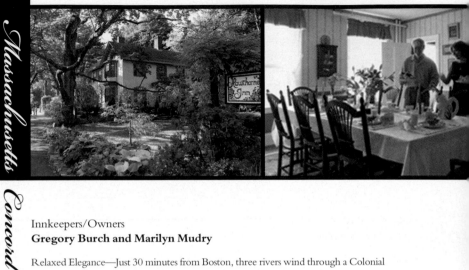

Innkeepers/Owners
Gregory Burch and Marilyn Mudry

Relaxed Elegance—Just 30 minutes from Boston, three rivers wind through a Colonial landscape of Minutemen's fields where moss-covered stonewalls embrace the homes of Hawthorne, Alcott, Thoreau and Emerson. Here you will find an intimate refuge, the Hawthorne Inn, filled with original artworks to delight your eyes, curious to excite the imagination, coverlets to snuggle on a crisp autumn eve and burnished antiques that speak of home and security. Seven vibrant Guestrooms, inspired by a refreshing mix of tradition and artistic expression, offer abundant comforts and modern amenities. Since 1976 the Inn has made welcome business-travelers, lovers, seekers, pilgrims and families to our historic 17th century village. As you amble in the footsteps of Patriots and Poets you will savor the Inn's unique location near the Authors Homes, Walden Pond, Minuteman National Park and Old North Bridge, where was fired, "the shot heard 'round the world." Many choose the Hawthorne as a base for day-trips to explore Boston, Cambridge, Sturbridge, Salem, Plymouth and the near by ocean beaches.

Rates
Graciously appointed rooms offering Canopy or Four-poster Bed, Refreshments at Check-in and Multi-course Breakfast. Rates vary by Seasonal Demand and length of stay. Nightly Accommodations from $159.- $349. See website for Specials. Number of Rooms: 7

Cuisine
Good food and fine conversation define breakfast at the inn. Daily-changing Specials include: Croissant French Toast with berry-infused maple syrup and laughter, Award-Winning Pears with Mascarpone and an anecdote, steamy Organic Coffee mixed with a smile. Enjoy our table, each other and life.

Nearest Airport
Boston Logan-30 min./ Manchester N.H.-50 min./ Private Planes at Hanscom Field- 10 min. See website for directions.

Emerson Inn By The Sea

www.EmersonInnByTheSea.com
One Cathedral Avenue, Pigeon Cove, Rockport, MA 01966
800-964-5550 • 978-546-6321 • Fax 978-546-7043
info@EmersonInnByTheSea.com

Member Since 1973

Massachusetts

Rockport

Innkeepers/Owners
Bruce and Michele Coates

Ralph Waldo Emerson called the Inn "Thy proper summer home." Today's guests enjoy the relaxed 19th Century atmosphere from our broad oceanfront veranda, but can savor the 21st Century amenities of a heated outdoor pool, room phones, data ports, high speed wireless internet, air conditioning, cable television, private baths and spa tubs. Nearby are hiking trails along the oceanfront, tennis, golf, sea kayaking, scuba diving and the always popular whale watches. Halibut Point State Park features the history of the Rockport Quarries and downtown Rockport is famous for shops and art galleries. The historic Emerson is the ideal ocean front location for weddings, retreats and conferences. "Editors Pick," Yankee Travel Guide to New England. And as featured in 1000 Places To See in the USA Before You Die and in Zagat's 2005 & 2006 Top U.S. Hotels, Resorts, and Spas. Mobil Three Star, AAA ◆◆◆.

Rates
$99/$399 B&B; Two Seaside Cottages, each accommodates 8, available for a weekly rental. Open all year. Number of Rooms: 36

Cuisine
Award-winning Restaurant. 'Unparalleled ambiance' - The Boston Globe. Outdoor oceanfront dining and elegant turn-of-the-century dining room serving breakfast daily; dinner and live music schedules vary by season. Wine Spectator Award of Excellence.

Nearest Airport
Boston Logan International Airport

🍽 🍽 🍽 ♀

Harbor Light Inn

www.harborlightinn.com
58 Washington Street, Marblehead, MA 01945
781-631-2186 • Fax 781-631-2216
info@harborlightinn.com

Member Since 1996

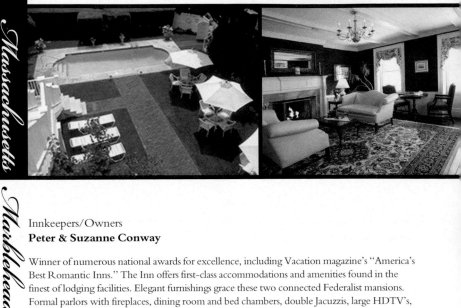

Innkeepers/Owners
Peter & Suzanne Conway

Winner of numerous national awards for excellence, including Vacation magazine's "America's Best Romantic Inns." The Inn offers first-class accommodations and amenities found in the finest of lodging facilities. Elegant furnishings grace these two connected Federalist mansions. Formal parlors with fireplaces, dining room and bed chambers, double Jacuzzis, large HDTV's, WIFI, sundecks, patio, quiet garden and outdoor heated pool combine to ensure the finest in New England hospitality. Located in the heart of historic Harbor District of fine shops, art galleries and restaurants. Our intimate tavern is open nightly and offers fine wines, beers and cordials along with our bar menu of local favorites.

Rates
20 Rooms, $155/$365; Suites, $195/$365 B&B. Open year-round. Number of Rooms: 20

Cuisine
Breakfast buffet featuring fresh homemade breads, fruit platters, yogurts, bagels, hot casseroles, salmon platter and daily specials. Wine, beer and cordials in new pub. Pub menu is available for lunch and dinner daily. 7 restaurants within 2 blocks.

Nearest Airport
Boston Logan International approximately 15 miles .

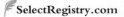
SelectRegistry.com

Charles Street Inn

www.charlesstreetinn.com
94 Charles St., Boston, MA 02114
877-772-8900 • 617-314-8900 • Fax 617-371-0009
info@charlesstreetinn.com

Member Since 2004

Massachusetts Boston

Innkeepers/Owners
Sally Deane & Louise Venden

A luxury inn located in historic Beacon Hill within blocks of Boston's shopping, touring, and subway stops, the Charles Street Inn offers unique comfort and privacy in nine spacious rooms with elevator access. Each room features a private bath with whirlpool tubs, working marble fireplaces, fresh flowers, BOSE radio/CD player, Cable TV, VCR, DVD, AC controls, DSL and Wireless Internet, and Sub-Zero refrigerator. Authentic Victorian-era antiques, king & queen size canopy and sleigh beds, and rich imported linens complete each elegant setting. Relax in front of a fire or enjoy any of the fabulous restaurants that are literally steps from the inn. Recognized among Boston's Best by Travel + Leisure, Boston Magazine, and as one of the top 10 romantic inns in the US by America's Historic Inns. Concierge services available.

Rates
$250/$525 depending on room, season, and day of the week. Call for rates (US toll-free 877-772-8900) or visit "Reservations" on our web site. Number of Rooms: 9

Cuisine
Arrive to sweets, fresh fruit, snacks and refreshments in the lobby and in your room . Then, schedule your in-room breakfast with so many choices including quiche and eggs, delicious bowls of fresh fruit, a variety of pastries, cereals, and cheeses.

Nearest Airport
Boston

Carpe Diem Guesthouse & Spa

www.carpediemguesthouse.com
12 - 14 Johnson Street, Provincetown, MA 02657-2312
800-487-0132 • 508-487-4242
info@carpediemguesthouse.com

Member Since 2003

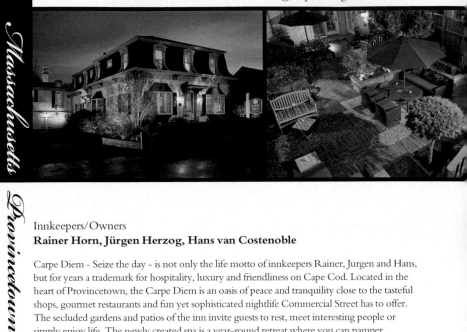

Innkeepers/Owners
Rainer Horn, Jürgen Herzog, Hans van Costenoble

Carpe Diem - Seize the day - is not only the life motto of innkeepers Rainer, Jurgen and Hans, but for years a trademark for hospitality, luxury and friendliness on Cape Cod. Located in the heart of Provincetown, the Carpe Diem is an oasis of peace and tranquility close to the tasteful shops, gourmet restaurants and fun yet sophisticated nightlife Commercial Street has to offer. The secluded gardens and patios of the inn invite guests to rest, meet interesting people or simply enjoy life. The newly created spa is a year-round retreat where you can pamper yourselves with a rejuvenating massage, a relaxing steam bath, a stimulating hot sauna or some lazy time in the outdoor Jacuzzi. The guestrooms are decorated with exquisite taste, many feature fireplaces and whirlpool tubs. Breakfast is a social event when the varied guests gather all morning in the sun lit dining area. Food aficionados can start their day with a wonderful hot cup of Carpe Diem Coffee, homemade breads and pastry, egg dishes and specials like Belgian Waffles, French Crepes or Austrian Kaiserschmarrn.

Rates
18 rooms and suites, $95/$425. Open year round. Number of Rooms: 18

Cuisine
Jurgen's homemade German-style breakfast is famous. Out&About: "Imagine a cross between Martha Stewart cozy and cool European design. Similarly, the breakfasts are classic American gourmet meets German bounty." Afternoon wine & cheese and refreshments.

Nearest Airport
Boston & Providence

Crowne Pointe Historic Inn & Spa

www.crownepointe.com
82 Bradford Street, Provincetown, MA 02657
877-276-9631 • 508-487-6767 • Fax 508-487-5554
welcome@crownepointe.com

Member Since 2003

Innkeepers/Owners
David M. Sanford & Thomas J. Walter

A prominent Sea Captain built this historic mansion, which has been fully restored to its 19th Century glory. The inn's stunning Victorian architecture includes two-story wrap around porches complete with turret and harbor views. The New York Daily News raves "Five Star Luxury Without the Cost." Revive at our full service on-site Shui Spa featuring many treatments and massage options. Shui Spa offers guests an intimate spa experience. Crowne Pointe is a AAA Four Diamond property located in the center of town, walk to everything. Our signature gourmet hot breakfast and afternoon wine and cheese social are included. Heated in-ground pool, two hot tubs, fireplaces and in-room whirlpools are offered. Spa packages are available. Our restaurant captures our guests with exquisite gourmet cuisine, and our hotel bar is a treasured place to socialize. The finest menu creations from our talented chefs, carefully selected labels from our wine cellar, and excellent service in a charming setting are waiting for you to indulge.

Rates
$99/$465 depending upon season. Minimum stay requirements may apply. Many special packages available, call for details. Number of Rooms: 40

Cuisine
The freshest regional ingredients arriving daily, our distinctive full hot breakfasts are unsurpassed. The main selections change daily and special dietary needs are accommodated.

Nearest Airport
Provincetown Airport (PVC) or Boston Logan Airport

Gabriel's at Ashbrooke Inn

www.gabriels.com
102 Bradford Street, Provincetown, MA 02657
508-487-3232
elizabethbrooke@me.com

Member Since 2011

Massachusetts

Provincetown

Innkeepers/Owners
Elizabeth & Elizabeth Brooke

Since 1979, Gabriel's at The Ashbrooke Inn has welcomed our family of friends to this unique and special inn. We welcome everyone including children and pets! We are located in the center of Provincetown bordering the Bas Relief Park. Once you arrive you will not need your car until you depart! Our beautifully appointed guest rooms all have Tempurpedic beds, Jacuzzi tubs, fireplaces, wet bars, TVs, DVD players, WiFi, amenity baskets and more. We offer an extensive free movie library, courtesy phone, bicycle storage and access to the Great Room/ Dining Room anytime. Enjoy our lovely gardens, lounge on the sun decks, meet new friends in the Great Room at breakfast, or set out at twilight towards the bright lights of Commercial Street, or the last purple light of day fading over Herring Cove. You're certain to experience the unique character of Provincetown and the amazing hospitality of Gabriel's.

Rates
$150/$380 depending on the room and the season. We are open year round. Off season specials and packages are often available. Call Elizabeth directly for information 508-487-2779. Number of Rooms: 8

Cuisine
Gourmet chocolates in your room upon arrival. Homemade breakfast each morning, in season, in our Great Room. Our famous home baked cookies, tea, coffee, and organic drinks available anytime. Special dietary needs can be accommodated.

Nearest Airport
Provincetown Airport (PVC), Boston Logan Airport (BOS), Providence T.F. Green Airport (PVD)

SelectRegistry.com

The Whalewalk Inn and Spa

www.whalewalkinn.com
220 Bridge Road, Eastham, Cape Cod, MA 02642
800-440-1281 • 508-255-0617 • Fax 508-240-0017
reservations@whalewalkinn.com

Member Since 1993

Innkeepers/Owners
Kevin & Elaine Conlin

Abandon every day life. Rekindle your romance and rejuvenate your body and mind. Relax at Cape Cod's most romantic country Inn and Spa. Secluded, but centrally located to all attractions which make Cape Cod so special. After a gourmet breakfast, walk the "Outer Cape" beaches while listening to the soothing sound of the waves lapping on Cape Cod Bay or crashing at the National Seashore. At the end of a day on the beach, riding the Rail Trail, kayaking, shopping or museum hopping, restore your inner balance and harmony at The Spa, a special place with your comfort and exercise regime in mind. Forget the weather; pamper your mind and body with a massage or facial; feel the heat of the dry sauna or workout in the indoor resistance pool or on cardiovascular machines. Have fun with Wii Sports and Fit. Stay in the luxurious Spa Penthouse or in one of 16 other beautiful accommodations. All are individually decorated having amenities such as air-conditioning, TV/DVD/CD, fireplace, refrigerator, and high speed WiFi. Come and enjoy our impeccable service and heartfelt hospitality.

Rates
$220/$420. Call for off-season rates. Open April to December. Number of Rooms: 17

Cuisine
Full-service gourmet breakfast with fresh home-baked delights and entrees: Waffle Sundaes, Eggs Benedict, Corn Pancakes with Dill Shallot Sauce and Salmon Rosettes, Grand Marnier Oatmeal Pie, Baked Omelet, and Granola Pizza. Evening hors d'oeuvres.

Nearest Airport
Boston, MA; Providence, RI

The Captain's House Inn

www.captainshouseinn.com
369-377 Old Harbor Rd, Chatham, MA 02633
800-315-0728 • 508-945-0127 • Fax 508-945-0866
info@captainshouseinn.com

Member Since 1989

Innkeepers/Owners
James & Jill Meyer

Perhaps Cape Cod's finest small Inn, this historic 1839 sea captain's estate on two acres is the perfect choice for a romantic getaway or elegant retreat. Gourmet breakfasts, English afternoon teas, beautifully decorated rooms with king and queen size beds, fireplaces, seating areas, telephones, WI-FI capability, iPod docking stations and TV's with DVD players; some with whirlpool tubs. Enjoy uncompromising service from our enthusiastic international staff and enjoy the Inn's many gardens and fountains, heated outdoor pool, fitness center, and savor the scenic beauty of the historic seafaring village of Chatham with its 70 miles of spectacular shoreline. The Captain's House Inn of Chatham has been a AAA ◆◆◆◆ award winner since 1987.

Rates
12 Rooms, $265 to $370 in Summer, $185 to $260 in Winter; 4 Suites, $265 to $480 in Summer, $185 to $315 Winter. Open year-round. Rates are per night, based upon double occupancy. Tax is not included. Number of Rooms: 16

Cuisine
Breakfast, poolside lunches, afternoon tea, evening snacks.

Nearest Airport
Providence or Boston

SelectRegistry.com

Old Harbor Inn

www.chathamoldharborinn.com
22 Old Harbor Road, Chatham, MA 02633
800-942-4434 • 508 945-4434 • Fax 508 945-7665
info@chathamoldharborinn.com

Member Since 2004

Innkeepers/Owners
Ray & Judy Braz

Originally built by the local doctor in 1932, The Old Harbor Inn is now entering its fourth decade of providing distinctive lodging to the discriminating traveler. The Inn is ideally located just steps from the center of the historic seaside village of Chatham. Guests frequently tell us how enjoyable it is not to use their cars for several days as they explore all the attractions that Chatham has to offer. Designer appointed rooms with king or queen beds are just the start of a luxurious experience. WiFi throughout the Inn, as well as flat screen/DVD combos with an extensive DVD library, add to your in room enjoyment. The professionally designed and meticulously maintained gardens and Koi ponds are sure to please. Judy, Ray and their knowledgeable international staff are always available to help plan your days. Chatham serves as a centralized base for exploring all of Cape Cod and the Islands. Provincetown, Falmouth, Martha's Vineyard or Nantucket are all easily accessible. Whether you are planning a romantic getaway or an elegant retreat, every day you get our best.

Rates
Rates are: $209/$349 summer-$159/$269 spring and fall-$139/$219 winter. Peak season min. stays apply. Number of Rooms: 11

Cuisine
The full breakfast includes fresh juices, gourmet teas and coffees, seasonal fresh fruit, assorted breads and cereals, plus a fresh prepared entree and a fresh bakery specialty.

Nearest Airport
Boston or Providence

Isaiah Jones Homestead

www.isaiahjones.com
165 Main Street, Sandwich, MA 02563
800-526-1625 • 508-888-9115 • Fax 508-888-9648
info@isaiahjones.com

Member Since 1989

Innkeepers/Owners
Don and Katherine Sanderson

Relax in pampered elegance in this 1849 Italianate Victorian Inn. The main house has five exquisitely appointed guest rooms with private baths featuring queen beds, antique furnishings, oriental carpets, all with fireplaces or glass-front stoves and two with oversize whirlpool tubs. The unique Carriage House includes two spacious junior suites each with a fireplace and whirlpool bath, one with a king bed. Located in the heart of Sandwich village, the inn is within easy walking distance of many shops, restaurants and attractions of Cape Cod's oldest town. Unwind by strolling the meandering garden paths around the goldfish pond, by sitting in comfortable Adirondack chairs placed around the well-manicured yard or by relaxing by the original antique-tiled fireplace in the gathering room. A full breakfast sets a warm tone to start your day. Chosen Editors Choice, Cape Cod Travel Guide. Selected as "Insider Pick" for Romantic Getaways by Destination Insider. Featured in "Checking In," Boston Sunday Globe and The Wall Street Journal's "Take Monday Off" on Cape Cod.

Rates
Seven rooms, $175/$300, including a full, three-course breakfast. Air conditioned. Open year-round. Complimentary parking and WiFi. Number of Rooms: 7

Cuisine
Breakfast is served in our sunny, cherry paneled dining room or on the deck overlooking the garden. Enjoy a full three-course breakfast of fresh fruit, juices, creative hot entrees, home-baked scones and muffins, and our special blend of gourmet coffee

Nearest Airport
Logan Airport, Boston, MA; TF Green, Providence, RI

Palmer House Inn

www.palmerhouseinn.com
81 Palmer Avenue, Falmouth, MA 02540
800-472-2632 • 508-548-1230 • Fax 508-540-1878
innkeepers@palmerhouseinn.com

Member Since 2001

Innkeepers/Owners
Bill & Pat O'Connell

On a tree-lined street in the heart of the Historic District, The Palmer House Inn is an elegant Victorian home. Stained glass windows, rich woodwork, gleaming hardwood floors and antique furnishings create an overall sense of warmth and harmony. Beautiful beaches, quaint shops, ferry shuttles, and excellent restaurants are only a short stroll away. The innkeepers pamper you with fresh flowers, extra pillows, fluffy robes, fine linens and meticulous housekeeping. The Palmer House Inn is the perfect place to stay, in splendid comfort and gracious care. Local activities include golf, swimming, cycling on the Shining Sea Bike Path on one of the Palmer House's bicycles, fishing, charter sailing, kayaking, hiking, bird watching and more.

Rates
16 Rooms, $169/$269; 1 Cottage Suites, $245/$299. K, Q & DBL beds. 7 rooms w/ whirlpool tubs and 3 w/ fireplaces. Rooms have 600 thread count sheets, TV, phones, hair dryers, irons & boards, ice buckets, AC and WiFi. Open year-round Number of Rooms: 17

Cuisine
Full two to three course gourmet breakfast served with candlelight and classical music. Afternoon and evening refreshments. Early morning coffee.

Nearest Airport
TF Green (Providence), Logan (Boston)

Massachusetts

Falmouth

Thorncroft Inn

www.thorncroft.com

460 Main St., P.O. Box 1022, Martha's Vineyard, MA 02568

800-332-1236 • 508-693-3333 • Fax 508-693-5419

innkeeper@thorncroft.com

Member Since 1994

Proprietors/Innkeepers
Karl & Lynn Buder

Thorncroft Inn is situated in three restored buildings on 2 1/2 acres of quiet, treed grounds on the Island of Martha's Vineyard. It is secluded, exclusively couples-oriented and first-class. All rooms have phone, TV, high-speed wireless and wired internet access, air-conditioning, deluxe bathrobes and an array of amenities. Most rooms have working, wood-burning fireplaces and canopied beds. Some have two-person whirlpool bathtubs or private 250-gallon hot tubs. Several offer private exterior entrances or furnished private porches or balconies. Full country breakfast is served in our two dining rooms or breakfast is delivered to the room. Our concierge service is renowned and focuses on the specific needs of each couple. Thorncroft Inn is an ideal setting for honeymoons, anniversaries, engagements, birthdays or any romantic getaway for couples. Voted best B&B on Martha's Vineyard-2011 by Martha's Vineyard Magazine.

Rates
14 antique appointed rooms, $195 to $495 B&B per evening with seasonal variations. European Plan offered year 'round excludes breakfast at a $50 per night discount. Number of Rooms: 14

Cuisine
Full country breakfast served in two dining rooms at individual tables for two or an ample continental breakfast delivered to room; Traditional or healthful entrees.

Nearest Airport
Martha's Vineyard Airport (MVY) 5 miles; Logan Airport in Boston (BOS)77 miles

SelectRegistry.com

Seven Sea Street Inn

www.sevenseastreetinn.com
7 Sea Street, Nantucket, MA 02554
800-651-9262 • 508-228-3577 • Fax 508-228-3578
innkeeper@sevenseastreetinn.com

Member Since 1996

Innkeeper/Owner
Matthew Parker

Enjoy Seven Sea Street Inn, a truly charming Nantucket bed and breakfast Inn, where we pride ourselves on the attentive service and elegant accommodations that will make your stay with us a fond memory. Our Inn is distinguished by its beautiful red oak post and beam style, designed and constructed with an authentic Nantucket ambiance in mind. In addition to providing exceptional comfort and hospitality, we offer a stunning view of Nantucket Harbor from our Widow's Walk deck. All of our guest rooms are furnished with luxurious Stearns and Foster queen or king mattresses, the world's finest bedding. Each Main house guest room and suite is furnished with rainshower showerheads, ACs, high definition TV, high speed wireless connectivity and a bow box of Nantucket's famous chocolate covered cranberries. Our location, nestled on a quiet tree-lined side street and less than a five-minute walk from Main Street shopping, restaurants, museums and the beach, couldn't be better. Indulge yourself at our lovely Inn this year.

Rates
13 Guest Rooms, $99/$349 B&B; 2 Suites, $159/$449 B&B. Seasonal rates. Number of Rooms: 15

Cuisine
Expanded Buffet Continental Breakfast served daily. Two seatings, 8 a.m. and 9 a.m. Gourmet coffee, tea, soda, bottled water and homemade cookies available anytime.

Nearest Airport
Nantucket Memorial Airport

Union Street Inn

www.UnionInn.com
7 Union Street, Nantucket, MA 02554
888-517-0707 • 508-228-9222 • Fax 508-325-0848
info@UnionInn.com

Member Since 2005

Innkeepers/Owners
Ken & Deborah Withrow

"Best Nantucket Boutique Hotel"-BEST OF BOSTON MAGAZINE. "This mint 1770 house in the middle of town has more style than most–not a surprise, given the previous careers of proprietors Ken (ex-GM of the Royalton in New York City) and Deborah (a display manager at Henri Bendel). They've decorated the 12 rooms in impeccable New England-by-way-of-France style–Pierre Deux wallpaper, high-poster beds, polished original floorboards, and a few non-fusty antiques. Six also have fireplaces. Add to the mix delicious breakfasts served on the outside patio (try the challah-bread French toast with fresh berries), a concierge to score hard-to-get dinner reservations, and just-baked cookies served every afternoon, and you'll see why this place has return guests every summer."- CONDE NAST TRAVELER. Rooms have private baths, A/C, flat screen TV's, Frette and Matouk bedding, bath amenities by (MALIN+GOETZ), and complimentary Wi-Fi. Restaurants, shops, galleries, museums, and ferries are a short stroll. Walk or bicycle to Nantucket's beautiful beaches.

Rates
12 Rooms. High Season: $299-$619; Shoulder Seasons: $149-$589. Closed November through March. Number of Rooms: 12

Cuisine
We are the only Nantucket B&B serving a Full Cooked-To-Order Breakfast. Available in the Dining Room, Garden Patio or In Bed. Afternoon Treats include Home-Baked Cookies, Carrot Cake & Brownies. Coffee, Tea, & Bottled Spring Water always available

Nearest Airport
Nantucket Memorial Airport-10 minute taxi ride.

Famous for: Great Lakes,(borders on four of the five Great Lakes), Fishing, Swimming, Water Sports, Holland (Tulip Center of America), Cherries, Farmland, Auto Manufacturing.

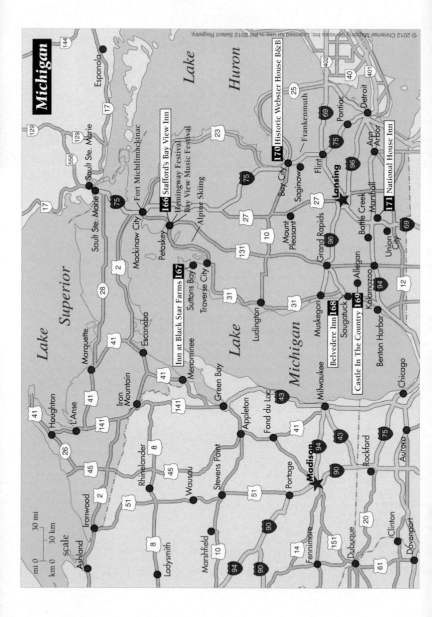

© 2012 Christmar Mapping Services Inc. Licensed for use in the 2012 Select Registry.

🍽️ 🍽️ 🍽️ 🍷

Stafford's Bay View Inn

www.staffords.com
2011 US 31 N, P.O. Box 657, Petoskey, MI 49770
800-258-1886 • 231-347-2771 • Fax 231-347-3413
bayview@staffords.com

Member Since 1972

Michigan

Petoskey

Proprietor
Stafford Smith

Stafford's Bay View Inn was purchased by Stafford and Janice Smith in 1961. Stafford and his family has owned, operated, and lovingly restored, this grand Victorian Country Inn on the shores of Lake Michigan's Little Traverse Bay. Built as a rooming house in 1886 in the Historic Landmark District of Bay View, this Inn sets the standard in country Inn dining and gracious service. Each beautifully appointed guest room features a private bath, and individual climate controls. Visitors to the area enjoy summer Chautauqua programs, championship golf, paved bike paths just out our front door, fall color tours, winter ski packages, and sleigh rides around the Bay View cottage grounds. Petoskey's Historic Gaslight Shopping District and marina are located nearby. Our inn is an exquisite place to hold weddings, rehearsal dinners, receptions and reunions. Many quiet corners offer a wonderful environment for company meetings and conferences. Voted 'Michigan's Best Brunch' by Michigan Living. This Inn is the flagship property of Stafford's Hospitality.

Rates
21 Victorian rooms $99/$219, 10 spa and fireplace Suites $139/$279. Number of Rooms: 31

Cuisine
Breakfast and Dinner: May-October and winter weekends. Lunch: Late May-October. Sunday Brunch: June-October and Holidays. Visit www.staffords.com for menus, dining schedules and info on full-service, year-round, innkeeper-owned properties nearby.

Nearest Airport
Pellston (PLN) - 17 miles, Traverse (TVC) - 65 miles

Inn at Black Star Farms

🍽️ 🍽️ 🍽️ 🍷

www.blackstarfarms.com
10844 E. Revold Rd., Suttons Bay, MI 49682
877-466-9463 • 231-944-1251 • Fax 231-944-1259
innkeeper@blackstarfarms.com

Member Since 2003

Michigan

Suttons Bay

Proprietor
Don Coe

Expect consistently exceptional experiences at our year-round Inn, nestled below a hillside of vineyards in the heart of Leelanau Peninsula wine country. Our ten contemporary guestrooms, each with private bath and some with fireplaces and spa tubs, have fine furniture, luxurious linens, and Aveda toiletries. Amenities include a bottle of our House wine, cozy robes, evening hospitality hour and complimentary tasting of our award-winning wines at our on-site tasting room. Massage services and sauna are available. A full gourmet breakfast is prepared daily using seasonal ingredients from the farm and region. Visit Leelanau Cheese Company for artisanal raclette and fromage blanc cheeses. Casual and upscale dining is available seasonally at our Hearth and Vine cafe or Arcturos dining room, both featuring breads baked on the property by 9 Bean Rows CSA. Meetings, reunions and receptions are welcomed. Our on-site catering for private events features locally sourced ingredients. The farm also has boarding stables and wooded recreational trails that are great in any season.

Rates
High season May 25, 2012-Oct 27,2012: $295-$395/night. Low season October 28, 2012-May 23, 2013: $225-$295/night rates subject to 6% sales tax and 5% destination fee. Number of Rooms: 10

Cuisine
Our breakfasts feature fresh fruit and juices, house made baked goods, a seasonal gourmet entree, and coffee and tea. For all meals we are committed to using as many ingredients from the farm and our region as each season will allow.

Nearest Airport
Cherry Capitol Airport (TVC)

Belvedere Inn

www.thebelvedereinn.com
3656 63rd Street, Saugatuck, MI 49453
877-858-5777 • 269-857-5777 • Fax 269-857-7557
info@thebelvedereinn.com

Member Since 2012

Michigan Saugatuck

Innkeepers/Owners:
Shaun Glynn & Pete Ta

Often referred to as Mini Versailles, The Belvedere Inn which translates to "Beautiful View" is a peaceful country estate & is one of the few European-style B&Bs in Michigan. The Inn's success relies on one main ingredient – Excellence – a single minded belief based on good taste, quality service, gourmet food & an exquisitely restored mansion. Built in 1913 & designed by Dwight Perkins, a colleague of Frank Lloyd Wright, the Inn sits on 5 acres of manicured gardens just 1.5 miles from downtown Saugatuck. The Inn's history is perpetuated through skillful restoration, gleaming hardwoods & the patina of fine antiques while discrete modernization offers the highest standard of guest comforts. The award winning restaurant is renowned for it's fine food & wine. Chef Shaun Glynn, Galway, Ireland offers eclectic classical dishes made from local ingredients & served in an intimate setting. The magnificent grounds make a picture perfect backdrop for a wedding or any special occasion. The unique setting also satisfies the demands of a successful business meeting or retreat.

Rates
Rooms & Suites $135-$345. All with fireplaces & deluxe amenities. Luxury suites feature plush memory foam top beds & two person whirlpools. Offering Bed Breakfast & Dinner packages year round. Come for Dinner, Stay for Breakfast! Number of Rooms: 10

Cuisine
Full breakfast at private tables in dining room or terrace & delicious treats throughout the day. Restaurant has seasonal hours for dinner. Guests enjoy complimentary 4 course dinner for two at various times during the year. Full bar service.

Nearest Airport
Tulip City (Holland 15 mins), Gerald Ford (Grand Rapids 45 mins), Midway (Chicago 2.5 hrs), O'Hare (Chicago 3 hrs).

 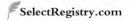

Castle in the Country

www.castleinthecountry.com
340 M-40 South, Allegan, MI 49010
888-673-8054 • 269-673-8054
info@castleinthecountry.com

Member Since 2008

Michigan

Allegan

Innkeepers/Owners
Herb & Ruth Boven

Escape the ordinary at Castle in the Country. Walk hand in hand through our wooded forest trails, sip a glass of wine in the screened porch beside our private lake or close the door to your own romantic suite with a whirlpool tub for two, fireplace and gourmet breakfast. Schedule a side-by-side couple's massage in our secluded Royal Retreat Spa Area. Awarded "Most Romantic Hideaway in North America!" & Best Getaway in the Great Lakes. When you choose Castle in the Country, you choose a Michigan getaway with extraordinary decor, amenities, and service! Scenic countryside provides a peaceful pastoral and wooded setting for your getaway. We offer 10 individually decorated Rooms/Suites within the timeless beauty of our century-old Victorian Castle and in our contemporary country manor house, the Castle Keep. Whether you're looking for a romantic getaway for two to celebrate a birthday, anniversary or honeymoon or, the perfect venue for an elopement or a Destination Wedding and Reception, our Innkeepers will help you create an experience that will exceed every expectation.

Rates
10 Rooms; 7 whirlpool/fireplace suites $199-$309 3 rooms fireplaces $149-$279
Midweek discounts; Spa & Dinner Packages; Wedding Packages; Business Retreats.
Number of Rooms: 10

Cuisine
Full breakfasts are artfully presented and served daily at your own individual table for two in our dining rooms overlooking the pond. Picnic baskets filled with fresh baked bread, and creative Dinner Packages may be added by advanced reservation.

Nearest Airport
Kalamazoo/Battle Creek International

Historic Webster House B&B

www.historicwebsterhouse.com
900 Fifth Street,, Bay City, MI 48708
989-316-2552 • 877-229-9704
info@historicwebsterhouse.com

Member Since 2011

Michigan

Bay City

Owner - **Deborah Ingersoll**
Innkeepers - **Gail & Frank Partee**

Luxurious. Exquisite. Ultimate comfort. These are just a few of the words that tell the story of the Webster House – Bay City, Michigan's pre-eminent bed and breakfast. Nestled in the city's historic district just blocks from a quaint but bustling riverfront downtown, the three-story house is full of history and modern amenities that are sure to make your visit memorable. Built in 1886 for Judge Thomas E. Webster, the six-bedroom, Queen Anne-style home has been fully renovated, with much of its original grandeur preserved. Our rooms pamper you with the finest in European-style sleeping, with feather-top, queen-size beds and down duvets in each. A delicious gourmet breakfast at our inn will be the perfect start to a day of shopping or taking in one of Bay City's many riverfront festivals and events, all just a short walk away. The historical touches inside the inn are as prevalent and breathtaking as they are outside, in a neighborhood that boasts some of the Midwest's finest majestic Victorian architecture.

Rates
Inn-Season: $166 - $206; Mid-Season: $156 - $196; Quiet-Season: $146 - $186 Open year-round. Cable TV, free WI-FI, DVD players. Number of Rooms: Six

Cuisine
A fireside candlelit gourmet breakfast is served on fine china accompanied by classical music; an evening social hour of wine and cheese; freshly baked cookies at turndown; unique local eateries for lunch and dinner just a short walk from the inn.

Nearest Airport
MBS International (Midland-Bay City-Saginaw) - 15 minFNT (Flint) - 45 minDTW (Detroit) - 2 hours

National House Inn

🍽 🍽

www.nationalhouseinn.com
102 S. Parkview, Marshall, MI 49068
269-781-7374
frontdesk@nationalhouseinn.com

Member Since 1978

Michigan

Marshall

Innkeeper/Owner
Barbara Bradley

The only thing we overlook is the Fountain Circle in the middle of picturesque Marshall. Discover why the National Trust of Historic Preservation named our town as one of their "Dozen Distinctive Destinations" in the country! Enjoy every aspect of our inn with its heritage and tradition that has welcomed guests for 170 years. Just steps from the inn, you'll find shopping, museums, galleries, ghost tours, carriage rides, Schuler's Restaurant and more.

Rates
$105-$170 Number of Rooms: 17

Cuisine
Breakfast, afternoon tea, catered dinners for receptions.

Nearest Airport
Kalamazoo & Detroit

Mississippi

"The Magnolia State"

Famous for: Mississippi River, Fertile Soil, Cotton, River Boats, Catfish, Old South, Red Bluff, Civil War Sites, Antebellum Mansions.

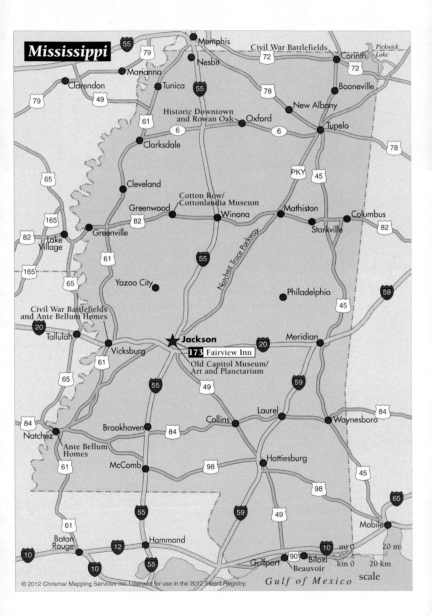

© 2012 Chrismar Mapping Services Inc. Licensed for use in the 2012 Select Registry.

SelectRegistry.com

Fairview Inn

www.fairviewinn.com
734 Fairview Street, Jackson, MS 39202
888-948-1908 • 601-948-3429 • Fax 601-948-1203
innkeeper@fairviewinn.com

Member Since 1994

Proprietors
Peter and Tamar Sharp

The Fairview Inn, Jackson's only AAA four-diamond small luxury hotel, invites you to experience this unique historic 1908 Colonial Revival mansion. This bed and breakfast Inn is one of the few architecturally designed homes of that period remaining, which exudes the rich history of Jackson, Mississippi. On the National Register of Historic Places and conveniently located in the Belhaven historic neighborhood adjacent to Millsaps and Belhaven Colleges, the Fairview Inn is minutes away from downtown Jackson's arts, theater, museums and shopping. Antique and boutique shops are also close by in the nearby Fondren District. More than a bed & breakfast, the Inn boasts 18 luxurious guest rooms, Sophia's restaurant serving lunch, dinner and Sunday brunch, nomiSpa for relaxation and rejuvenation, a game room and private guest lounge. The Fairview Inn is popular not only for leisure travelers seeking the history and culture of the South, but also with business travelers looking for unique, comfortable accommodations where they can entertain clients in a luxury and discreet setting.

Rates
5 Rooms and 13 Suites, $149/$319 Luxury Inn. Open year-round. Rates Include Full Breakfast. Number of Rooms: 18

Cuisine
Full breakfast each morning for Inn guests. Fine Dining: Lunch Monday-Friday 11:00 a.m to 2:00 p.m. Dinner Tuesday-Saturday 5:30 p.m. to 9:30 p.m. Sunday Brunch 11:00 a.m. to 2:00 p.m. Full Bar and extensive wine list available.

Nearest Airport
Jackson-Evers International Airport

Famous for: Center of Continental United States, "Gateway to the West," Livestock, Ozark Plateau, Cottontail Rabbits, Dairy, Corn, Wheat, Cotton, Lead, Zinc, Lime, Cement, Timber, Aircraft, Automobiles, Spacecraft.

Southmoreland on the Plaza

www.southmoreland.com
116 East 46th St., Kansas City, MO 64112
816-531-7979 • Fax 816-531-2407
innkeeper@southmoreland.com

Member Since 1992

Innkeepers/Owners
Mark Reichle and Nancy Miller Reichle

Southmoreland on the Plaza-an Urban Inn sets the standard for B & B hospitality and comfort. Located just one and one-half blocks off of the Country Club Plaza and two blocks from the Nelson Atkins Museum of Art, the Inn blends classic New England Bed and Breakfast ambiance with small hotel amenities. Twelve guestrooms and the Carriage House suite offer private baths, telephones, and off-street parking. Guests enjoy individually decorated rooms featuring decks, fireplaces or Jacuzzi baths. Business travelers find respite at Southmoreland. We are pleased to offer corporate rates and a rare mix of services conducive to business travel: in-room phones, Wi-Fi, fax, copier, voice mail, 24-hour access and switchboard, and guest privileges at a local full-service fitness center. Southmoreland on the Plaza is an Inn of national reputation, worthy of its Plaza locale; warm and accommodating like Kansas City itself. Featured on the Food Network's "Barbecue with Bobby Flay." Visit us at www.southmoreland.com.

Rates
12 Rooms in Main House, $135/$200 Summer $130/$215 Winter $250 Carriage House (less $20 SGL.). Number of Rooms: 13

Cuisine
Gourmet breakfast served daily. Complimentary afternoon wine and hors d'oeuvres, with hot beverages and sweets served in the evening. Courtyard breakfast BBQ served Saturdays, Apr 15-Oct 15.

Nearest Airport
Kansas City International

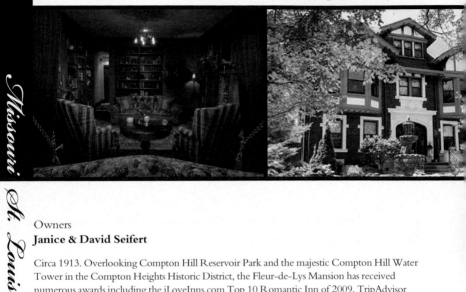

Fleur-de-Lys Mansion

www.thefleurdelys.com
3500 Russell Blvd, St. Louis, MO 63104
314-773-3500 • 1-888-693-3500
seifert@thefleurdelys.com

Member Since 2011

Missouri

St. Louis

Owners
Janice & David Seifert

Circa 1913. Overlooking Compton Hill Reservoir Park and the majestic Compton Hill Water Tower in the Compton Heights Historic District, the Fleur-de-Lys Mansion has received numerous awards including the iLoveInns.com Top 10 Romantic Inn of 2009, TripAdvisor Traveler's Choice Award Winner 2010, rated #7 Best in the World and #5 Best in the U.S. by TripAdvisor, and among Midwest Living's "Best of the Midwest" in 2011. The Fleur-de-Lys is a meticulously restored Tudor Revival mansion. The atmosphere exudes a comfortable elegance and luxury amenities that make it perfect for business or leisure. Stay in a Parkside Room or Jacuzzi Suite with antiques, period reproductions, towel warmers and free wireless internet. Guests have said our beds are like "sleeping on a cloud" with down comforters and ironed, lavender-scented linens. Relax in a terry-lined robe, take a private dip in our hot tub, or enjoy the beauty of our urban garden. Awaken to the aromas of the gourmet breakfast that is waiting for you in our Parkside Dining Room. Enjoy the TLC while we serve you!

Rates
King Rooms: $235 (Sunday-Thursday) $305 (Friday-Saturday) Queen Rooms: $160 (Sunday-Thursday) $205 (Friday-Saturday) Number of Rooms: 4

Cuisine
A gourmet breakfast is included in your room rate. Our menu changes daily & includes imaginative uses of fresh fruits, yogurt, homemade granola, sweet and savory crepes, and a variety of luscious baked eggs and decadent French toasts.

Nearest Airport
Lambert St. Louis International Airport

SelectRegistry.com

Yates House Bed & Breakfast

🍽️ 🍽️ 🍽️

www.yateshouse.com

305 Second Street, Rocheport, MO 65279

573-698-2129

info@yateshouse.com

Member Since 2005

Missouri

Rocheport

Innkeepers/Owners
Conrad & Dixie Yates

Midwest Living Magazine "2010 Best In the Midwest" Where to Stay category selection. Located in "One of America's Top Ten Coolest Small Towns" Frommers Budget Travel Guide. Everything you'll need for luxurious and relaxing lodging is provided. All rooms are large, beautifully furnished, and well equipped. King beds, jetted tubs, and fireplace are available. Wireless Internet and other business services are provided. Twenty-six seat dining/meeting room available and catering for small groups. Individual table or in-room breakfast provided. Famous for seasonal, gourmet breakfast menu and cooking classes. "Dixie can flat cook," observed Southern Living magazine. Within a block of most scenic section of Katy Trail State Park. Photogenic trails, bluffs, tunnels, and Missouri River within short walking distance. Vineyards, winery, shops and restaurants nearby. Voted "Favorite Day Trip" by readers of the Kansas City Star. Fortunately located midway between Kansas City and St. Louis and fifteen minutes from University of Missouri town of Columbia.

Rates
Five Rooms:$179-$289 One Suite:$269-$309 Number of Rooms: 6

Cuisine
Full, seasonally changing, gourmet breakfast menu with individual table or inroom service (Some rooms).Meal ingredients from local providers whenever possible.Afternoon cookies and beverage.

Nearest Airport
Columbia Regional Airport, 30 min. Delta/NWA nonstop connection to Memphis.

Hermann Hill Vineyard & Inn, Riverbluff Cottages, and Wedding Chapel

www.hermannhill.com
P.O. Box 555, 711 Wein Street, Hermann, MO 65041
573-486-4455 • Fax 573-486-5373
info@hermannhill.com

Member Since 2005

Innkeepers/Owners
Terry & Peggy Hammer

Enjoy the ultimate wine country inn experience at Missouri's most popular Bed and Breakfast. While both properties were built for upscale lodging, you can choose the inn's traditional bed and breakfast amenities and service or opt for more privacy at our Hermann Hill Riverbluff cottages. The inn's eight exquisitely appointed guest rooms offer spectacular views from your own balcony or patio, luxurious private baths with Jacuzzi-style tubs, spa room, hot tubs and steam showers in select suites, and the privacy and freedom to set your own pace. Sited on a bluff and surrounded by a vineyard, the inn rooms create the ideal backdrop for your stay in an ever-changing panorama of Hermann and the Missouri River Valley. Our Riverbluff cottages offer even higher amenities, including private outdoor hot tubs overlooking the Missouri River, aromatherapy fireplaces, kitchens, outdoor gas grills, steam showers, and laundry facilities. We supply your cottage with breakfast entrees prior to your arrival, provide daily make up service and also samples of our Port Chocolate Raspberry sauce.

Rates
Suites range from $181/$471 for all eight Inn rooms and all 12 cottage rooms. Rates vary by season and day. We offer multiple night mid-week discounts and American hero discounts mid-week discounts at both properties. Number of Rooms: 20

Cuisine
The Inn offers a full country breakfast with choice of entree served in the kitchen, dining room, deck or brought to your room. The Cottages have your breakfast stocked in your refrigerator for you to warm at your leisure.

Nearest Airport
70 miles west of St. Louis Lambert Airport

SelectRegistry.com

Inn at Hermannhof

www.theinnathermannhof.com
237 E. First Street, Hermann, MO 65041
888-268-1422 • 573-486-5199
info@innathermannhof.com

Member Since 2008

Innkeeper
Krissy Zumsteg

For a truly memorable experience, visit us in Hermann Missouri. The inn at Hermannhof features spacious, historically decorated Suites with luxurious amenities and a full breakfast. The Inn offers 8 Suites in the Festhalle and 6 Haus Wineries with 19 Suites. The Inn is located in the heart of the historic district, placing you in the center of Hermann activities. Nineteen of our unique guest rooms are located in six hillside cottages. Each Cottage is a fully restored historic house winery, originally built in the mid 1800s. Guest rooms range from classic to luxury. Each is designed with exquisite style to offer you choices, which include magnificent bedchambers, wine cellars, sitting rooms, fireplaces, whirlpool tubs, extensive steam showers, deep soaking tubs, wrap-around porches, and much more. All of our guest rooms provide the highest standard of excellence, with the comfort of you, our guest, as our first priority. Our Cottages are located behind the Hermannhof Winery, just a short distance from the historic district and the Amtrak Station.

Rates
Rates starting from $198 to $368. Number of Rooms: 27

Cuisine
Enjoy a full gourmet breakfast in our fireplace gathering room, or have a lighter fare delievered to your room if you prefer.

Nearest Airport
Lambert St. Louis International Airport

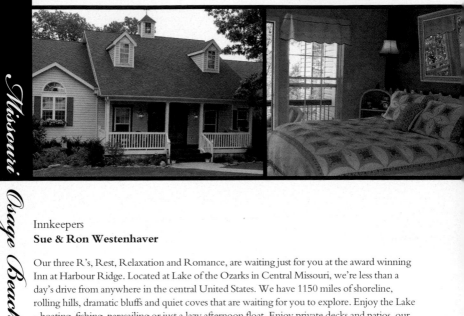

Inn at Harbour Ridge

www.harbourridgeinn.com
6334 Red Barn Road, Osage Beach, MO 65065
877-744-6020 • 573-302-0411
stay@harbourridgeinn.com

Member Since 2012

Missouri

Osage Beach

Innkeepers
Sue & Ron Westenhaver

Our three R's, Rest, Relaxation and Romance, are waiting just for you at the award winning Inn at Harbour Ridge. Located at Lake of the Ozarks in Central Missouri, we're less than a day's drive from anywhere in the central United States. We have 1150 miles of shoreline, rolling hills, dramatic bluffs and quiet coves that are waiting for you to explore. Enjoy the Lake – boating, fishing, parasailing or just a lazy afternoon float. Enjoy private decks and patios, our gazebo or the Inn's dock. Play championship golf on any one of fourteen golf courses. Hike at nearby state parks. Visit our wineries and eateries both on and off the water. Retail therapy is available at over 100 stores at the Osage Beach Premium Outlets, and at local boutiques nearby Mennonit markets. We've received two Certificates of Excellence from Trip Advisor, and have received top awards from BedandBreakfast.com.

Rates
$129 - $189 Our guestrooms offer luxurious linens, flicker fireplaces, Cable TV and DVD players, as well as complimentary Wi-Fi. Choose a private starlit hot tub, twosome tubby, or innside hot tub for your romantic getaway. Number of Rooms: 5

Cuisine
We serve comfort gourmet breakfasts and can plan fun and fabulous breakfast parties. We use fresh herbs from our own herb garden when possible and every lady is served a flower on her breakfast plate.

Nearest Airport
Kansas City International, Lambert-Saint Louis International

 SelectRegistry.com

New Hampshire

"The Granite State"

Famous for: Granite, White Mountains, Lakes, Beaches, Prime Primary (the first state to hold presidential primary elections).

🍴 🍴 🍴 🍷

Bedford Village Inn

www.bedfordvillageinn.com
2 Olde Bedford Way, Bedford, NH 03110
603-472-2001 • 800-852-1166 • Fax 603-472-2379
Member Since 2011
jack@bedfordvillageinn.com

Innkeeper/Owner
Jack Carnevale

The Bedford Village Inn was once the site of a working farm built in 1890. Through a multi-million dollar restoration, the original residence became the home of our nationally acclaimed AAA Four Diamond restaurant. The original barn was transformed into a luxury inn offering AAA Four Diamond lodging for the most discerning travelers from all over the world. Twin silos from the original property stand sentry to our magnificent Great Hall that soars three stories high and provides the most unique event site in New England. Its huge bay window overlooks an ever-changing seasonal courtyard garden. The inn rooms, also awarded Four Diamonds, were individually designed and decorated in the original barn and each one features a king-size four poster bed, sitting area with flat screen tv, free high speed internet access and elegant Italian marble baths with whirlpool tubs. The Federal architecture is elegantly complimented by miles of granite walkways throughout the estate and native rock walls that serve to highlight the manicured gardens filled with lush seasonal plantings.

Rates
There are several choices. Luxury $195-$520 Deluxe and Executive $325-$750 Summit Suite $375 with fireplace and two bedrooms 1,100 sq. ft. The Woodbury House with 3,200 sq. ft. offers a wonderful historic stay. Number of Rooms: 14

Cuisine
The culinary offerings are diverse. The Dining Rooms serves Contemporary Regional New England cuisine in several individually decorated rooms. The Tavern is the spot for casual dining. Corks Wine bar is perfect for its own menu and great wine choices

Nearest Airport
The Manchester Boston Regional Airport is a short 5 minute drive and is served by our free Mercedes ML suittle.

Adair Country Inn & Restaurant

www.adairinn.com
80 Guider Lane, Bethlehem, NH 03574
888-444-2600 • 603-444-2600 • Fax 603-444-4823
innkeeper@adairinn.com

Member Since 1995

Owners **Betsy and Nick Young**
Innkeepers **Ilja and Brad Chapman**

"Adair Country Inn & Restaurant is everything you dreamed a New England country inn would be." – USA Today. Get away from it all and unwind at this peaceful country inn. Enter a woodland oasis via a long winding drive surrounded by stone walls, stately pines, ponds, gardens and 200 acres. The Inn's scenic grounds were originally created by the Olmsted Brothers. This elegant Inn sits atop a knoll and enjoys magnificent views of the Presidential Range and comfortably appointed guest rooms with fireplaces, antiques, reproductions and air conditioning. Adair serves as an intimate, romantic retreat for adults who enjoy observing wildlife, hiking, golfing, skiing and more in the nearby White Mountains. The Inn's relaxing ambiance and casual dress belie uncompromising attention to detail, highly personalized, warm service and award-winning New England style cuisine. Adair is within a short drive of Franconia Notch, Mt. Washington, Mt. Lafayette, The Flume, superb hiking, numerous cross-country venues and major ski areas. Deliberately small... Naturally quiet!

Rates
$195/$325 B&B. Spacious rooms w/ views and private baths, 7 w/fireplaces, 3 w/2-person tubs, Queen or King feather beds. Complimentary wireless internet. Number of Rooms: 9

Cuisine
Breakfast features fresh fruit, homemade granola, steaming popovers and a hot entree. Afternoon tea with homemade goodies. New England style cuisine Thursday thru Monday in a cozy fireside restaurant with seasonal patio seating. Full beverage service.

Nearest Airport
Manchester NH 95 miles, Boston MA 155 miles, Montreal 180 miles

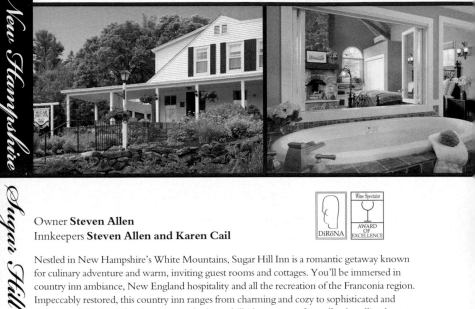

Sugar Hill Inn

www.sugarhillinn.com
116 Route 117, Sugar Hill, NH 03586
800-548-4748 • 603-823-5621
info@sugarhillinn.com

Member Since 2001

New Hampshire

Sugar Hill

Owner **Steven Allen**
Innkeepers **Steven Allen and Karen Cail**

Nestled in New Hampshire's White Mountains, Sugar Hill Inn is a romantic getaway known for culinary adventure and warm, inviting guest rooms and cottages. You'll be immersed in country inn ambiance, New England hospitality and all the recreation of the Franconia region. Impeccably restored, this country inn ranges from charming and cozy to sophisticated and distinctive. This 1789 farmhouse is perched on a hillside on acres of woodlands, rolling lawns and gardens, enhanced by White Mountains view. All rooms have a/c, and many have fireplaces, whirlpool tubs, and private decks. The Dream Cottage with a cathedral ceiling, stone fireplace, whirlpool and sauna has been featured in "Everyday with Rachael Ray" magazine. Whether you seek a convenient base for the attractions and outdoor activities of Franconia Notch and the White Mountains or a special private hideaway to snuggle in front of a fireplace...come share the good life at the Sugar Hill Inn...your destination of choice. Yankee Magazine Editors' Choice. Best of New Hampshire.

Rates
Classic Rooms: $165/$280; Cottages: $170/$465; Luxury Rooms: $200/$405. Open year-round. Number of Rooms: 14

Cuisine
Full breakfast, afternoon small bites and cocktails. Dinner Thurs.- Mon. by reservations. Relax in the Tavern with your favorite drink before dinner. Over 100 wines from around the world. Distinguished Restaurants of North America (DiRoNA) award.

Nearest Airport
Manchester Airport - 100 miles.

SelectRegistry.com

The Notchland Inn

www.notchland.com
2 Morey Road, Hart's Location, NH 03812-4105
800-866-6131 • 603-374-6131 • Fax 603-374-6168
innkeepers@notchland.com

Member Since 1996

New Hampshire

Hart's Location

Innkeepers/Owners
Les Schoof and Ed Butler

Get away from it all, relax and rejuvenate at our comfortable granite manor house, completed in 1862, within the White Mountain National Forest. Settle into one of our spacious guest rooms, individually appointed and each with a wood-burning fireplace and private bath. Children and pets are welcome in our newly completed mountain view cottages, ranging in size from 1 to 2 bedrooms and all with whirlpool baths. A wonderful 5-course dinner and full country breakfast are served in a fireplaced dining room overlooking the gardens. Nature's wonders abound at Notchland. We have Saco River frontage on our property and two of the area's best swimming holes! Visit with Crawford and Felonie, our Bernese Mountain Dogs. Secluded, yet near to all the Mt. Washington Valley has to offer. Notchland...a magical location.

Rates
8 Deluxe Rooms, 5 Suites, 2 Cottages $199/$385, B&B.Open year-round. Number of Rooms: 15

Cuisine
5-course distinctive dinners Weds-Sun, hearty country breakfast daily. Fully licensed: wine/spirits/beer. Dinner is a leisurely affair, taking about 2 hours. $40 per person for in-house guests. $45 Wed, Thurs, Sun; $48 Fri, Sat & Holidays for others.

Nearest Airport
Manchester, NH, approx. 125 miles; Burlington, VT, approx. 130 miles

Inn at Thorn Hill

www.innatthornhill.com
Thorn Hill Road, P.O. Box A, Jackson Village, NH 03846
800-289-8990 • 603-383-4242 • Fax 603-383-8062
stay@innatthornhill.com

Member Since 1998

Innkeepers/Owners
James and Ibby Cooper

Situated grandly on a knoll overlooking Jackson Village and the Presidential Mountains, the Inn offers 25 uniquely decorated guestrooms, suites, and cottages. The Main Inn features four suites and 12 luxury rooms, all with fireplaces, spa baths, and TV/DVDs, some with steam showers, wet bars, and mountain views. Common areas include a wrap-around porch; a lounge with a separate, casual menu; library; and spa level. Spa Facilities include an exercise room, sauna, yoga, and manicure/pedicure. Activities are available in all seasons at the Inn and throughout the White Mountains. Outdoor pool, year-round outdoor hot tub, cross-country skiing, and tobogganing at the Inn-hiking, golf, tennis, shopping, skiing, and sleigh rides are all nearby. Only AAA Four Diamond Inn and Restaurant in Mt. Washington Valley. Conde Nast Traveler's Gold List 2006. Travel & Leisure's World's Best Awards 2006.

Rates
Main Inn: 4 suites, 12 luxury rooms; Carriage House: 6 North Country rooms; 3 Cottages; Open year round. Breakfast, tea and three-course dinner included. $195/$430. Off Season Spa Packages. Number of Rooms: 25

Cuisine
New England Cuisine with Mediterranean influences and mountain views. Separate lounge menu. Well stocked bar with over thirty single malt scotches and the wine list has over 1300 selections.

Nearest Airport
Portland, ME

Inn at Ellis River

www.innatellisriver.com
P.O. Box 656, 17 Harriman Road, Jackson, NH 03846
800-233-8309 • 603-383-9339 • Fax 603-383-4142
stay@innatellisriver.com

Member Since 2009

Innkeepers/Owners
Lyn Norris-Baker and Frank Baker

Nestled by a sparkling stream on several acres at the edge of picturesque Jackson Village in the heart of the White Mountains, the Inn's rooms and rustic cottage for two are appointed with period furnishings, many with two-person whirlpool tubs and/or balconies and most with fireplaces. Let the river's soothing sounds lull you to sleep, and awaken to clear mountain air and a bountiful homemade breakfast. Spend your days exploring waterfalls or enjoy scenic drives, hiking, golf, canoeing, fishing, mountain biking, or tax-free shopping. In summer, scale Mount Washington by road or cog railway, take a moose tour, or relax by our heated pool. In winter, cross-country ski, snowshoe, take a sleigh ride, or choose from one of five Alpine Ski Centers nearby. Return each day to enjoy afternoon refreshments, a game of darts or billiards in our cozy gameroom/pub, the challenge of a Stave puzzle or board game in our sitting room, or the relaxing view of the river as you soak in our atrium-enclosed hot tub. Recipient of multiple Best of BedandBreakfast.com Awards, Mobil ☆☆☆.

Rates
Classic rooms $129/$199; Fireplace rooms $149/$219; 7 rooms & one cottage w/ whirlpool tubs & fireplaces $199/$299. Number of Rooms: 21

Cuisine
Gourmet country breakfast with menu changing daily. Afternoon refreshments include home-baked sweets and seasonal beverages. Several restaurants within walking distance.

Nearest Airport
Portland, ME ~ 75 miles; Manchester, NH ~ 110 miles; Boston (Logan) ~ 140 miles.

The Buttonwood Inn on Mt. Surprise

www.buttonwoodinn.com

P.O. Box 1817, 64 Mount Surprise Road, North Conway, NH 03860-1817

800-258-2625 • 603-356-2625 • Fax 603-356-3140

Member Since 1999

innkeeper@buttonwoodinn.com

Innkeepers/Owners

Bill and Paula Petrone

Awarded "THE MOST PERFECT STAY" by Arrington's Inn Traveler, an America's Favorite Inns Award winner, and Winner of 2010-2011 "Best of New England" and 2009-2010 "Best Food" on BedandBreakfast.Com. Our inn is situated on more than five secluded acres of field and forests near the villages of North Conway and Jackson. Offering a peaceful, rural setting and the convenience of being close to area activities, the Inn was originally an 1820s farmhouse and retains a comfortable country atmosphere with wide pine floors, antiques, quilts, and stenciling. Unwind with afternoon tea and home baked treats in front of one of our wood burning fireplaces in either the spacious living room or the Mt. Surprise Room media and game room when days are cool. You can select a spot of sun or shade in our award-winning gardens, take a dip in our heated pool or soak in our open air hot tub with a view of the mountains and forest by day and stars by night. Watch outside for the appearance of deer, wild turkeys, moose, hawks and our active and entertaining hummingbirds.

Rates

QUIET Season: Week: $79-$179 Weekends: $99-$199 April to mid-June & Nov to mid-Dec. INN Season: Week: $89 - $189 Weekends: $109 - $209 mid-December to March & mid-June to mid-September. PEAK Season: $149-$239 mid-Sept to October. Number of Rooms: 10

Cuisine

A full gourmet breakfast with delicious starters and entrees is prepared with fresh ingredients by Paula alternating savory one morning and sweet the next day. An afternoon beverage service with English teas and homemade baked treats is provided.

Nearest Airport

Portland, ME - 65 miles; Manchester, NH - 100 miles; Boston, MA - 139 miles

Home Hill Country Inn & Restaurant

www.homehillinn.com
703 River Road, Plainfield, NH 03781
(603) 675–6165 • Fax (603) 675–5220
inquiries@homehillinn.com

Member Since 2010

New Hampshire

Plainfield

General Manager
Paula Snow

Welcome to Home Hill Inn, a romantic, tranquil retreat set on 25 secluded acres in Plainfield, New Hampshire. Experience the luxury of our beautifully appointed rooms, inventive cuisine, pampering body massage treatments, and a boutique of local wares and crafts. Our seasonal packages include access to nearby golf courses and ski resorts. Breathtaking views, soul satisfying meals and attentive service make Home Hill Inn the ideal location for special functions, corporate retreats, family reunions or a romantic getaway. Bathed in light, Home Hill's dining room features dramatic floor-to-ceiling French doors, a decor awash in country reds and yellows and elegant furnishings accented by custom-designed chandeliers, an inviting atmosphere for unforgettable dining. Dinner is served Wednesday through Sunday from 5 pm until 9 pm. Brunch is served Sundays from 10 am until 2 pm.

Rates
Rates start at $100 off season mid week and up to $250 high season. Number of Rooms: 11

Cuisine
Farm to Table is Chef Paula Snow's passion and with so many farms on River Road alone that vision is realized in a tasty, creative and international style. Seasonal dining menu and tavern menu, Sunday Brunch and sumptuous breakfast are sure to please.

Nearest Airport
10 minutes from the Lebanon Airport, 90 minutes from Manchester airport.

The Darby Field Inn

www.darbyfield.com
185 Chase Hill Road, Albany, NH 03818
603-447-2181 • 800-426-4147
marc@darbyfield.com

Member Since 1981

Innkeepers/Owners
Marc & Maria Donaldson

Wander off the beaten path and discover the Darby Field Inn, a romantic country inn nestled on a quiet hill overlooking the White Mountains of New Hampshire. This inn is much more than a little bed and breakfast. It is a romantic getaway, offering deluxe rooms/suites with fireplaces and Jacuzzis, soothing spa services, and elopement, romance and wedding packages. It is an escape from the ordinary, offering candlelight dining, special weekend cookie and herb tour packages, and four seasons of local outdoor adventures! It is a relaxing mountain retreat that invites you to wander through on-site flower gardens, socialize with other guests in cozy Littlefield's Tavern, or swim in our outdoor heated pool (seasonal). On-site wooded nature trails are the perfect way to work off breakfast, whether by snowshoe, by foot! The Inn is located only a few miles from local shopping and area attractions, and is only two hours North of Boston. No matter what initially brings you to the Darby Field Inn, we bet you'll find many reasons to return, year after year.

Rates
7 standard rooms ranging from $150 - $195 per night. 6 deluxe rooms/suites ranging from $220 - $280 per night. All with private bath and WiFi. Rates are before 9% tax and 6% service. Number of Rooms: 13

Cuisine
Full country breakfast is included in room rates. Relaxed dining available most nights in either our mountain-view dining room, or Littlefield's Tavern. Enhance your meal with a bottle of wine from our international list, or local NH beer.

Nearest Airport
(1) Portland, ME: 60 Mi. (2) Manchester, NH: 100 Mi. (3) Logan Airport (Boston), MA : 135 Mi.

The Manor on Golden Pond

www.manorongoldenpond.com
P.O. Box T Route 3, 31 Manor Drive, Holderness, NH 03245
800-545-2141 Reservations • 603-968-3348 • Fax 603-968-2116
info@manorongoldenpond.com

Member Since 1995

Innkeepers/Owners
Brian and Mary Ellen Shields

It was the sheer romantic beauty of its mountain and lake view setting that inspired the building of The Manor on Golden Pond. And while the view still inspires, so does the hotel's cuisine and leisure facilities. The romantic story behind the resort began in 1904, when a wealthy Englishman fell in love with the mountain and lake view setting and built the Manor for his bride. In many senses, the idyll continues, inspiring the Oscar-winning Hepburn and Fonda film 'On Golden Pond.' Enjoy tea and dreamy end-of-day reveries in the library or alternatively retreat to the excellent restaurant. Guests awaken to our delectable Gourmet breakfasts each morning. The cuisine is the finest in the region, complemented by a celebrated cellar. Seasons Spa offers New Hampshire indigenous spa treatments to relax and soothe the most seasoned spa goers. Perhaps the best way to enjoy The Manor On Golden Pond is fireside after dinner, with a large Port and entertaining company. Fodor's 2011 Choice Hotel, Andrew Harper's "Hideaway Report" recommended. Zagat's Recommended. AAA Four Diamond rated.

Rates
22 rooms & 2 Suites $220/$550 B&B for 2 ppl per night. Open year-round. Log-burning fireplaces, oversized jacuzzis & flat screen TV. Keurig coffee makers. Complimentary use of heated outdoor pool, clay tennis court & lawn games. Number of Rooms: 24

Cuisine
Our chef's innovative creations showcase award-winning New England cuisine using the freshest local products & complemented by his wide-ranging culinary training. Experience our Van Horn Dining Room or "M" Bistro. Full gourmet breakfast each morning

Nearest Airport
Manchester, NH(MHT) (1 hour); Boston, MA (BOS)(2 hours); Portland, ME(PWM) (1.5 hour); Laconia, NH(LCI) (.5 hours)

Glynn House Inn

www.glynnhouse.com
59 Highland Street, Ashland, NH 03217
866-686-4362 • 603-968-3775
innkeeper@glynnhouse.com

Member Since 2005

Innkeepers/Owners
Pamela, Ingrid & Glenn Heidenreich

"New Hampshire's Finest Small Inn", this historic 1896 Victorian is the perfect choice for romance, recreation and relaxation. Delicious breakfasts are served at individual tables in the elegant Victorian dining room. Afternoon refreshments and complimentary wine & hors d'oeuvres are offered in the sitting room or outside on the wraparound porches. Tastefully decorated guest rooms include WiFi, private bathrooms, fireplaces, A/C, satellite TV, DVD players and iPod radios. In room massage is available. Seven suites, many with separate sitting rooms, also have double whirlpool baths. Venture away from the Inn and experience NH's spectacular lakes and mountains. Enjoy antiquing, art galleries, boating, fine dining, fishing, golf, hiking, historic sites, skiing, sleigh rides and snowmobiling. The innkeepers will make your visit an experience to remember by providing genuine hospitality and uncompromising service. Bring your favorite four-footed canine pal and reserve one of four pet friendly rooms.

Rates
Low season: $149 - $279; High season: $159 - $289; Peak season: $169 - $299; Number of Rooms: 12

Cuisine
A gourmet breakfast with a choice of entrees is served each morning. Afternoon refreshments are offered daily. Guests love our delicious cookies. In the evening, join other guests and the innkeepers for complimentary wine & appetizing hors d'oeuvres.

Nearest Airport
Manchester - 50 miles; Boston - 78 miles

Colby Hill Inn

🍴 🍴 ♟

www.colbyhillinn.com
33 The Oaks, P.O. Box 779, Henniker, NH 03242
800-531-0330 • 603-428-3281 • Fax 603-428-9218
innkeeper@colbyhillinn.com

Member Since 1993

New Hampshire

Henniker

Innkeepers/Owners
Cyndi and Mason Cobb

Intimate and romantic country inn located in the charming unspoiled village of Henniker. Enjoy romantic touches including down comforters, plush bathrobes, two-person whirlpools, crackling fireplaces and luxurious linens. 14 romantic guest rooms including two intimate suites with period antiques. All guest rooms have private baths, phones and WiFi access. Award winning candlelight dining nightly overlooking lush gardens, antique barns and gazebo. "Exquisite and Romantic Dining..." says Getaways for Gourmets. Bountiful breakfasts and candlelight dinners. Genuine hospitality and central New England location make this an ideal getaway spot. Enjoy cooking classes and theme weekends including "Chocolate Lovers Weekend" and "WineFest Weekends." Outdoor pool, lawn chess, cross country and downhill skiing, hiking, biking, and tennis all nearby. Yankee Magazine Editor's Pick. Featured in The Boston Globe and Ski Magazine. 90 Minutes North of Boston.

Rates
$140/$279 depending on season. Some guest rooms have two-person whirlpools/ fireplaces. Gourmet breakfast included. Number of Rooms: 14

Cuisine
Full gourmet breakfast including specialties like pumpkin pancakes with warm maple cream. Afternoon cookies. Award-winning romantic candlelight dining with full service bar, fine wines and spirits. Dinner available nightly for inn guests and public.

Nearest Airport
Manchester

Chesterfield Inn

www.chesterfieldinn.com
20 Cross Road, West Chesterfield, NH 03466
800-365-5515 • 603-256-3211 • Fax 603-256-6131
info@chesterfieldinn.com

Member Since 1990

New Hampshire

West Chesterfield

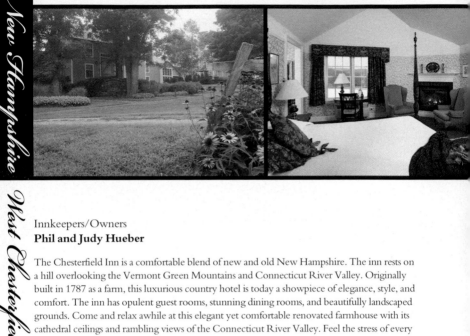

Innkeepers/Owners
Phil and Judy Hueber

The Chesterfield Inn is a comfortable blend of new and old New Hampshire. The inn rests on a hill overlooking the Vermont Green Mountains and Connecticut River Valley. Originally built in 1787 as a farm, this luxurious country hotel is today a showpiece of elegance, style, and comfort. The inn has opulent guest rooms, stunning dining rooms, and beautifully landscaped grounds. Come and relax awhile at this elegant yet comfortable renovated farmhouse with its cathedral ceilings and rambling views of the Connecticut River Valley. Feel the stress of every day life disappear as you sit in front of the fire in the parlor of this small country hotel. Spend the day reading in one of the Adirondack chairs in the back yard or explore local villages and countryside. Return at dusk to a sumptuous dinner in our candlelit dining room. Privacy, delicious cuisine, and relaxation are yours at one of the most unique and accommodating inns in New England. This is a perfect place for a romantic getaway in the country!

Rates
15 Rooms, $149/$344; 2 Suites, $269/$294. Open year-round except Christmas Eve and Christmas Day. Number of Rooms: 15

Cuisine
Full Country Breakfast cooked to order and served daily. Dinner is served Monday through Saturday in our candlelit dining room with sweeping views of the Green Mountains. Room service is available. Wine list and full bar available.

Nearest Airport
Hartford, CT is a one and a half hour drive and Boston is a two and a half hour drive.

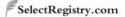
SelectRegistry.com

The Hancock Inn

www.hancockinn.com www.facebook/hancockinn
33 Main Street , P.O. Box 96, Hancock, NH 03449
800-525-1789 • 603-525-3318
innkeeper@hancockinn.com

Member Since 1971

Innkeepers/Owners
Jarvis & Marcia Coffin

CELEBRATE THE SEASONS AT NEW HAMPSHIRE'S OLDEST INN. In New England it's all about the weather. From warm summer nights to crisp autumn days and snowy winter woods to babbling spring brooks ~ there's something to enjoy each season at the historic Hancock Inn. The town of Hancock, located in the beautiful Monadnock Region of Southern New Hampshire, is considered by many to be one of the prettiest villages in New England. Situated inbetween Norway Hill to the East ~ with an apple orchard, Christmas tree farm and panoramic views ~ and Norway Pond to the West ~ you'll also find a church with Paul Revere bell #236 that rings in each hour, a friendly local general store, a delightful café and many homes that are listed on the National Historic Register. Named a Top Ten Historic Inn by YANKEE MAGAZINE in 2011, today, the Inn maintains authentic colonial charm combined with familial warmth and modern amenities. Our family includes Potter, the golden retriever, who will be waiting by the front door to greet you.

Rates
Rates: $105 ~ $240. 12 rooms & 1 suite. 1 room is handicap-accessible & dog friendly. All rooms have private baths, air conditioning, hairdryers, & free phone (limited cell signal). Some rooms have jetted tubs and fireplaces. Number of Rooms: 13

Cuisine
Room rate includes full cooked-to-order breakfast. Fine New England cuisine is served Tuesday-Saturday between 5:30-8pm in our colonial dining room and tavern. On Sunday night enjoy a simple Innkeepers' 1-dish-menu; check weekly for the bill of fare.

Nearest Airport
Manchester, NH - 50 miles ~ Boston Logan - 90 miles

The Inn at Crotched Mountain

www.innatcrotchedmt.com
534 Mountain Rd., Francestown, NH 03043
603-588-6840 • Fax 603-588-6623
innkeeper@innatcrotchedmt.com

Member Since 1981

Innkeepers/Owners
John and Rose Perry

A quaint country Inn, built in 1822, located on 65 acres, on the side of Crotched Mt. with spectacular views of the Piscatiqoug Valley. During the summer and fall, one may stroll among the vegetable, herb and flower gardens, sit, relax and enjoy the view by the swimming pool, or enjoy a game of tennis on one of the two clay tennis courts. For the more adventurous, take in the professional productions of The Peterborough Players, concerts and cultural events at The Old Meeting House of Francestown, hiking, or enjoying the many antique shops. During the Winter, one can relax in front of the fireplace in one of the two sitting rooms, there is also skiing at Crotched Mt Ski & Ride, 1 mi. from the Inn or Pats Peak, 30 minutes away. Enjoy a full country breakfast. Light fare is served in The Winslow Tavern on Saturday nights. There are a wide variety of restaurants in the area for those evenings the inn does not serve. The Inn is a wonderful place to relax and unwind. John, Rose and their 2 English Cockers look forward to welcoming you to their comfortable and casual inn.

Rates
13 Rooms, 8 with private baths, 5 with shared,3 with fireplaces, $80/$160 B&B. Open year round, except first two weeks in November. WiFi, Pet friendly. Number of Rooms: 13

Cuisine
Full breakfast daily. Light fare served in The Winslow Tavern on Saturday. Wine and liquor available.

Nearest Airport
Manchester-Boston Regional, Manchester, N.H.

Famous for: Princeton University, Battle of Trenton, Atlantic City, Atlantic Coastline, Industry, Menlo Park.

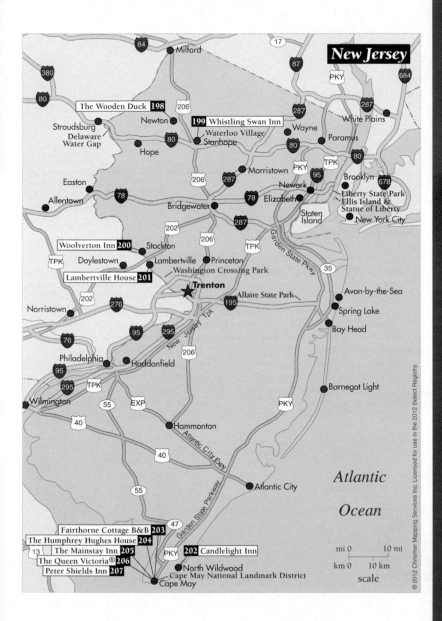

The Wooden Duck B&B

www.woodenduckinn.com
140 Goodale Road, Newton, NJ 07860
973-300-0395
woodenduckinn@aol.com

Member Since 2003

New Jersey Newton

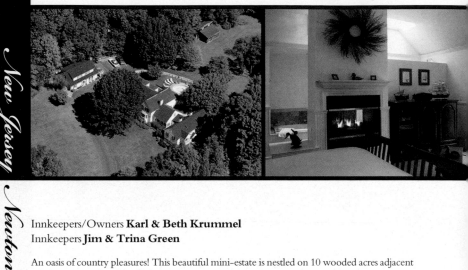

Innkeepers/Owners **Karl & Beth Krummel**
Innkeepers **Jim & Trina Green**

An oasis of country pleasures! This beautiful mini-estate is nestled on 10 wooded acres adjacent to the 1600-acre Kittatinny Valley State Park, abounding with wildlife and hiking trails. In-ground pool open all summer. All guestrooms have queen bed, private bath, clock radio, satellite TV/VCR, telephone, hair dryer, iron/ironing board, comfortable sitting area and a desk. Complimentary wireless Internet available throughout. Some rooms have soaking tub for two, 2-sided gas fireplace, DVD player and private balcony. Guests are welcome to use the game room with fireplace, TV/VCR, board games, and video library. The Guest Pantry with complimentary snacks, homemade cookies, soda, coffee, and tea is available 24/7. Nearby are many antique and craft shops, fine dining, winter and summer sports, horseback riding, hiking and fishing, mineral and mining museums, and numerous golf courses. Rated Mobil ☆☆☆. Less than an hour to the Crossings Outlet Mall in PA and only 55 miles to Times Square in Manhattan.

Rates
10 rooms, $135-$299 per night/double. Corporate rates Sunday thru Thursday. Open all year. Number of Rooms: 10

Cuisine
Full country breakfast featuring a rotating menu of delicious baked French toast or egg casseroles, meat and fruit, with homebaked bread or coffee cake, juice, tea, and coffee. Trail mix, cookies, snacks, hot and cold beverages available 24/7.

Nearest Airport
Newark Airport, 45 Miles. Aeroflex private airport in walking distance.

SelectRegistry.com

Whistling Swan Inn

www.whistlingswaninn.com
110 Main St., Stanhope, NJ 07874
888-507-2337 • 973-347-6369 • Fax 973-347-6379
info@whistlingswaninn.com

Member Since 1992

Innkeepers
Tom and Rosalind Bruno

"One of the Top Ten B&B's in the US" says the Inn Traveler magazine. Set amidst a spectacular garden on a quiet, tree-lined street, the Whistling Swan Inn exudes romance and warmth. This elegant 1905 Queen Anne Victorian features a gracious wraparound veranda where leisurely breakfasts are served on pleasant mornings. Each room embraces you with comfort and warmth with period antiques and modern conveniences; TV/VCR/DVD, A/C, wireless Internet, plus refrigerators, gas fireplaces and Jacuzzis in our suites. Whatever the season, a myriad of activities awaits you. After a busy day of hiking, biking, shopping or antiquing, relax in a hammock or share pleasant conversations with new-found friends. Enjoy fine dining at one of the area gourmet restaurants, some within walking distance. At day's end, snuggle up with your special someone next to a crackling fire. Sink into your featherbed and fall asleep to a movie from our DVD library.

Rates
5 Rooms (all with private bath), $119-$169; 4 Suites (Jacuzzi, fireplace), $189-$269. Corporate/Government/Single rates available. Number of Rooms: 9

Cuisine
Full country buffet breakfast, 24-hour complimentary guest snack bar, including our signature chocolate chip cookies. Special diets accommodated.

Nearest Airport
Newark - 45 minutes; Allentown, PA - 1 hour

Woolverton Inn

www.woolvertoninn.com
6 Woolverton Road, Stockton, NJ 08559
888-264-6648 • 609-397-0802 • Fax 609-397-0987
sheep@woolvertoninn.com

Member Since 2002

Innkeepers/Owners
Carolyn McGavin and Bob Haas

Perched high above the Delaware River, surrounded by 300 acres of rolling farmland and forest, The Woolverton Inn provides the seclusion of a grand country estate, yet the activities of New Hope and Lambertville are just five minutes away. Enjoy the glorious setting and relaxed elegance of this 1792 stone manor, while feeling as comfortable as you would at your own home in the country. All guestrooms are unique and thoughtfully decorated; they feature bucolic views, fireplaces, whirlpool tubs and showers for two, private outdoor sitting areas, stocked refrigerators, and Bose CD Wave radios. Dogs are permitted in the Garden Cottage. As recommended by "1000 Places to See Before You Die in the USA and Canada" and National Geographic Traveler, among others.

Rates
6 Rooms $150/$345; 2 Suites $285/$365; 5 Cottages $305/$435. Rooms offer featherbeds, fresh flowers, robes, luxury linens, CD Players, two person whirlpool tubs, two person showers, fireplaces. Number of Rooms: 13

Cuisine
Full gourmet breakfast served in our gardens or in bed. Signature Dishes include: homemade apple-cranberry turkey sausage, lemon-ricotta hotcakes, pina colada scones and fabulous cookies.

Nearest Airport
Philadelphia International and Newark

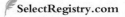

Lambertville House

🍽️ 🍽️ 🍽️ 🍷

www.lambertvillehouse.com
32 Bridge Street, Lambertville, NJ 08530
888-867-8859 • 609-397-0200 • Fax 609-397-0511
innkeeper@lambertvillehouse.com

Member Since 2009

New Jersey

Lambertville

Proprietors
Edric & Mary Ellen Mason

Four Diamond Award

The Lambertville House has been a landmark in the Delaware Valley area since 1812 providing gracious hospitality to American presidents, business leaders, dignitaries and discriminating guests from around the world. Proud recipients of the AAA ◆◆◆◆ for the past 12 years and listed on National Historic Register. Centrally located, yet a world apart this sophisticated boutique hotel offers amenities and attention to detail found only in the finest upscale properties. Each guest room features a private bath with whirlpool tub, fireplace, iPod docking radio, flat screen TV, Wireless Internet and exquisite ambiance. A short walk away is a complimentary health club, shops, antiques and award winning restaurants. A cozy hotel bar and restaurant serving breakfast, lunch and dinner every day. Uncompromising service and an experienced and knowledgeable staff always available to assist you. An ideal choice for a romantic getaway, a business meeting designed to refresh people and ideas or, an all-inclusive event venue for a wedding, rehearsal dinner or special celebration.

Rates
Rates: 26 Rooms/Suites $180/$350. Beautifully appointed baths with large whirlpool tubs, complimentary bathrobes, exclusive Aveda amenities, Evening turndown service, daily paper, complimentary bottled water, coffee and tea. Number of Rooms: 26

Cuisine
Left Bank Bistro features imaginative and fresh dining options in a handsome setting. Breakfast, lunch and dinner is served daily. Classic cocktails, an impressive wine list and the "best martini in town" is offered in the bar. Outdoor patio seating.

Nearest Airport
Philadelphia International, Newark International

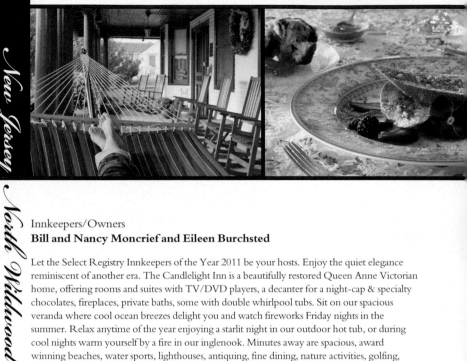

¶O¶

Candlelight Inn

www.candlelight-inn.com
2310 Central Avenue, North Wildwood, NJ 08260
800-992-2632 • 509-522-6200 • Fax 609-522-6125
Member Since 2001
info@candlelight-inn.com

New Jersey

North Wildwood

Innkeepers/Owners
Bill and Nancy Moncrief and Eileen Burchsted

Let the Select Registry Innkeepers of the Year 2011 be your hosts. Enjoy the quiet elegance reminiscent of another era. The Candlelight Inn is a beautifully restored Queen Anne Victorian home, offering rooms and suites with TV/DVD players, a decanter for a night-cap & specialty chocolates, fireplaces, private baths, some with double whirlpool tubs. Sit on our spacious veranda where cool ocean breezes delight you and watch fireworks Friday nights in the summer. Relax anytime of the year enjoying a starlit night in our outdoor hot tub, or during cool nights warm yourself by a fire in our inglenook. Minutes away are spacious, award winning beaches, water sports, lighthouses, antiquing, fine dining, nature activities, golfing, shopping, history, and a fun-filled boardwalk...something for everyone. Cape May County has islands with great Atlantic Ocean beaches, a Naval Air Station Museum, Historic Cold Spring Village, and Leaming's Gardens - the country's largest garden of annuals. Our inn is a small piece of the New Jersey Coast that we would like to share with you and your special someone.

Rates
7 Rooms, $115/$215; 3 Suites, $135/$275. Some have double whirlpool tubs. All rooms have either queen or king beds, private baths, air conditioning, gas or electric fire places plus many other amenities. Open year-round. Number of Rooms: 10

Cuisine
A 3-course, sit-down breakfast with a choice of entrees, afternoon refreshments, and complimentary soft-drinks, coffee & teas all day.

Nearest Airport
Atlantic City (ACY) - 40 minutes; Philadelphia Intern'l (PHL) - 90 minutes; Newark 'Liberty' Intern'l - 2 hours

The Fairthorne Cottage Bed & Breakfast

IOI

www.fairthorne.com
115 Ocean Street, Cape May, NJ 08204
800-438-8742 • 609-884-8791 • Fax 609-898-6129
fairthornebnb@aol.com

Member Since 2001

New Jersey

Cape May

Innkeepers/Owners
Ed & Diane Hutchinson

Diane and Ed welcome you to their intimate seaside inn. With just four rooms that feature King Sleep Number Beds complimented by cool luxury linens. All rooms have complimentary on site parking, flat screen tv's, ipod, iphone docking stations and wi fi access. Each bathroom is a haven to relax with rain shower heads or perhaps one of our two person air tub rooms. Fireplaces to take the chill off while you sip some sherry. Bicycles and beach chairs and towels are available for your use. You won't be disappointed in your choice to stay at The Fairthorne.

Rates
Rooms, $175/$295, Shoulder season specials. Number of Rooms: 4

Cuisine
Full breakfast and afternoon cookies. Make yourself a hot cup to cocoa, tea or coffee from our 24 hour Flavia Service. Also a fully stocked fridge with complimentary soft drinks.

Nearest Airport
Philadelphia and Atlantic City

The Humphrey Hughes House

www.humphreyhugheshouse.com
29 Ocean Street, Cape May, NJ 08204
609-884-4428
TheHumphreyHughes@comcast.net

Member Since 1999

Innkeepers/Owners
Terry & Lorraine Schmidt

Nestled in the heart of Cape May's primary historic district, The Humphrey Hughes House is one of the most spacious and gracious Inns. Expansive common rooms are filled with beautiful antiques. Relax on the large wraparound veranda filled with rockers and enjoy the ocean view and colorful gardens. Our large, comfortable guest rooms offer pleasant, clean accommodations. All rooms are air-conditioned with cable TV and Wireless Internet. Our location offers the visitor the opportunity to walk to the beach, restaurants, shops, theatre, concerts, nature trails. A full breakfast is served to all guests at 9:00 a.m. each day.

Rates
$175/$350 per night, Dbl. Weekday discounts Fall and Spring. All rooms and suites with queen or king. Number of Rooms: 10

Cuisine
Delicious,and beautifully presented, Hot Breakfast is served in our Dining room each morning.When weather permits, is served on the front Veranada which provides both neighborhood and ocean views. Refreshments are available 24/7 on the sunporch.

Nearest Airport
Atlantic City International

SelectRegistry.com

The Mainstay Inn

www.mainstayinn.com
635 Columbia Ave., Cape May, NJ 08204
609-884-8690 • Fax 609-884-1498
mainstayinn@comcast.net

Member Since 1976

Innkeeper **Diane Clark/**
Owners **David and Susan Macrae**

The Mainstay is a Landmark within a National Historic Town, and is but a short walk to restaurants, shops, theater, concerts, nature trails and beautiful beaches. All rooms are like stepping back in time and have queen, king and full beds. All are air-conditioned with cable TV and a private bath. Relax in the morning with our fresh brewed coffee or our Afternoon Tea each day in our rockers on our wrap around veranda while enjoying the Gardens and Horse and Carriages as they go by. Beach chairs, towels, and small umbrellas are provided free of charge. We are listed in the book "1,000 Places to See Before You Die."

Rates
9 Rooms, $165/360 B&B; 3 Suites, $195/$350 Opens April 1st closes January 1st,
Number of Rooms: 12

Cuisine
A Full Sit Down Breakfast served April to May, Hearty Buffet served June to September. All fresh baked Cakes and Fresh Seasonal Fruit Served Daily Fresh baked goodies with Savories served each day at our Afternoon Tea starting at 4 pm

Nearest Airport
Atlantic City International 45 minutes away.

The Queen Victoria

www.queenvictoria.com
102 Ocean Street, Cape May, NJ 08204-2320
609-884-8702
reservations@queenvictoria.com

Member Since 1992

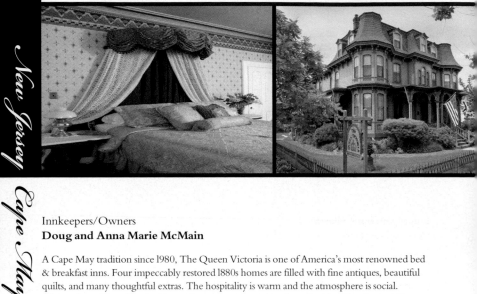

Innkeepers/Owners
Doug and Anna Marie McMain

A Cape May tradition since l980, The Queen Victoria is one of America's most renowned bed & breakfast inns. Four impeccably restored l880s homes are filled with fine antiques, beautiful quilts, and many thoughtful extras. The hospitality is warm and the atmosphere is social. Choose from thirty-four inviting and spacious rooms and suites, all with private bath, AC, mini-refrigerator, safe, robes and TV with DVD. Pamper yourself with a whirlpool tub or gas-log fireplace. For your Victorian enjoyment, rocking chairs fill porches and gardens. Wicker swings carry you back to a quieter time. Bicycles are provided free of charge, as are beach chairs and beach towels. The Queen Victoria is open all year and is located in the heart of the historic district, one block from the Atlantic Ocean, tours, shopping, and fine restaurants. Victorian Cape May offers tours, special events, and activities all year including the Spring Music Festival, Victorian Weekend, the Food & Wine Festival and Christmas in Cape May.

Rates
25 Rooms: $125/$285. 9 Suites: $175/$515. Weekday discounts Fall, Winter and Spring. Always open. Complimentary WiFi. Number of Rooms: 34

Cuisine
Rates include generous buffet breakfast and afternoon tea with sweets and savories. Complimentary juices, soft drinks, bottled water, coffee and teas. Baked treats and fresh fruit always available. Casual and fine dining within walking distance.

Nearest Airport
Atlantic City (ACY), Philadelphia (PHL)

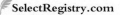

Peter Shields Inn

www.petershieldsinn.com
1301 Beach Avenue, Cape May, NJ 08204
609-884-9090
petershieldsinn@comcast.net

Member Since 2008

New Jersey

Cape May

Proprietor
Jeff Gernitis

This 1907 Georgian revival mansion is an architectural masterpiece, directly across from the Atlantic Ocean in Cape May, New Jersey with golfing, fishing and Atlantic City all within reach. The Peter Shields Inn is the ideal choice for a relaxing getaway. Just a short stroll from Cape May's historic district, the inn offers a charming sanctuary. Enjoy easy access to our beautiful beaches in the summer season or sip a glass of wine next to a cozy fireplace in the fall and winter. We provide the perfect setting any time of year. Each of our nine guest rooms offers individual ambiance with private baths, most have Jacuzzi tubs and fireplaces, flat screen cable television, plush bedding, exclusive bath amenities, nightly turn down service, individual climate control for heat and air conditioning. The inn also specializes in both casual and elegant ocean front weddings and special events. With our inviting guest rooms, fine dining restaurant, beautiful location and an attentive and caring staff, your visit to the Peter Shields Inn is sure to be a memorable one.

Rates
$150-$425 Includes full breakfast daily, afternoon wine & cheese, 24 hour hospitality suite with complimentary soft drinks, & snacks, concierge service, free Wifi, private parking, beach chairs, towels, umbrellas and bicycles. Number of Rooms: 9

Cuisine
Whether you're in the mood to dine indoors next to a warm fireplace or on our porch overlooking the sea, our award-winning, Zagat-rated restaurant offers Cape May's finest dining. The chef serves creative cuisine using the freshest local ingredients.

Nearest Airport
Atlantic City or Philadelphia International

New Mexico

"The Land of Enchantment"

Famous for: Taos, Santa Fe, Pueblos, Adobe, Cliff Dwellings, Carlsbad Caverns (the largest in the world), White Sands, National Monument, Ghost Ranch, Ship Rock, Pecos National Historical Park, Pancho Villa State Park.

Hacienda del Sol

www.taoshaciendadelsol.com
P.O. Box 177, 109 Mabel Dodge Lane, Taos, NM 87571
866-333-4459 • 575-758-0287 • Fax 575-758-5895
sunhouse@newmex.com

Member Since 2003

Innkeepers/Owners
Gerd and Luellen Hertel

Taos Mountain provides a magnificent backdrop to our Hacienda, which borders thousands of acres of panoramic and peaceful Indian Pueblo land. Enjoy a serene and beautiful view from the tranquil gardens or steaming jacuzzi as you stargaze in the stillness of our many clear nights. The original 1804 adobe once belonged to legendary art patroness Mabel Dodge Luhan. This historic inn has hosted guests such as D.H. Lawrence, Georgia O'Keefe, Frank Waters and Ansel Adams. Southwestern rooms enchant our guests with kiva fireplaces, viga and latilla ceilings, and handcrafted furniture. In the heat of summer, Taos elevation combined with the shade of towering cottonwoods, elms, willows and blue spruce on the property provide blissful conditions. Experience the culinary talents of award winning chef/owner Gerd Hertel every Thursday night for a fun cooking demonstration followed by a 4 course meal including wine. We also offer gourmet theme dinners for holidays and special occasions. Weddings can be arranged in either of our garden courtyards with full catering services provided.

Rates
7 Rooms, $135/$325 B&B. 4 Suites, $190/$540 B&B. Open year round. Number of Rooms: 11

Cuisine
2-course breakfast with hot entree. Gourmet Coffees and tea and hot cocoa available all day. Afternoon homemade snacks and sweets are available in the Dining room. Breakfast served on the patio in summer or by the open kiva fireplace in winter.

Nearest Airport
Santa Fe and Albuquerque Airport

El Farolito and Four Kachinas Inn

www.farolito.com and www.fourkachinas.com

514 Galisteo Street (El Farolito), 512 Webber Street (Four Kachinas), Santa Fe, NM 87501

888-634-8782 • 505-988-1631 • Fax 505-989-1323

Member Since 2001

innkeeper@farolito.com

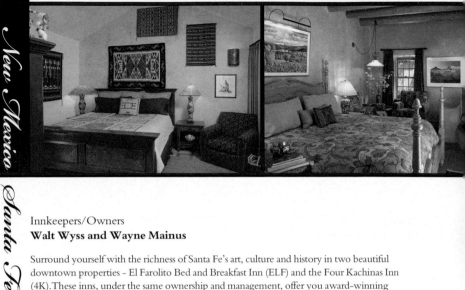

Innkeepers/Owners

Walt Wyss and Wayne Mainus

Surround yourself with the richness of Santa Fe's art, culture and history in two beautiful downtown properties - El Farolito Bed and Breakfast Inn (ELF) and the Four Kachinas Inn (4K). These inns, under the same ownership and management, offer you award-winning accommodations, showcasing exquisite original Southwestern art and handcrafted furnishings. The rooms are decorated in styles relevant to Santa Fe's rich cultural heritage of native American, Spanish and Anglo inhabitants. Modern amenities also abound including fine linens, rich fabrics, AC, private entrances, TVs, telephones and free Internet access. The two inns are conveniently located in the downtown historic district, a short pleasant walk to numerous galleries, shops, museums, world-class fine dining, and the central Plaza. Savor a leisurely breakfast on the back portal and relax on your garden patio. At ELF, enjoy a fireside breakfast in the brightly decorated dining room and the coziness of a fireplace in your room. At the 4K Inn, enjoy access to the cozy lounge and relax on one of our many garden patios.

Rates
13 Rooms, $130/$240; 1 Suite, $210/$275. 7 rooms/1 suite at El Farolito and 6 rooms at Four Kachinas. Features: TV, phones, fine linens, AC, garden patios. Fireplaces, in-room coffee and refrigerators at ELF. Number of Rooms: 14

Cuisine
Complete healthy breakfast with quality home-baked goods, hot entree, fresh fruit, yogurts, and ample accompaniment. Complimentary afternoon light refreshments. Walking distance to numerous world-class fine dining restaurants.

Nearest Airport
Santa Fe and Albuquerque

Los Poblanos Historic Inn & Organic Farm

www.lospoblanos.com
4803 Rio Grande Blvd. NW, Los Ranchos de Albuquerque, NM 87107
866-344-9297 • 505-344-9297 • Fax 505-342-1302
info@lospoblanos.com

Member Since 2005

Innkeepers/Owners
The Rembe Family

Set among 25 acres of lavender fields and lush formal gardens, Los Poblanos Inn is one of the most prestigious historic properties in the Southwest. The Inn was designed by the region's foremost architect, John Gaw Meem, the "Father of Santa Fe Style," and is listed on both the New Mexico and National Registers of Historic Places. Guest rooms are in a classic New Mexican style with kiva fireplaces, carved ceiling beams, hardwood floors, and antique New Mexican furnishings. Guests can relax around the Spanish hacienda-style courtyard or spend hours exploring the property's extensive gardens and organic farm. The buildings feature significant artwork commissioned during the WPA period by some of New Mexico's most prominent artists, including a fresco by Peter Hurd and carvings by Gustave Baumann. Detailed tours highlighting the property's cultural, political, agricultural and architectural history are available to every guest. "One could spend a lifetime at Los Poblanos and never fall out of love." - Su Casa Magazine

Rates
20 Guest Rooms and Suites, seasonal rates from $145 to $300. Fireplaces, spa services upon request, wireless internet, flatscreen tvs, fitness center, free onsite parking. Open year-round. Number of Rooms: 20

Cuisine
Complimentary gourmet breakfast with fresh organic produce and ingredients from our farm. Add on options for guests include an in-room charcuterie and pantry, La Merienda dinner, cooking classes and workshops.

Nearest Airport
Albuquerque International Sunport

New York

From Niagara Falls to New York City, New York, the Empire State, is peppered with a plethora of lakes and over 40,000 miles of rivers and streams. Home to rugged mountains, New York offers exciting opportunities to downhill or cross-country ski as well as snowshoe. Large cities and small towns feature numerous attractions, from the Baseball Hall of Fame in Cooperstown, to the wine trails of the Finger Lakes to national parks to historical sites across the State.

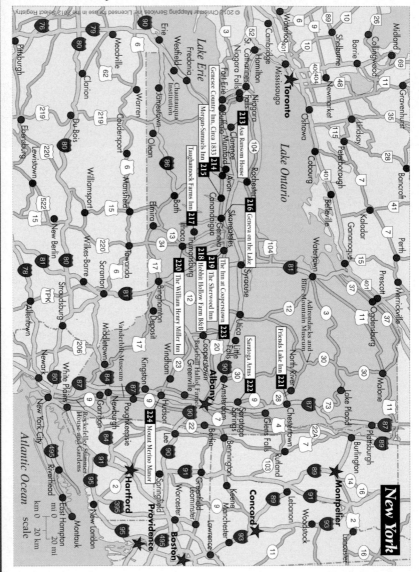

© 2012 Christian Mapping Services Inc. Licensed for use in the 2012 Select Registry.

SelectRegistry.com

Asa Ransom House

www.asaransom.com

10529 Main St. Rt. 5, Clarence, NY 14031

800-841-2340 • 716-759-2315 • Fax 716-759-2791

innfo@asaransom.com

Member Since 1976

New York

Clarence

Innkeepers/Owners

Robert Lenz and Abigail Lenz

On the site of the first gristmill built in Erie County (1803), where guests are romanced in the winter by the glowing fireplaces and spacious grounds full of herbs and flowers in the summer. Many rooms have porches or balconies to view the grounds or just relax. Experience world-class cuisine and full country breakfasts with delicious regional accents. Voted best food, service, hospitality, romantic setting and historical charm in Buffalo News readers survey. Often upon arrival you will find the aroma of fresh pies and breads lingering in the air! Clarence is known throughout the east for its antiques and treasures, along with unusual shops full of gifts, art and crafts. Explore the hiking/bike trails or visit the nearby Opera House, Erie Canal Cruises, Albright-Knox Art Gallery and Frank Lloyd Wright's Martin House Complex. Also Niagara wineries, Fort Niagara, Letchworth State Park and much more. Only 28 miles from Niagara Falls. AAA ◆◆◆

Rates
10 Rooms, $129/$195 B&B; $195/$330 MAP. Single rates available. All private baths. Full country breakfast included, queen or king beds, 9 with fireplace, 2 with whirlpool. Complimentary wireless internet. Number of Rooms: 10

Cuisine
Fine country dining with regional specialties. Fully licensed - NYS Wine award. "Best Place to Take Out-of-Town Guests" award.

Nearest Airport
Buffalo/Niagara 9 miles, Amtrak 11 miles

Genesee Country Inn Bed and Breakfast

www.geneseecountryinn.com
948 George Street, P.O. Box 226, Mumford-Rochester, NY 14511
585-538-2500 • 800-697-8297 • Fax 585-538-9867

Member Since 1988
stay@geneseecountryinn.com

New York

Mumford-Rochester

Innkeepers/Owners
Deborah & Richard Stankevich

Step back to an era of simple elegance, fine hospitality and natural beauty. This historic Bed and Breakfast/Country Inn, an 1833 plaster-paper mill, is situated on eight acres along Spring Creek with mill ponds and a waterfall to enthrall any traveler. Hike the grounds, the MacKay Wildlife Preserve, or the Genesee Country Village & Museum Nature Center. Enjoy the art of fly-fishing on our private Spring Creek, fish the famed Oatka Creek, and visit the historic NYS Fish Hatchery. The Inn's idyllic country ambiance is perfect for a secluded, romantic getaway, yet it is close enough to the arts, entertainment, Finger Lakes wineries, antique shops, and over 70 golf courses. The Inn is a wonderful location for family reunions, birthday parties, corporate events, bridal or baby showers, and intimate weddings or elopements. Romance, spa, and fly-fishing packages are available! The Inn has wireless Internet, TVs with DVD players, an extensive DVD collection, fax, and meeting facilities. Check our web site for additional special packages and getaway weekends. See you at the Inn!

Rates
Six Old Mill Rooms-$120/$160; Three Garden Rooms-$160/$185; and One King Suite-$180/$200. Number of Rooms: 10

Cuisine
Full hot country breakfast daily. Refreshments available throughout the day.

Nearest Airport
Rochester International Airport (13 miles east); Buffalo International Airport (41 miles west)

Morgan–Samuels Inn

www.morgansamuelsinn.com
2920 Smith Rd., Canandaigua, NY 14424
585-721-6656 • 585-721-3383
MorSamBB@aol.com

Member Since 1992

Innkeepers/Owners
Julie & John Sullivan

Travel the 2000 foot tree lined drive to this secluded and exquisite 1810 English style mansion. The Inn sits on a rise like a plantation surrounded by 46 acres. Four patios, trickling waterfall, tennis court, beautiful landscaped grounds canopied by 300 noble trees. Relax in a romantic atmosphere with soft music piped throughout the common areas. Enjoy an elegantly appointed common room with an open stone fireplace, baby grand piano and many museum quality oil paintings. Cozy library just off the common room. Innkeeper dinners and a sumptuous gourmet breakfast is served in three areas; the beamed dining room with a mural surrounding you, the tea room with floor to ceiling windows with garden views and the Victorian porch is glass enclosed with expansive views of the property and bird watching. There are five guest rooms and the Morgan Suite. All rooms have wood burning or English coal grate fireplaces. Rooms with fireplaces, 3 rooms with double Jacuzzies, 3 rooms with French doors and balconies with the sound of trickling water over the rocks below. Newly completed Spa.

Rates
5 Rooms, $169/$269 B&B; 1 Suite, $299/$325 B&B; Number of Rooms: 6

Cuisine
Innkeeper dinner by reservation and Breakfast served privately if desired. The signature fruit tray with a variety of 24 seasonal fruits starts the day followed by a verbalized menu which includes our renowned open faced omelets.

Nearest Airport
Rochester & Syracuse International are about the same distance

Geneva On The Lake

www.genevaonthelake.com
1001 Lochland Road, Route 14, Geneva, NY 14456
800-3-GENEVA • 315-789-7190 • Fax 315-789-0322
info@genevaonthelake.com

Member Since 2003

General Manager
William J. Schickel

Experience European elegance and friendly hospitality in the heart of Finger Lakes Wine Country. Amidst an ambiance of Italian Renaissance architecture, classical sculptures, luxurious suites and Stickley furnishings, guests from around the world enjoy vacation getaways, family gatherings, weddings and conferences. Rest, relax and surrender yourself to gracious service and breathtaking surroundings. Candlelight dining with live music. A complimentary bottle of wine and flowers are in your suite on arrival and The New York Times is at your door each morning. Complimentary high-speed wireless Internet is available. Glorious formal gardens for lawn games, a 70' outdoor pool, and a boat-house with dock and moorings. Adjacent are Geneva's charming Historic District and the campus of Hobart and William Smith Colleges, both replete with architectural gems. Enjoy magnificent scenic beauty on the Seneca Lake Wine Trail. Golf is nearby. "The food is extraordinarily good." – Bon Appetit. "One of the 10 most romantic inns in the United States." – American Historic Inns.

Rates
29 Guest Accommodations (13 one bedroom suites, 10 two bedroom suites and 6 studios). Room Rates from $165 to $795 per night. Many Packages with candlelight dinner and full breakfast from $284 to $1115 per night. Number of Rooms: 29

Cuisine
Gourmet dinner is served with a smile in the warmth of candlelight and live music. Breakfast daily and Sunday Brunch. Lunch On The Terrace in summer.

Nearest Airport
Rochester International

SelectRegistry.com

Taughannock Farms Inn

www.t-farms.com
2030 Gorge Road, Trumansburg, NY 14886
888-387-7711 • 607-387-7711 • Fax 607-387-7721
www.t-farms.com

Member Since 2002

Innkeepers/Owners
Tom & Susan Sheridan

Relax and enjoy a bygone era at this Victorian country inn. Majestically situated above Cayuga's waters, the inn offers commanding views of the lake. This Finger Lake's wine region landmark, built in 1873, is known for its gracious hospitality, abundant American cuisine, and charming accommodations. In addition to the five rooms in the Main inn that are furnished with antiques, we also have four guesthouses for a total of 23 rooms. Our newest guesthouse, Edgewood, has 10 rooms with either covered balconies/patios that have outstanding views of Cayuga Lake, and 4 king units featuring jacuzzis. Savor a romantic dinner in the 150-seat fine dining restaurant overlooking the lake. The four-course meal features American cuisine and is complemented by wonderful Finger Lakes wines.

Rates
Main Inn rooms $95/$200. 3 Guesthouses $130/$210 per room. Full cottage $365/ $505. Seasonal rates. Number of Rooms: 23

Cuisine
Expanded Continental breakfast of juice, coffee, fruit, breakfast pastries, cereal, yogurt and at least one hot item. Dinner includes appetizer, salad or sorbet, entree, and dessert. Banquets available.

Nearest Airport
Tompkins County Airport

Hobbit Hollow Farm

www.hobbithollow.com
3061 West Lake Road, Skaneateles, NY 13152
800-374-3796 • 315-685-2791 • Fax 315-685-3426
innkeeper@hobbithollow.com

Member Since 1998

New York

Skaneateles

Proprietor
William B. Eberhardt

Hobbit Hollow Farm has been carefully restored inside and out to recreate the casual comfort of an elegant country farmhouse. Hobbit Hollow serves a full, gourmet breakfast as part of the room price. Overlooking Skaneateles Lake, Hobbit Hollow Farm is situated on 320 acres of farmland with trails and ponds as well as private equestrian stables. Spend time contemplating the lake on our east veranda. Enjoy afternoon tea or coffee and watch the light play on the water in the soft wash of dusk. Rediscover what it means to be truly relaxed in a setting of tranquility. This is the perfect spot for a quiet, romantic getaway.

Rates
5 rooms with master-crafted period furniture and antiques, $175/$325. Amenities include four-poster beds, whirlpool baths and fireplaces. We are open year-round. Number of Rooms: 5

Cuisine
Full gourmet country breakfast. Find excellent dinner and lunches at the Sherwood Inn, Blue Water Grill, and Kabuki.

Nearest Airport
Syracuse (Hancock International)

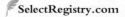

The Sherwood Inn

www.thesherwoodinn.com
26 West Genesee Street, Skaneateles, NY 13152
800-374-3796 • 315-685-3405 • Fax 315-685-8983
info@thesherwoodinn.com

Member Since 1979

Owner
William B. Eberhardt

Built as a stagecoach stop in 1807, The Sherwood Inn has always been a favorite resting place for travelers. The handsome lobby with fireplace, gift shop, antiques and orientals offers a warm reception. Each room has been restored to the beauty of a bygone era to create a relaxing harmony away from everyday cares. Our newly renovated dining and banquet rooms are able to accommodate groups of all sizes. In addition to our dining rooms, many of our 25 guest rooms overlook beautiful Skaneateles Lake. Casual lakeside dining and The Sherwood are synonymous, and we have been recognized by the New York Times, Bon Appetit, Country Living, Harper's Bazaar and New Yorker magazines. Our extensive menu offers American cooking with a continental touch, accompanied by an impressive wine list which received the Wine Spectator "Award of Excellence."

Rates
17 Suites and 8 Rooms, $175/$295. Suites have fireplaces/whirlpool baths. All have private baths, telephones and televisions. Complimentary continental breakfast buffet is served daily. We are open year-round. Number of Rooms: 25

Cuisine
Our Tavern serves traditional American fare in a relaxed atmosphere. Our Dining Room offers candlelight dining in a lovely setting overlooking Skaneateles Lake. Serving Daily.

Nearest Airport
Syracuse (Hancock International)

William Henry Miller Inn

www.MillerInn.com
303 North Aurora Street, Ithaca, NY 14850
877-256-4553 • 607-256-4553 • Fax 607-256-0092
millerinn@aol.com

Member Since 2003

New York *Ithaca*

Innkeepers/Owners
Lynnette Scofield & David Dier

Experience the Finger Lakes! There is so much to see and do in this lovely (and surprising) part of New York State. The William Henry Miller Inn is located in the heart of downtown Ithaca and is perfect for the business traveler, vacationer or guests coming in conjunction with Cornell University or Ithaca College. The Inn is ten blocks from Cornell University, a mile from Ithaca College and twenty minutes to The Finger Lakes Wine Trail. Our goal is to make your stay as comfortable and easy as possible starting with hand ironed sheets, private baths and wireless throughout. Our nine guest rooms offer a variety of configurations and our pet friendly room is located in The Carriage House if you're bringing a four pawed friend with you. Kiplinger's Magazine voted Ithaca one of the top ten places to live in the US. It has recently been named as one of the top ten places to retire in the country. There is something for everyone in this interesting, busy town.

Rates
$165 to $275/night. Full breakfast, evening dessert, beverages, wireless and parking included. Number of Rooms: 9

Cuisine
Breakfast with choice of two main dishes served during a two hour period. Homemade evening dessert and always available coffee and tea. Wonderful restaurants nearby including the world famous Moosewood. We gladly accommodate dietary requests.

Nearest Airport
Tompkins County (Ithaca) Airport is just ten minutes away. Syracuse is seventy-five minutes.

SelectRegistry.com

Friends Lake Inn

www.friendslake.com

963 Friends Lake Road, Chestertown, NY 12817

518-494-4751 • Fax 518-494-4616

friends@friendslake.com

Member Since 1998

New York

Chestertown

Innkeepers/Owners
John and Trudy Phillips

Experience the comfort and intimate ambiance of this elegantly restored inn, surrounded by the natural beauty of the Adirondacks. Guest rooms feature antiques, fine fabrics, featherbeds, Jacuzzis, steam showers and/or fireplaces. Nationally acclaimed cuisine is served daily in the candlelit Nineteenth Century dining room, complemented by gracious service and a Wine Spectator Grand Award–winning wine list. During the summer swim in the lake or the pool, canoe, kayak or fish on Friends Lake. In the winter ski, snowshoe or hike on 32 kilometers of trails. Many activities are close to the Inn.

Rates
Choose from 17 luxurious guest rooms, all with private baths. Rooms with Jacuzzis or Adirondack Rooms with fireplaces available. Rooms range from $349-$499 per couple. (MAP, full country breakfast and three course dinner included). Number of Rooms: 17

Cuisine
Full country breakfast and candlelit dinner served daily, bistro open at 2:00 pm on weekends, 4:00 pm weekdays. Inquire about conferences, rehearsal dinners, and weddings. Lighter Wine Bar Menu available. Extensive wine collection.

Nearest Airport
Albany

Saratoga Arms

www.SaratogaArms.com
497 Broadway, Saratoga Springs, NY 12866
518-584-1775 • Fax 518-581-4064
info@SaratogaArms.com

Member Since 2008

New York

Saratoga Springs

Innkeepers/Owners
The Smith Family

An award winning 1870 Second Empire brick concierge hotel located in the heart of Saratoga's downtown district. Walking distance to restaurants, museums, shopping, and colleges. Beautifully decorated rooms with high ceilings, fireplaces, double whirlpool tubs. State-of-the-art executive conference room. Individually appointed guest rooms blend nineteenth century ambiance and modern amenities for the best of both worlds including cable TV, WiFi, voice mail and personal climate control. Period antiques, family treasures and custom decor throughout the hotel carry on the genteel Saratoga style. The jewel of Saratoga Arms is the beautiful wraparound Saratoga porch that welcomes you as you approach the hotel and begs you to linger as you depart. It serves as a gathering place for guests and visitors. A collection of antique wicker extends an invitation to engage in lively conversation with other guests or to leisurely enjoy the passers-by.

Rates
$195-$375, Racing Season $350-$625. Cable TV with HBO. Individually controlled heat and air-conditioning WiFi. Number of Rooms: 31

Cuisine
Full Irish breakfast served each morning. Coffee and tea all day.

Nearest Airport
Albany, NY (ALB) 28 miles; Saratoga (private) 3 miles.

The Inn at Cooperstown

www.innatcooperstown.com
16 Chestnut Street, Cooperstown, NY 13326
607-547-5756 • Fax 607-547-8779
info@innatcooperstown.com

Member Since 1998

New York Cooperstown

Innkeepers/Owners
Marc and Sherrie Kingsley

A stay at The Inn at Cooperstown is a special treat. This award-winning historic hotel is ideally situated to enjoy all that Cooperstown offers. The Inn was built in 1874 and is thoughtfully improved upon every year. Spotless rooms are individually decorated with many charming touches. The new luxury suite is filled with upscale amenities. The relaxing atmosphere at the inn enables guests to escape the hectic pace of the modern world. After exploring the lovely village of Cooperstown, visitors unwind in rockers on The Inn's sweeping veranda or enjoy the fireplace in a cozy sitting room. The National Baseball Hall of Fame is just two blocks away. It is a brief trolley ride to experience another century at The Farmers' Museum, where exhibits, a recreated village and costumed staff depict life over 150 years ago. Nearby, the Fenimore Art Museum displays a premier collection of Native American Indian art, American paintings and folk art. The Glimmerglass Opera, beautiful Otsego Lake and many other treasures are located just beyond the village.

Rates
Guest rooms have private bath, A/C, CD/clock radio, hair dryer, iron, wireless internet. Televisions in sitting rooms and suites. Standard: $110/$185, Classic: $135/$210, Suites: $190/$308, $280/$498. Open year-round. Number of Rooms: 18

Cuisine
Expanded continental breakfast, afternoon refreshments, and fine restaurants within walking distance.

Nearest Airport
Albany, NY (ALB) or Syracuse, NY (SYR).

Mount Merino Manor

www.mountmerinomanor.com
4317 Route 23, Hudson, NY 12534
518-828-5583 • Fax 518-828-4292
info@mountmerinomanor.com

Member Since 2009

New York

Hudson

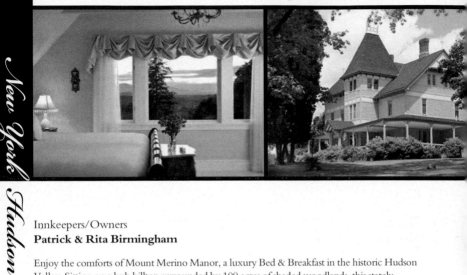

Innkeepers/Owners
Patrick & Rita Birmingham

Enjoy the comforts of Mount Merino Manor, a luxury Bed & Breakfast in the historic Hudson Valley. Sitting on a lush hilltop surrounded by 100 acres of shaded woodlands, this stately Victorian has magnificent views of the Catskill Mountains and Hudson River. Decorated with an eclectic mix of treasured furniture, period pieces and fine fabrics, each guest room has a distinct personality. All guest rooms have spacious private baths and many have mountain views, candle-lit fireplaces, whirlpool tubs, spa showers and king beds. Special amenities such as thick Egyptian cotton towels, luxury bed linens, spa robes, aromatherapy bath products, fresh flowers and bedside chocolates pamper every guest. This 1870's mansion also provides modern amenities such as complimentary WiFi, TV/DVD and in-room climate control. Just outside the city of Hudson and a neighbor to Olana State Historic site, Mount Merino Manor is minutes to fine dining, shopping, art, antiques and all outdoor activities.

Rates
$175-$375. All private baths. Mid-week rates/packages. 1 Room ADA compliant.
Number of Rooms: 7

Cuisine
Breakfast is served in our light-filled dining room at individual tables. Locally grown seasonal fruit, fresh baked muffins or bread and a hot entree including gourmet coffee and teas. A guest kitchen provides hot and cold beverages and snacks anytime.

Nearest Airport
Albany International Airport 45 miles. Columbia County Airport 10 miles.

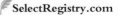

Famous for: Blue Ridge Mountains, Smoky Mountains, Outer Banks, Roanoke Island, Cape Hatteras, Kitty Hawk, Tobacco, Textiles, Furniture.

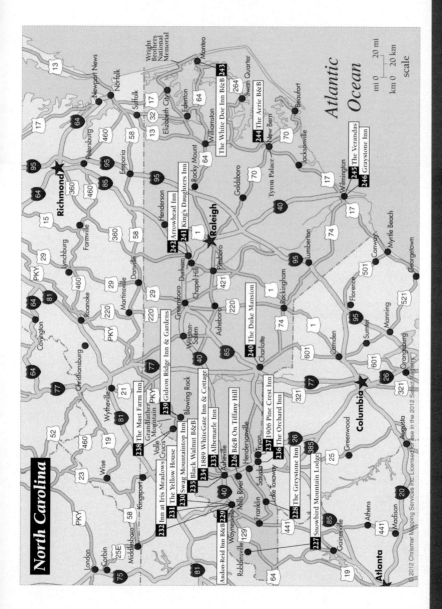

Bed & Breakfast on Tiffany Hill

www.BBonTiffanyHill.com
400 Ray Hill Rd , Mills River, NC 28759
828-290-6080
vacation@BBonTiffanyHill.com

Member Since 2010

North Carolina

Mills River

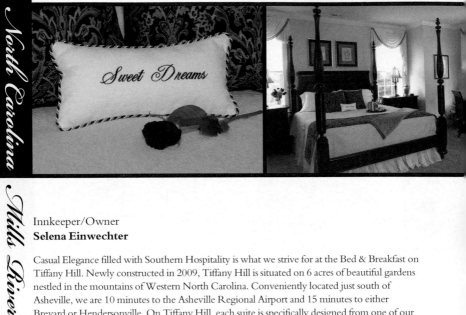

Innkeeper/Owner
Selena Einwechter

Casual Elegance filled with Southern Hospitality is what we strive for at the Bed & Breakfast on Tiffany Hill. Newly constructed in 2009, Tiffany Hill is situated on 6 acres of beautiful gardens nestled in the mountains of Western North Carolina. Conveniently located just south of Asheville, we are 10 minutes to the Asheville Regional Airport and 15 minutes to either Brevard or Hendersonville. On Tiffany Hill, each suite is specifically designed from one of our favorite southern towns. Suites include private baths, 7 layer beds, flat Screen TV/DVD players, wireless hi-speed internet access, piped-in music, luxurious robes, writing desks, keyless entry and 24 hour access to complimentary beverages and snacks. Second floor suites also have individual temperature controls. Your stay comes with a 3-course gourmet breakfast and lots of southern hospitality. Come do as much or as little as you like on Tiffany Hill.

Rates
5 Suites: Rates range from $185 to $235 per night before taxes. Natchez Suite - $185; Madison Suite - $185; Seaside Suite - $215; Beaufort Suite - $215; Charlottesville Suite - $235. Number of Rooms: 5

Cuisine
Join us at breakfast at Tiffany's as we serve a three course gourmet breakfast daily. Let us know if it is your anniversary & we will make it candlelit. Happy to accommodate individual breakfast dietary requests. Breakfast to go is also available.

Nearest Airport
Asheville Regional - 10 minutes Greenville, South Carolina - 45 minutes Charlotte, North Carolina - 2 hours

SelectRegistry.com

Snowbird Mountain Lodge

www.snowbirdlodge.com
4633 Santeetlah Rd., Robbinsville, NC 28771
800-941-9290 • 828-479-3433 • Fax 828-479-3473
innkeeper@snowbirdlodge.com

Member Since 1973

North Carolina

Robbinsville

Innkeeper/Owner
Robert Rankin

High up in Santeetlah Gap, on the Southern border of the Great Smoky Mountains National Park, lies this secluded, rustic yet elegant, historic lodge built of stone and huge chestnut logs. Offering the finest in modern convenience and traditional comfort, Snowbird is the perfect retreat from the pressures of a busy world. The view from the lovely mountaintop terrace is one of the best in the Smokies. An excellent library, huge stone fireplaces, tennis courts and hiking trails on 100 acres of forest with numerous "quiet getaway" spots, offer guests a rare chance to relax. Award-winning gourmet cuisine and a lovely fireside bar with an exceptionally well-stocked wine cellar will have you looking forward to your next meal. Whether it's fly-fishing, hiking, biking, or just relaxing in front of the fire, we can make your next trip to the mountains picture-perfect. It's no wonder that guests have been coming to Snowbird to relax and renew themselves for over 60 years.

Rates
23 Rooms, $255-$365 FAP. In-room fireplaces, air conditioning, whirlpool tubs, steam showers and private hot tubs available. Number of Rooms: 23

Cuisine
Full gourmet breakfast, packed picnic lunch and four course gourmet dinner.

Nearest Airport
Knoxville, Atlanta

The Greystone Inn

www.greystoneinn.com
220 Greystone Lane, Lake Toxaway, NC 28747
800-587-5351 • 828-966-4700 • Fax 828-862-5689
info@greystoneinn.com

Member Since 1991

North Carolina

Lake Toxaway

Owner
Reg Heinitsh, Jr.

All of the intimacies of a charming & historic inn are combined with the luxurious amenities of a full service resort at The Greystone Inn. Our AAA Four Diamond rated property is situated on the shores of North Carolina's largest private lake in the heart of the Blue Ridge Mountains, and is an ideal setting for those looking to truly get away from it all. Highlights include a pampering spa, lake activities, a new Kris Spence designed golf course, tennis, croquet, a fitness center, and more. Of course, our signature amenity is our daily Champagne cruise aboard our 26-passenger mahogany launch "Miss Lucy". Each guestroom is unique with amenities that include gas and wood fireplaces, private porches, lake views, Jacuzzi bathtubs, wet bars and more. We pride ourselves on attentive and personal service - our goal is to make folks feel like guests in our home. We hope to see you soon!

Rates
Rooms & Suites ranging from $380-$590. Rate includes MAP meals, tennis, croquet, canoe/kayaks, fitness center, and our daily Champagne cruise. Spa, Golf, Romance, and Hiking Packages are available. Number of Rooms: 31

Cuisine
A full breakfast, afternoon tea & treats, hors d'oeuvres, and a six-course dinner are included in our Modified American Plan (MAP) rates. A la carte lunch is available at the adjacent country club. We have a full bar and an extensive wine list.

Nearest Airport
Asheville (AVL)

🏴 SelectRegistry.com

Andon-Reid Inn Bed & Breakfast

www.andonreidinn.com
92 Daisy Ave., Waynesville, NC 28786
828-452-3089 • 800-293-6190
info@andonreidinn.com

Member Since 2011

Innkeeper
Rachel Reid

Experience Southern hospitality in our meticulously restored turn-of-the-century bed and breakfast, originally constructed in 1902. Welcome to a special place where you can lose yourself in our complimentary mountain views and find some much needed solitude. We are an excellent choice for your romantic getaway, outdoor fun or just an escape for some "me time". Our award winning bed and breakfast has 5 beautifully appointed guest rooms all with private baths, fireplaces, glorious views and many distinctive features that will contribute to your comfort, relaxation, and romance. Take advantage of our complete fitness studio, recreation room and sauna. Relax on our wraparound porch or enjoy a glass of wine while sitting under the stars around our fire pit. Situated in a residential area we are surrounded by the Great Smoky Mountains, Blue Ridge Parkway and Pisgah National Forest. The quaint town of Waynesville is only a short walk from our bed and breakfast and is filled with an array of art studios, galleries, outstanding restaurants and antique shops.

Rates
Rooms and Suites $149.00-$209.00. Seasonal Rates and Packages available. Complimentary hot and cold beverages, snacks and freshly baked afternoon sweets. Number of Rooms: 5

Cuisine
Our full served breakfast is not to be missed! Menus change daily with entrees such as sweet potato pancakes, lemon-baked eggs and homemade chicken sausage, Mexican frittata and turkey kielbasa with our special cornbread and honey butter plus dessert!

Nearest Airport
Asheville Regional (AVL)

The Swag MountainTop Inn

🍽 🍽 🍽

www.theswag.com
2300 Swag Road, Waynesville, NC 28785
800-789-7672 • 828-926-0430 • Fax 828-926-2036
stay@theswag.com

Member Since 1991

Innkeepers/Owners
Dan & Deener Matthews

Where stress disappears ... has an address ... 30 miles west of Asheville. The Swag Mountaintop Inn is an intimate hideaway that invites you to discover the wonders of nature just steps from your bedroom. The Swag is where our favorite amenity –nature – meets the luxury resort. Great Smoky Mountains National Park shares an old split rail fence boundary with our inn that stretches more than a mile. The spectacular beauty of this Appalachian high country is captured architecturally in our historic hand-hewn logs and local field stone design. The construction was inspired by the past while built for the future. This hidden and secluded mountaintop setting at 5,000 feet reveals to you well-marked nature trails the crowds have yet to find. It all starts to unfold at the bottom of our driveway where the pavement stops, the gate opens and your romantic adventure begins. The Swag – an award-winning luxury resort – captures the Appalachians as they used to be.

Rates
8 Rooms $490/$695; 6 Cabins/Suites $695/$785. Open mid-April through November.
Number of Rooms: 14

Cuisine
A not-to-be-missed hors d'oeuvre hour precedes our superb four-course cuisine nightly. All three meals are included for two guests in the room rate. We are in a dry county. Guests are welcome to bring their own spirits.

Nearest Airport
Asheville, NC (AVL)

🪶 SelectRegistry.com

The Yellow House on Plott Creek Road

🍽

www.theyellowhouse.com
89 Oakview Drive, Waynesville, NC 28786
800-563-1236 • 828-452-0991
info@theyellowhouse.com

Member Since 1998

North Carolina

Waynesville

General Managers
Don Cerise/Shawn Bresnahan

A European-style inn of casual elegance, the 19th century Yellow House accents fine service in a romantic, intimate setting. Located a mile from the lovely mountain community of Waynesville, NC, the Inn sits atop a knoll 3,000 feet above sea level. Five beautifully landscaped acres of lawns and gardens feature two ponds, a waterfall, a footbridge and a deck. The Inn offers three rooms and seven suites, each with luxury linens, private bath, gas fireplace, coffee service, refrigerator and bathrobes; suites also have wet bar and 2-person jetted tub. Most accommodations include private balcony or patio. The Yellow House offers a quiet rural setting with exceptional views, soothing music, and complimentary wireless internet service for guests. Minutes from the Blue Ridge Parkway, Great Smoky Mountains National Park, Pisgah National Forest, Cherokee Indian Reservation, horseback riding and ski area, and Maggie Valley. Close to four mountain golf courses, Asheville and the spectacular Biltmore Estate. Picked by Lanierbb.com as BEST INN for changing of the leaves for 2011.

Rates
3 Rooms, 7 Suites, $165-$275. Seasonal Rates and Packages Available. Entire Inn can be rented for weddings, reunions and business retreats. Number of Rooms: 10

Cuisine
Gourmet breakfast each morning served en suite, on private balcony, veranda or dining room depending on accommodation; sweets always and appetizers each evening. Picnics by request. Lunches, teas, and parties can be arranged with notice.

Nearest Airport
Asheville (AVL), Greenville/Spartanburg (GSP)

Inn at Iris Meadows

www.irismeadows.com
304 Love Lane, Waynesville, NC 28786
888-466-4747 • 828-456-3877 • Fax 828-456-3847
irismeadows@aol.com

Member Since 2006

Innkeepers/Owners
George & Becky Fain

High upon rolling meadows and iris gardens with commanding views of the picturesque town of Waynesville and the surrounding mountains, this stately Inn is the perfect destination for romantic getaways, honeymoons, celebrations, and relaxing escapes. Seven lavishly appointed guest rooms, all with fireplaces, private designer baths, large jetted tubs, heavenly king/queen beds, fluffy robes, TV/VCR/DVDs, phones, WiFi, A/C, and intriguing antiques. A meticulously restored turn-of-the-century Greek Revival mansion in Waynesville's historic Love Lane neighborhood. Iris Meadows has spacious gathering areas including a library, music room, grand halls with leaded glass doors throughout, intricate woodwork, carved mantels, and wraparound porches. Chosen as "one of our new favorites" by the Atlanta Journal Constitution's "Go Guide" of southern retreats and one of the Palm Beach Daily Post's "Seven Southern Spots to Sit a Spell." Walking distance of 1/2 mile to area shops, galleries, and fine restaurants; 8 minutes to the Blue Ridge Parkway: 1/2 hr to Asheville's Biltmore Estate.

Rates
$225/$275 weeknights; $250/$300 weekends, holidays, and October. Corporate rates midweek. Number of Rooms: 7

Cuisine
Bountiful 3-course breakfast. Cookies/treats 4 pm. Complimentary beverages, fruits, coffee/tea service, guest refrigerator, microwave, 24 hr. a day in guest kitchen.

Nearest Airport
Asheville, NC; Greenville, SC

Albemarle Inn

www.albemarleinn.com
86 Edgemont Road, Asheville, NC 28801-1544
800-621-7435 • 828-255-0027 • Fax 828-236-3397
info@albemarleinn.com

Member Since 2002

Innkeepers/Owners
Fabrizio & Rosemary Chiariello

A classic turn-of-the-century Southern mansion on the National Register, the Albemarle Inn offers elegance in a warm atmosphere. The main parlor glows with restored oak wainscoting. An intricately carved staircase leads to period guest rooms, appointed with antiques, fresh flowers, cozy robes and fine linens. Morning begins with coffee or tea by the Arts & Crafts style marble fireplace and a gourmet breakfast served on the enclosed, plant-filled sunporch enhanced by candlelight, gleaming silver and soft music. In late afternoon guests relax on the massive stone veranda overlooking lush gardens enjoying refreshments and conversation. While minutes to downtown, The Biltmore Estate and the Blue Ridge Parkway, the inn is set in a secluded period neighborhood. The perfect spot for romantic getaways and girlfriend escapes, the inn offers in-room massage and a romance package complete with our hand dipped chocolate covered strawberries. Let us pamper you with a vacation you will never forget.

Rates
$100/$370. Elegantly appointed period rooms with claw-foot tubs, fine linens and fresh flowers. Number of Rooms: 11

Cuisine
Full multi-course gourmet breakfast served at private tables, late afternoon refreshments on the veranda or by the fire, complimentary chilled beverages and 24-hour coffee and tea.

Nearest Airport
Asheville/Hendersonvillle Airport (AVL)

1889 WhiteGate Inn and Cottage

www.whitegate.net
173 East Chestnut Street, Asheville, NC 28801
800-485-3045 • 828-253-2553 • Fax 828-281-1883
innkeeper@whitegate.net

Member Since 2005

North Carolina

Asheville

Owners / Innkeepers
Ralph Coffey and Frank Salvo

The historic 1889 WhiteGate Inn & Cottage is a AAA 4 Diamond property that tempts travelers with the delightful charm of a historic Asheville Bed and Breakfast and the luxurious amenities of a boutique hotel. For couples craving a romantic Asheville getaway or those seeking serenity in a long weekend, our inn offers a respite from the distractions of everyday life. A sumptuous 3 course breakfast begins each day. Wander the stunning award winning gardens or stroll through the downtown shops, galleries and restaurants. Enjoy hors d'oeuvres and beverages served every evening in the garden. Treat yourself, or you and a loved one, to the ultimate in luxury when staying in one of our Carriage House suites. Complete handicapped accessible suite available. 1 & 2 bedroom Bungalow suites offer ultimate privacy including a full kitchen. In room couples massage and spa treatments available by appointment. Our fitness room offers workout equipment and a dry sauna. Pet friendly units available.

Rates
$159/$379. Separate cottages with full kitchens, on site orchid greenhouse, gym, dry sauna. Some Pet Friendly rooms, complete ADA suite available. No Smoking or Children. Number of Rooms: 11

Cuisine
3 Course Gourmet Breakfast, complimentary hors d'oeuvres & wine served each evening in garden, 24 hour cakes, cookies, fresh fruit, hot & cold beverages. Picnic baskets & bag lunch by order.

Nearest Airport
Asheville

Black Walnut Bed & Breakfast

www.blackwalnut.com
288 Montford Avenue, Asheville, NC 28801
800-381-3878 • 828-254-3878
info@blackwalnut.com

Member Since 2007

Innkeepers/Owners
Peter & Lori White

The perfect in-town location in the heart of the Historic District of Montford. Within walking distance to the shops, restaurants and galleries of the city. Surrounded by manicured gardens and waterfall Koi ponds. Relax in the rockers on the porch, or the terrace when the weather is fair, or enjoy a fire in one of the 11 fireplaces. All guest rooms are complete with private bath en-suite and King or Queen luxury kingsdown mattresses, most with working fireplaces . Fresh flowers, chocolates and luxury bedding compliment the antiques. Indulge in a gourmet 3-course breakfast with homemade pastries, fruit and hot entree. Your innkeepers have more than 50 years of experience as professional bakers and chefs! In the late afternoon, relax with complimentary fine wines and hors d'oeuvres with your hosts. We are always happy to help with suggestions, recommendations and reservations!

Rates
6 rooms in the main house, 2 pet-friendly suites located in the carriage house. $185/$325. Full breakfast, complimentary beverages, WiFi, computer station, afternoon tea included. Off season rates available. Open all Year. Number of Rooms: 8

Cuisine
Decadent 3 course breakfasts. Afternoon tea with selection of fine wines and hot and cold hors d'oeuvres, homemade pastries. 24 hour complimentary beverages.

Nearest Airport
Asheville (AVL)

The Orchard Inn

www.orchardinn.com

100 Orchard Inn Lane, on Rt 176, .5 mi. east of Ozone Dr., Saluda, NC 28773-0128

800-581-3800 • 828-749-5471

innkeeper@orchardinn.com

Member Since 1985

Innkeepers/Owners
Marc & Marianne Blazar

Located just 30 miles south of Asheville in the foothills of the Blue Ridge Mountains, the rest of the world melts away the moment you enter the long winding driveway and approach our elegant mountain top escape, comfortably nestled on 12 peaceful acres. All rooms have private bathrooms and are furnished with period pieces and antiques. Cozy cottages feature fireplaces, whirlpools and private decks. Our ultra luxurious linens and cool fresh mountain air are a perfect recipe for a great night's sleep. Enjoy award-winning cuisine in our fine dining restaurant which overlooks the organic garden, vineyard, orchard and surrounding mountains. Hike nearby trails and waterfalls; fly fish native trout streams; paddle the nationally acclaimed Green River; schedule a massage or yoga class; play golf on a private course; watch over 50 species of native and migrating birds; visit the Biltmore Estate, Carl Sandburg home or local craft galleries in historic Saluda; then experience the peace & tranquility of this gracious historic Inn. An ideal setting for weddings and corporate retreats.

Rates
9 Rooms in the Inn, $130/$195 B&B; 5 Cottages, $180/$520 B&B. All rooms have private baths, some w/ gas fireplaces, whirlpool & steam shower. Ultra luxurious linens and towels. Many rooms have spectacular mountain views. Number of Rooms: 14

Cuisine
Full gourmet breakfast included in room rate. Award-winning European inspired cuisine served Thurs-Sat evenings, featuring farm to table fresh local produce. Fine wine & beer. Listed as a "Food Find" by Southern Living. Member Chaine des Rotisseur.

Nearest Airport
Asheville (AVL) 25 min, Greenville (GSP) 45 min, Charlotte (CLT) 90 min.

1906 Pine Crest Inn & Restaurant

🍽 🍽 🍽 ♉

www.pinecrestinn.com
85 Pine Crest Lane, Tryon, NC 28782
800-633-3001 • 828-859-9135 • Fax 828-859-9136
select@pinecrestinn.com

Member Since 1991

Innkeeper/Owner
Carl Caudle

Imagine 250-year old cabins so captivating they inspired literary greats F. Scott Fitzgerald & Ernest Hemingway. Or pamper yourself with a Jacuzzi tub, a massage, artisan cheese & a bottle of wine with a dozen roses. Tranquility & relaxation await you in any of our 32 romantic rooms, suites or private cottages on our beautifully landscaped 10-acre property. Art & antique shopping, golf, waterfall hikes & winery tours, white water rafting, drives along the Blue Ridge Parkway, The Biltmore Estate... these experiences & more can be found at our distinctive retreat just south of Asheville. Renowned for our "Best Breakfast in the Southeast," exceptional fine dining, & celebrity wine dinners. Our cellar has received the prestigious Wine Spectator 'Best of Award of Excellence'. Recognized in Southern Living, Fodor's, Our State Magazine, & on the National Historic Registry. Romance packages, destination weddings, reunions, or executive retreats in our conference center can all be managed with ease by our professional staff. Our guests create memories that will last a lifetime.

Rates
20 Rooms $99-229; 8 Suites $179-279; 4 Cottages $189-599. Seasonal specials & packages available. Number of Rooms: 32

Cuisine
Sumptuous, made-to-order 3-course breakfast... that can be served in bed! Distinctive a la carte dinner menu with regional accents, organic ingredients & fresh herbs from our gardens. Afternoon tea, award-winning wine list, & evening port and sherry.

Nearest Airport
Asheville, NC (AVL), Greenville,SC (GSP), Charlotte, NC (CLT)

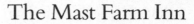

The Mast Farm Inn

www.MastFarmInn.com

2543 Broadstone Road, P.O. Box 704, Valle Crucis, NC 28691

888-963-5857 • 828-963-5857 • Fax 828-963-6404

Member Since 1988

stay@mastfarminn.com

North Carolina

Valle Crucis

Innkeepers/Owners
Sandra Siano and Danielle Deschamps

The Mast Farm Inn is more than a bed and breakfast, with inn rooms, private getaway cottages, fine dining and great wines, organic gardens, and unique gifts that complete our historic country appeal. The key to the Inn's success, however, lies in the exceptionally friendly and caring service offered to lodging and dinner guests alike. With inspired restoration and continuing care, the inn continues to welcome guests, as it did over 100 years ago. Choose from eight guest rooms in our 1880's farmhouse and seven cottages, some restored from original farm buildings. Cottages range in size from cozy ones suitable for a couple to large ones for up to six guests. All are unique spaces. The Inn's restaurant is celebrated, enjoyed by lodging guests and locals. The service is attentive, yet relaxed and friendly. Enjoy fireside or terrace dining, depending on the season. The current innkeepers place special emphasis on the environment, creating a "green" inn where recycling, reducing waste, and buying organic produce locally are taken seriously.

Rates
8 guest rooms: $145/$250. 7 private cottages: $225/$450. Number of Rooms: 15

Cuisine
Full 2-course gourmet breakfast included with lodging. Dinner features fresh, organic delightfully creative cuisine. Dining schedule varies seasonally. Fine wines and beer available. Private parties.

Nearest Airport
Greensboro (GSO) or Charlotte (CLT)

Gideon Ridge Inn

www.gideonridge.com
202 Gideon Ridge Rd., P.O. Box 1929, Blowing Rock, NC 28605
888-889-4036 • 828-295-3644 • Fax 828-295-4586
Innkeeper@gideonridge.com

Member Since 1990

Innkeepers/Owners
Cindy & Cobb Milner

Gideon Ridge Inn is ten delightful guest rooms with mountain breezes, French doors and stone terraces. Ceiling fans and wicker chairs. Antiques and good books. Bedrooms with warm fireplaces and comfortable sitting areas. Crisp cotton bed linens and well-appointed bathrooms. Suites with whirlpool tubs and king beds. Fine breakfasts to linger over. Afternoon tea with fresh-baked shortbread to savor. Evening dining at Restaurant G, where guests and local residents enjoy farm to table fresh ingredients prepared by Chef Michael Foreman in the classic style. And in the library, a piano with a breathtaking view of the mountains. Really..... Guests enjoy hiking and walking the Blue Ridge Parkway. Golf at nearby clubs. Shopping and dining at Blowing Rock Village shops & restaurants. Biking in summer and skiing in winter. Or just sitting on our beautiful stone terrace and enjoying the cool mountain air.

Rates
3 Deluxe Suites with king bed and separate sitting area. 3 Terrace Rooms with private stone terrace. 9 rooms have fireplaces. 4 have whirlpools. All rooms B&B. A/C $155/ $325. Open year-round. Number of Rooms: 10

Cuisine
Full breakfast included, featuring our apple cornmeal pancakes, blueberry-stuffed French toast or other signature entrees. Afternoon tea with fresh-made shortbread cookies or scones. Dinner served Tues.-Sat. Cocktails and full wine list.

Nearest Airport
Charlotte, NC, 1.5 hours, (CLT); Greensboro, NC, 2 hours, (GSO)

The Duke Mansion

www.dukemansion.com
400 Hermitage Road, Charlotte, NC 28207
888-202-1009 • 704-714-4400 • Fax 704-714-4435
frontdesk@tlwf.org

Member Since 2005

General Manager
Becky Farris

The Duke Mansion, built in 1915 and listed on the National Register of Historic Places, offers 20 unique guest rooms in true Southern splendor with a full breakfast. The rooms are residential in their decor, and appointed with beautiful artwork and furnishings, giving you a breathtaking image of what it was like to be a member of the prestigious Duke family who made The Mansion their home. All rooms have queen or king sized beds, private baths, exquisite linens, luxurious robes, and a gourmet goodnight treat. The Mansion is an integral part of Charlotte's most prestigious and beautiful neighborhood, and is situated on four and a half acres of beautiful grounds. Its professional culinary staff and beautiful public rooms can accommodate family or business celebrations of 10–300 guests. When you select The Duke Mansion, you are supporting a nonprofit where all of the proceeds are used to preserve and protect it.

Rates
20 Rooms. $179-$279, including breakfast, plus tax. Special seasonal rates also available. Number of Rooms: 20

Cuisine
Full-time onsite professional culinary staff featuring New South cuisine. A deluxe, made to order breakfast is included with every guest room.

Nearest Airport
Charlotte-Douglas International Airport, 20 minutes

King's Daughters Inn

www.TheKingsDaughtersInn.com
204 N Buchanan Blvd, Durham, NC 27701
919-354-7000 • 877-534-8534 • Fax 866-489-2029
info@TheKingsDaughtersInn.com

Member Since 2011

Owners/Innkeepers
Colin and Deanna Crossman

With funds donated by the Duke family in the 1920's, the King's Daughters of Durham built a grand building located in the heart of Trinity Park to care for single elderly women. The King's Daughters Home closed in 2006 and now this piece of Durham's history has been reborn as a 17 room Boutique Bed & Breakfast. Varied in their décor and well appointed with beautiful and unique furnishings, the rooms offer a breathtaking image of what it was like to be in the Opulent or Roaring Twenties. The King's Daughters Inn is a short walk to Duke University, Brightleaf Square, Ninth Street and minutes from the Durham Performing Arts Center, Research Triangle Park and Raleigh–Durham International Airport. Modern Amenities Include: • Mac Mini and wireless internet access • Plasma HDTV • Turn–down service with Port & Chocolate Truffles • Triple sheeting with Pillow Top Mattress • Luxurious Bathrobe & Slippers • In Room Massage Services • Full, Hot Complimentary Breakfast.

Rates
Rates include a full hot breakfast, afternoon tea, and turn down service, as well as complimentary wireless internet and parking. Rates begin at $170.00. Number of Rooms: 17

Cuisine
The Inn serves a full, hot breakfast every morning. Focusing on fresh produce & homemade dishes, the Inn provides a hearty list of options. Alternatives include breakfast-to-go or in-room service. Afternoon Tea and evening spirits are also available.

Nearest Airport
Raleigh-Durham International Airport (RDU)

Arrowhead Inn

www.arrowheadinn.com
106 Mason Road, Durham, NC 27712
919-477-8430 • 800-528-2207 • Fax 919-471-9538
info@arrowheadinn.com

Member Since 2003

North Carolina

Durham

Innkeepers/Owners
Phil & Gloria Teber

Relax in the quiet comfort of our 18th Century plantation home. The Inn rests on six acres of stunning gardens and lawns amid venerable magnolia and pecan trees. Each of our elegant guest rooms, Carolina Log Cabin and Garden Cottage provide a serene respite with the amenities of a fine hotel. The Arrowhead Inn, circa 1775, has been carefully renovated retaining original moldings, mantelpieces, and heart-of-pine floors. Watch hummingbirds flutter on flowering hibiscus while relaxing with friends on our sun-warmed patio. Drift off for an afternoon nap next to your cozy fireplace. Unwind in your private whirlpool tub while enjoying fine wine & delicacies. Slip into your luxurious soft terry robe after refreshing yourself in a soothing steam shower. Awake to the delight of our abundant breakfast. Savor the cuisine of our fine inn dining, along with Durham's nationally famous chefs and restaurants. The Arrowhead Inn welcomes you for peaceful and romantic getaways, family & friend gatherings, and business retreats. Our Tiffany Gazebo provides a lovely setting for small weddings.

Rates
Rooms & Suites in Manor House $140-$265. Cottage & Log Cabin $265-$325. Rates include full breakfast & afternoon refreshments. Seasonal specials & packages available. Working fireplaces, whirlpool tubs, steam showers and free Wi-Fi. Number of Rooms: 9

Cuisine
Delicious gourmet breakfast: puffed soufflé, ricotta pancakes, fresh vegetable quiche, glazed scones, & fresh fruit. Chef/Owner prepares mouth-watering tasting dinners served in romantic setting or in the privacy of your suite. Fine wine & beer cellar.

Nearest Airport
Raleigh/Durham International Airport (RDU)

White Doe Inn

www.whitedoeinn.com
319 Sir Walter Raleigh Street, Post Office Box 1029, Manteo, NC 27954
800-473-6091 • 252-473-9851 • Fax 252-473-4708
whitedoe@whitedoeinn.com

Member Since 2005

Proprietors
Robert & Bebe Woody

The White Doe Inn is situated in the quaint coastal waterfront village of Manteo on Roanoke Island, which we believe is the best part of the Outer Banks of North Carolina. Luxury lodging, quality service, and a piece of the island life await you here. Centrally located, it's the perfect place to take advantage of all that the Outer Banks has to offer. Guests come from near and far to experience gracious hospitality in this lovely historic Victorian home. The Inn offers a four course complimentary breakfast each morning, afternoon & evening refreshments, bicycles for our guests, concierge services, and much more. The Inn's staff is available to make reservations or to arrange the purchase of advance tickets to events and activities. The White Doe Inn is listed on the National Register of Historic Places and is noted for its historic and architectural significance. The Inn is also a member of the North Carolina Bed & Breakfast Inns and the Professional Association of Innkeepers International.

Rates
Off: $175/$265, Mid: $199/$290, In: $232/335. Number of Rooms: 8

Cuisine
The White Doe Inn is pleased to provide outstanding service and a delicious full four-course seated and served breakfast that will delight your palate and be pleasing to the eye. Afternoon tea and pastries are set out daily as is evening sherry.

Nearest Airport
Norfolk International Airport, VA

The Aerie Bed & Breakfast

www.aeriebedandbreakfast.com
509 Pollock Street, New Bern, NC 28562
800-849-5553 • 252-636-5553 • Fax 252-514-2157
info@aeriebedandbreakfast.com

Member Since 2008

Innkeepers/Owners
Michael and Marty Gunhus

This stunning circa 1882 Late Victorian property is a favorite year-round Eastern Coastal North Carolina luxury accommodation. Experience the warmth and charm of historic New Bern by day and relax in The Aerie's comfort and elegance by night. An inviting welcome pervades the Inn as the staff surrounds guests with detailed service, striking the perfect balance between personal attention and individual freedom. Recognized in "Our State" magazine, The Washington Post and featured on PBS, The Aerie's many awards and acclimations include repeatedly being voted as "Simply The Best B&B" by North Carolina's Sun Journal. A gourmet breakfast features a menu that changes daily and guests may choose between three delicious hot-entree selections. Nine delightfully distinctive guest rooms are ready to pamper with luxurious linens, exquisite furnishings and modern amenities. Suites offer whirlpool baths and king or queen beds. Period antiques complement modern conveniences such as Cable TV, DVD/CD players, WiFi Internet, and a state-of-the-art Conference Center with reception area.

Rates
Nine rooms including several whirlpool suites. Rooms $129-$159 Suites $169-$199.
Number of Rooms: 9

Cuisine
Full breakfast included with an inspired menu that changes daily. Starter course and choice of three entrees. Evening wine and hors d'oeuvres. Coffee, tea, ice, and various cold beverages available 24 hrs.

Nearest Airport
New Bern (EWN), Raleigh (RDU)

SelectRegistry.com

The Verandas

www.verandas.com
202 Nun Street, Wilmington, NC 28401
910-251-2212 • Fax 910-251-8932
verandas4@aol.com

Member Since 2001

Owners
Dennis Madsen and Chuck Pennington

Towering above a quiet tree-lined street in the historic district stands this grand antebellum mansion. Built in 1854, the 13 year award-winning Inn is a blend of history, luxury, charm and hospitality. Guest space abounds with wonderful colors, original art, French and English antiques. Four verandas, garden terrace and cupola offer hideaways. Professionally decorated guestrooms have sitting areas, telephone, cable TV. Hand-ironed linens dress comfortable beds. Baths have soaking tubs, showers, marble floors, luxury amenities and robes. French pressed coffee with a gourmet breakfast. Complimentary beverages and snacks and social wine hour. Walking distance to the Riverwalk and restaurants and shopping. High speed wireless internet. Enjoy The Verandas – "An Inn Second to Nun!" ◆◆◆◆

Rates
8 Corner Rooms $169/$269. Two-nights min. on weekends Dec.,Jan.,Feb.,special: 3 nights for two. Number of Rooms: 8

Cuisine
Included with the room rate is a full gourmet breakfast with French pressed coffee served in our beautiful dining room. Complimentary beverages and snacks are available and white wine is served in the evening.

Nearest Airport
Wilmington International

Graystone Inn

www.graystoneinn.com
100 South 3rd Street, Wilmington, NC 28401
888-763-4773 • 910-763-2000 • Fax 910-763-5555
www.graystoneinn.com

Member Since 2005

Innkeepers/Owners
Rich & Marcia Moore

The Graystone Inn, one of the most elegant historical structures in Wilmington, is located in the heart of the historic district and just three blocks from shopping, fine dining and the River Walk. The Graystone, originally the "Bridgers Mansion," was built as a private residence in 1905 by Elizabeth Haywood Bridgers and is an excellent representation of the neo-classical revival style. Each elegantly decorated bedroom has its own private bath, telephones with voicemail and data port, WiFi and cable TV. All rooms contain period furnishings, exquisite draperies and fine pima cotton linens, towels and robes. Intricately carved fireplaces grace seven of the nine bedrooms. The Graystone has frequently been used as a set for motion pictures and television and lists many notable personalities among its guests.

Rates
6 rooms $159/$269. 3 Jr. suites $209/$369. Two night weekends. Open year round.
Number of Rooms: 9

Cuisine
Full gourmet breakfast prepared by chef-owner. Early morning coffee bar. Complimentary beverages. Evening wine.

Nearest Airport
Wilmington International

 SelectRegistry.com

Famous for: Cincinnati Zoo, Cincinnati Union Terminal, Taft Museum, Neil Armstrong Air and Space Museum, Put-in-Bay Village and Perry Memorial (largest Doric column in the world), Rolling Hills, Farmlands, Burial Mounds.

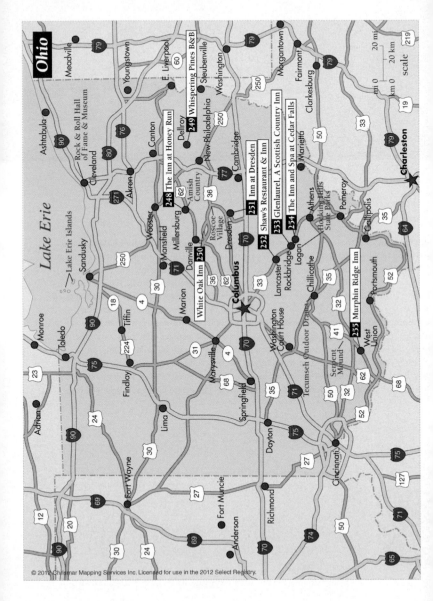

The Inn at Honey Run

www.innathoneyrun.com
6920 County Road 203, Millersburg, OH 44654
800-468-6639 • 330-674-0011 • Fax 330-674-2623
info@innathoneyrun.com

Member Since 1984

Ohio

Millersburg

Proprietor
Jason W. Nies

Our boutique country Inn is located in the heart of Amish country in Holmes County within two hours of Cleveland and Columbus. We invite you to indulge in our serene oasis of nature and wildlife, upscale casual dining and warm hospitality. Accommodations include well-appointed woodland inn rooms with plush king beds. For a unique getaway, stay in our earth-sheltered Club Level Honeycombs with stone patios, fireplaces, and valley views. Private guest cottages feature fireplaces and two person Jacuzzi tub or four person hot tub. Relax and rejuvenate at our spa with our serenity therapies. Watch birds from picture windows, read by blazing fireplaces, hike trails on our 50 acres, or explore the back roads of the countryside and nearby villages. Our experience packages enhance your stay with us – take a ride in an authentic Amish buggy, celebrate your Babymoon, or schedule a tee time. Plan your event with distinctive meeting spaces including an executive conference center, intimate Honeycomb Boardroom, TreeTop Pavilion, and picturesque views for your idyllic destination wedding.

Rates
Seasonal rates as low as $129.00 per night. Take advantage of our Guest Loyalty Program and save 10% off your next stay when you reserve upon departure. Number of Rooms: 40

Cuisine
Tarragon is a full service, upscale casual restaurant featuring American contemporary cuisine and seasonal menus inspired by local ingredients - prepared by our highly decorated chef and his team. Rooms include complimentary continental breakfast.

Nearest Airport
Millersburg, local airport – 15 minutesAkron/Canton – 60 minutesPort Columbus International Airport – 2 hours

Whispering Pines Bed & Breakfast

www.atwoodlake.com

1268 Magnolia Road, P.O. Box 340, Dellroy, OH 44620

866-4LAKEVU (452-5388) • 330-735-2824 • Fax 330-735-7006

whisperingpines@atwoodlake.com *Member Since 2006*

Ohio Dellroy

Innkeepers/Owners
Bill & Linda Horn

Whispering Pines is located in gently rolling hills overlooking beautiful Atwood Lake and its picturesque lush landscape. The lake views will take your breath away and the surroundings are indescribably tranquil. Enjoy a quiet conversation in an outdoor space – hammock, blanket on the hillside, or deck & gather around the warmth of the firepit in the evening roasting s'mores. Nine guest rooms with 2-person whirlpool tubs, wonderful views, Bose music system, exquisite authentic antiques, fireplace, private balcony and upscale amenities. Breakfast is served in our new very large sun-room overlooking the lake – the view is spectacular. We offer additional services such as an in-room massage, and other gift and seasonal packages. We can also accommodate small weddings. There are several restaurants in the area for dining. Endless activities with 28 miles of shoreline – a walk/hike in the park, kayak, pontoon, swimming, fishing, golf, museums, wineries, motorcycles and the Amish area. Whispering Pines – the perfect place for celebrating a special occasion or a brief getaway.

Rates
Inn-Season: $210 - $250, Quiet-Season: $190 - $240. Number of Rooms: 9

Cuisine
A delicious breakfast of seasonal fruit or cobblers, freshly baked breakfast sweets, & a variety of hot entrees served between 9-10:30 a.m., earlier upon request. Morning coffee delivered to your room. Afternoon cookies, tea, coffee, popcorn, s'mores.

Nearest Airport
Akron/Canton

The White Oak Inn

www.whiteoakinn.com
29683 Walhonding Rd (SR715), Danville, OH 43014
877-908-5923 • 740-599-6107
info@whiteoakinn.com

Member Since 1989

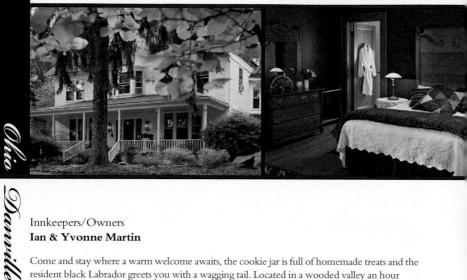

Innkeepers/Owners
Ian & Yvonne Martin

Come and stay where a warm welcome awaits, the cookie jar is full of homemade treats and the resident black Labrador greets you with a wagging tail. Located in a wooded valley an hour from Columbus and close to Kenyon College, The White Oak Inn has ten comfortable guest rooms and two luxury log cabin cottages. It's the perfect location to explore Amish Country, enjoy outdoor activities, take a wine tour, or just sit on the front porch and watch the hummingbirds. Let us entertain you at a Murder Mystery, or just enjoy a pampering weekend with in-room massages and dinner delivered to your room. Innkeeper Yvonne, one of the Eight Broads of the bedandbreakfastfoodie.com blog, creates delicious breakfasts and dinners daily, using fresh local ingredients and herbs from the Inn's gardens. Whether your visit is to celebrate something special or just recharge your batteries, The White Oak Inn has the perfect recipes for romance and relaxation. See our website for more information about our packages, including elopements, honeymoons and girlfriends' getaways.

Rates
Traditional queen rooms from $140 to $160 a night, fireplace rooms from $165 to $185, Whirlpool/fireplace rooms $175 to $195 and luxury cottages from $195 to $240 a night. See our website for package rates and specials. Number of Rooms: 12

Cuisine
Generous country breakfast daily. Evening meals available for inn guests, either as a delicious 4-course dinner in the dining room or a romantic dinner basket delivered to the room. Advance reservations requested. Lunches available for groups. BYOB

Nearest Airport
Port Columbus - 55 miles

The Inn at Dresden

www.theinnatdresden.com
209 Ames Drive, Dresden, OH 43821
800-373-7336 • 740-754-1122 • Fax 740-754-9856
info@theinnatdresden.com

Member Since 2000

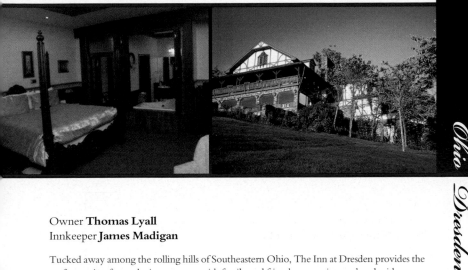

Ohio

Dresden

Owner **Thomas Lyall**
Innkeeper **James Madigan**

Tucked away among the rolling hills of Southeastern Ohio, The Inn at Dresden provides the perfect setting for a relaxing getaway with family and friends, or a quiet weekend with someone special. Originally built by Dave Longaberger, founder of Longaberger Baskets, this elegant Tudor home offers guests a panoramic view of Dresden and the surrounding countryside. Guests at the inn enjoy a full gourmet breakfast, an evening social hour and optional fine dining. Individually decorated rooms feature CD/DVD players (350 movies available) and special amenities such as wraparound private decks, single and two person Jacuzzi tubs and gas-log fireplaces. In season there is access to a 10,000 sq.ft. pavilion for guest enjoyment.

Rates
10 Rooms $115/$190 per night. Each room is individually decorated to depict the area.
Number of Rooms: 10

Cuisine
The Inn provides a full breakfast; an evening social hour of wine and cheese, followed by optional evening fine dining, by reservation for guests and their guests only.

Nearest Airport
Columbus Airport-60 min./ Akron Canton Airport-90 min.

🍴 🍴 🍴 🍷

Shaw's Restaurant & Inn

www.shawsinn.com
123 North Broad St., Lancaster, OH 43130
800-654-2477 • 740-654-1842 • Fax 740-654-7032
shaws@greenapple.com

Member Since 2005

Innkeepers/Owners
Bruce & Nancy Cork, Susie Cork

Located on a tree-shaded square in historic downtown Lancaster, Shaw's has been described as "a unique blend of country freshness and well traveled sophistication." Just minutes from Hocking Hills, Shaw's Inn offers 25 individually decorated theme rooms. Ten have large in-room whirlpool tubs, in which some are called the Napa Valley, the Savannah, The Caribbean, and Louis XIV. Full breakfast in the restaurant is included with all rooms. Shaw's Restaurant has a reputation for New York Strip, Filet Mignon, Prime Rib, and Fresh Seafood. The Chef creates a daily changing menu with seasonal items–Spring Lamb, Soft Shell Crab, Fresh Walleye, 4-pound Lobster, and many others. Add to your Holiday Festivities with four weeks of Christmas Dinners. There are Cooking Classes every Saturday. Cork's Bar, serving every day, has a warm setting of dark wood and brass. Free High-Speed Wireless Internet access throughout. Nearby attractions include: The Sherman House, The Decorative Arts Center of Ohio, The Georgian, and The Ohio Glass Museum.

Rates
Whirlpool Rooms $152/$218, Deluxe Rooms $125/$145, Corporate Rooms $86/$96, Double Occupancy. Full Breakfast is Included in the Restaurant. Number of Rooms: 25

Cuisine
Known for Steaks, Prime Rib, and Seafood. Pasta, Small Plates. Changing Seasonal Menu–Holiday Dinners. Wine Spectator Award of Excellence.

Nearest Airport
Port Columbus Airport

Glenlaurel, Scottish Inn & Cottages

🍽 🍽 🍽 ♀

www.glenlaurel.com

14940 Mount Olive Road, Hocking Hills Region, Rockbridge, OH 43149-9736

800-809-REST • 740-385-4070 • Fax 740-385-9669

Info@glenlaurel.com

Member Since 1998

Innkeeper
Greg Leonard

Sometimes at dinner, the story is told of how Glenlaurel was first imagined–300 years ago in the heart of the Scottish Highlands. Today, the heavily wooded 140-acre estate has the look of the old world, a veil of romance, and a pace of times gone by. Whether in the stately Manor House, the nearby Carriage House, or one of the crofts or cottages, luxury abounds with sumptuous fine dining, hot tub frolics, intimate fireside secrets, hiking through our Camusfearna Gorge, and a round of golf on our Scottish Links course ~ as it was played 100 years ago! The old-world elegance of the Inn and the secluded, peaceful setting are ideal for romantic nights for two, peaceful getaways for one, intimate weddings, and small group events. Our Anniversary Club honors a successful marriage, year after year; so make Glenlaurel your anniversary destination.

Rates
You will undoubtedly enjoy an extra level of comfort while admiring our refined decor & spaciousness. 1 Garrett $159/$189, 2 Rooms $189/$229, 3 Suites $219/$269, 7 Crofts $249/$299, 6 Cottages $299/$349. Open year-round. Number of Rooms: 19

Cuisine
Dinner is "a private invitation to dine at an estate house in the country" with social time, greetings from your host, and a candlelit culinary adventure-in the European tradition.

Nearest Airport
Port Columbus Airport (CMH) - 55 minutes. Onsite helipad.

Inn & Spa At Cedar Falls

www.innatcedarfalls.com
21190 State Route 374, Logan, OH 43138
800-653-2557 • 740-385-7489 • Fax 740-385-0820
info@innatcedarfalls.com

Member Since 1989

Ohio

Logan

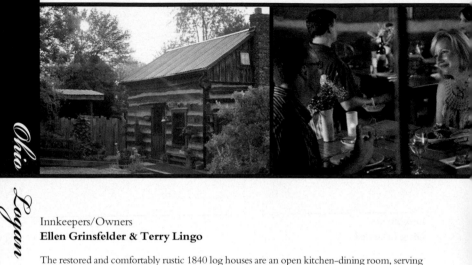

Innkeepers/Owners
Ellen Grinsfelder & Terry Lingo

The restored and comfortably rustic 1840 log houses are an open kitchen-dining room, serving the most refined of American cuisine. Antique appointed guest rooms in a barn-like structure have rockers and writing desks and offer sweeping views of meadows, woods and wildlife. Quaint cottages are ideal for two, or secluded, fully-equipped 19th century log cabins accommodate up to six. Some dog friendly. Casual fine dining for lunch and dinner is served on the patio or the 1840's log cabins. Enjoy spirits in the tavern with a drink before dinner. Discover a new degree of relaxation as you escape into a sanctuary of natural beauty and personal discovery at the Spa At Cedar Falls. The Gathering Place, a state-of-the-art green meeting/wedding location is a perfect fit for meetings and events. The rugged and beautiful Hocking Hills State Parks with glorious caves and waterfalls flanks the Inn's 75 acres on three sides. Casual and avid hikers will enjoy Old Man's Cave, Cedar Falls and Ash Cave. A variety of cooking classes, wine tastings, and hikes are scheduled year round.

Rates
9 Rooms, $129/$204 B&B; 12 Cottages, $179/$284 B&B; 5 Cabins, $199/$334 B&B and based on two people occupancy. Number of Rooms: 26

Cuisine
Watch meals being created in the open kitchen. Hearty country breakfasts, delectable lunches, sumptuous dinners. Picnic baskets for romantic dinners in your room. Brown bag lunches to take hiking. Patio dining in the warm months. Seasonal menus.

Nearest Airport
Columbus which is 50 miles.

254

SelectRegistry.com

Murphin Ridge Inn

www.murphinridgeinn.com
750 Murphin Ridge Rd., West Union, OH 45693
877-687-7446 • 937-544-2263 • Fax 937-544-8442
murphinn@bright.net

Member Since 1992

Innkeepers/Owners
Sherry & Darryl McKenney

As one of National Geographic Traveler's top 54 inns in the U.S. and achieving a prestigious spot on its Geotourism MapGuide, this prize-winning Inn welçomes you to 142 acres of year-round beauty. The Guest House has spacious rooms, some with fireplaces or porches, and romantic cabins with fireplace, two person whirlpool, luxurious shower and porch; all decorated with David T. Smith furniture. The 1828 farmhouse features dining rooms with original fireplaces and a gift shop. Dining is more than an amenity. Chef takes seriously the mandate to use the freshest, healthiest, regional and seasonal ingredients skillfully prepared to keep our award-winning reputation. Our full breakfast is the dessert of your stay. Fine wine, beer and liquors available every day, but Sunday. By night, view the Appalachian foothills by the firepit. By day, visit Amish Shops and the Great Serpent Mound or be pampered by an in-room massage. Murphin boasts an in-season pool, hiking, birding, tennis, and lawn games. Wi-fi makes us perfect for conferences. At Murphin Ridge, Innkeeping is in the details.

Rates
10 Inn Rooms $135/$155 and 9 Cabins $215/$260. Call for business rates. Special rates Sunday through Thursday. Number of Rooms: 19

Cuisine
Chef Brad uses ours, and our Amish neighbors' gardens, sourcing only the best for our "farm to table" cuisine. Bountiful breakfast daily. Boxed Lunches available. Seasonal Patio Dining. Pleasing our guests' palettes is our mission. No Sunday alcohol.

Nearest Airport
Cincinnati/Northern Kentucky International

Oklahoma

"The Sooner State"

Famous for: Will Rogers Memorial, Alabaster Caverns, State Park, National Cowboy Hall of Fame, Pioneer Woman Statue, Cattle Ranching, Oral Roberts University, Oil, Plastics, Rubber, Cotton.

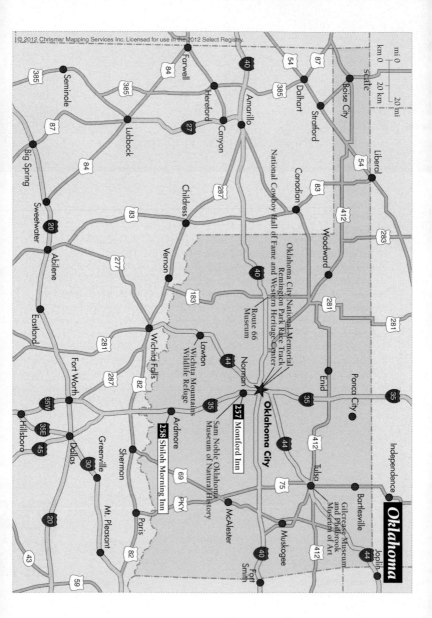

SelectRegistry.com

Montford Inn & Cottages

www.montfordinn.com
322 W. Tonhawa, Norman, OK 73069
800-321-8969 • 405-321-2200 • Fax 405-321-8347
innkeeper@montfordinn.com

Member Since 1997

Innkeepers/Owners
William & Ginger Murray, Phyllis & Ron Murray

Designed and built in 1994, the Murrays welcome you to the award-winning Montford Inn and Cottages. With its ten uniquely decorated rooms in the main house, and six incredible cottage suites, the Montford Inn has everything the discriminating inngoer is looking for in lodging. Located in the heart of Norman's Historic District, this Prairie-style Inn envelops travelers in a relaxing atmosphere. Antiques, family heirlooms and Native American art accent the individually decorated guest rooms and suites. Awaken to rich coffees and a gourmet country breakfast served in the beautifully appointed dining room or in the more intimate setting of the suites. Relax in private hot tubs. Escape in luxurious whirlpool bathtubs. Unwind in elegant cottage suites. Stroll through beautiful gardens. Find your heart...at the Montford Inn and Cottages! Featured in Southern Living, Country, Holiday, Fodor's, and Oklahoma Today.

Rates
10 Rooms, $99/$169; 6 Cottage Suites, $209/$239. Open year-round, possible restrictions for Christmas. Number of Rooms: 16

Cuisine
Full breakfast served in cottages and dining room. Complimentary wine and refreshments served early evening.

Nearest Airport
Will Rogers World Airport in Oklahoma City

Shiloh Morning Inn & Cottages

www.shilohmorning.com
2179 Ponderosa Road, Ardmore, OK 73401
888-554-7674 • 580-223-9500
innkeepers@shilohmorning.com

Member Since 2004

Oklahoma

Ardmore

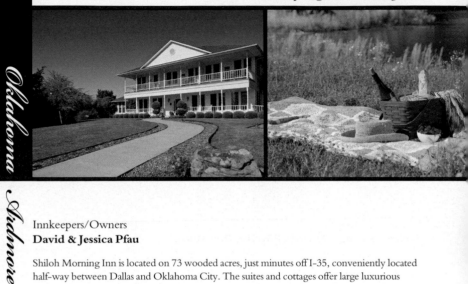

Innkeepers/Owners
David & Jessica Pfau

Shiloh Morning Inn is located on 73 wooded acres, just minutes off I-35, conveniently located half-way between Dallas and Oklahoma City. The suites and cottages offer large luxurious baths, king-size beds, fireplaces, TV/DVD, private hot tubs or jetted tubs for two, and a private balcony, patio, or deck. Guests choose from an extensive library of movies and books. The 73 acres include a large pond perfect for a picnic and/or fishing. Walking trails are dotted with hammocks and park benches. Wildlife abounds. With luxury and privacy as priorities, Shiloh Morning Inn is the perfect romantic getaway for couples seeking the quiet seclusion of a rural countryside.

Rates
5 suites and 4 cottages; $165 to $300. Full breakfast included. Number of Rooms: 9

Cuisine
Three-course, gourmet breakfast in the dining room at tables for two. Dinner available by reservation for intimate, room-service dining.

Nearest Airport
Dallas (DFW); Oklahoma City (OKC)

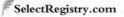

Famous for: The Oregon Trail, Mount Hood, Flowers, Lumber, Wineries, Rose Festival, Crater Lake, Painted Hills National Monument, Columbia River, Gorge, Coast Range, Cascade Range, Redwoods.

© 2012 Chrismar Mapping Services Inc. Licensed for use in the 2012 Select Registry.

Portland's White House B&B

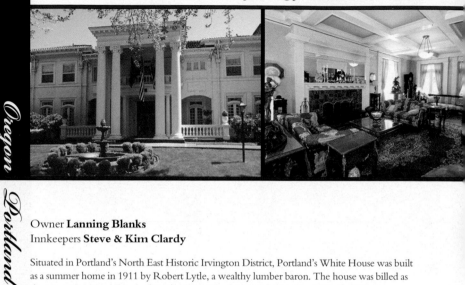

www.portlandswhitehouse.com
1914 NE 22nd Avenue, Portland, OR 97212
800-272-7131 • 503-287-7131 • Fax 503-249-1641
pdxwhi@portlandswhitehouse.com

Member Since 2004

Oregon

Portland

Owner **Lanning Blanks**
Innkeepers **Steve & Kim Clardy**

Situated in Portland's North East Historic Irvington District, Portland's White House was built as a summer home in 1911 by Robert Lytle, a wealthy lumber baron. The house was billed as the most expensive home built in the district for the period. This Greek Revival Mansion boasts a lifestyle of past years with 14 massive columns, circular drive and fountain to greet you. Summer days show impressive hanging baskets and wonderful flowers to warm your senses. Restored to its original splendor by Lanning with sparkling European Chandeliers, formal linened dining room, large parlor, grand staircase, magnificent leaded glass windows, gilt-gold ceilings, Trompe loeil and Grande Ballroom. Extensive collections of European and Continental Porcelains, 18th and 19th Century oil paintings. Guest rooms are appointed with period antiques, paintings, king or queen size feather beds and exquisite linens. Fresh local breakfast, utilizing SLOW FOODS when possible, served in the Main Dining room by candlelight. Romantic weddings, events, offered. "Top 10 City Inns" - Sunset Magazine

Rates
$135/$235. Molton Brown amenities in all rooms, Complimentary secured wireless, and each room has a flat screen cable TV. Number of Rooms: 8

Cuisine
Candlelight gourmet breakfast, always vegetarian, breakfast meat offered on the side. Housemade Bread Pudding French Toast, Crab Cake Eggs Benedict, Balsamic reduced Vegetable Fritatta, Oregon Blueberry Muffins, Pear Ginger Scones. Full Espresso bar.

Nearest Airport
Portland International Airport, 15 minutes. Located 2 blocks from public transportation.

Arch Cape Inn and Retreat

www.archcapeinn.com
31970 East Ocean Lane, Arch Cape, OR 97102
800-436-2848 • 503-436-2800 • Fax 503-436-1206
innkeeper@archcapeinn.com

Member Since 2009

Oregon

Arch Cape

Proprietors
Stephen & Cynthia Malkowski

Step out of your vehicle and into a place with beauty so dramatic it quiets the mind and stirs the heart. Here, at Arch Cape Inn, nature takes center stage and the rigors of everyday life are washed away. With romantic architecture, our Inn offers pristine views of the Pacific Ocean and the lush Oregon Coast Mountains. The Inn will carry you away from the trials of everyday life. Our Oregon Coast getaway boasts many outdoor activities that lead to beaches, mountain overlooks and the historic Oregon Coast Trail. Old Growth forests give way to spectacular views of the Pacific Ocean and many creeks that meet it. Walks on the beach delight beachcombers as they skirt the waves while tide pools await their discovery. Nature lovers keep a watchful eye open for the many species of birds and wildlife that call Arch Cape home. For urban adventurers, the nearby town of Cannon Beach offers world-class shopping, art & cultural activities. Guests return to the Inn to find a warm fire, comfortable surroundings and delicious food & wine in a first class dining destination experience.

Rates
Seasonally adjusted average rates of $240 per night during the Low Season and $320 in our High Season. Number of Rooms: 10

Cuisine
Our Inn delights in preparing gastronomic delights for our guests in the morning, and during our wine social hour. We are members of the James Beard Foundation.

Nearest Airport
The Portland Airport is a 2 hour drive of 105 miles.

🍽   🍷
Youngberg Hill Vineyards & Inn

www.youngberghill.com
10660 SW Youngberg Hill Road, McMinnville, OR 97128
888-657-8668 • 503-472-2727 • Fax 503-472-1313

Member Since 2008

info@youngberghill.com

Oregon

McMinnville

Innkeeper/Owner
Nicolette Bailey

Oregon's premier wine country estate and one of Wine Spectator's favorite locations; set on a 50 acre hilltop surrounded by vineyard. We have an amazing 22 year old vineyard that is farmed organically. We are well known for producing award winning Pinot Noir and Pinot Gris wines. As passionate farmers and winemakers we are thrilled to share, educate, and talk wine. We respect the environment and believe that we can make a difference in how we treat the land and each other every day. We care for our wine and guests with this same respect and philosophy. Youngberg Hill will take your breath away with the most beautiful views, warm luxurious Inn, personal and impeccable service and exceptional estate wines. Youngberg Hill provides the perfect location for those seeking a quiet, romantic getaway and a great base for touring Oregon wine country. We are centrally located in the Willamette Valley and have over 100 wineries and tasting rooms within 20 minute drive.

Rates
$200-$350. Number of Rooms: 8

Cuisine
We create a 2 course gourmet breakfast each morning focusing on regional food and products. Our menu changes because of this regularly. Some of our guest favorites are sure to be around.* Cornished baked eggs * Salmon Hash * Pinot Poached Pears

Nearest Airport
Portland International (PDX)

Channel House Inn

www.channelhouse.com
35 Ellingson Street, P.O. Box 56, Depoe Bay, OR 97341
800-447-2140 • 541-765-2140 • Fax 541-765-2191
info@channelhouse.com

Member Since 1997

Oregon

Depoe Bay

General Manager **Sarah Jincks**
Proprietors **Carl & Vicki Finseth**

Nestled in the Oregon Coast's magnificent scenery, Channel House combines the comforts of a first-class hotel with the congeniality of a small country inn. Imagine fresh ocean breezes, sweeping panoramic views, powerful surf, truly unbelievable sunsets and whales within a stone's throw. Perched on an oceanfront bluff, guestrooms have an understated natural elegance and contemporary decor, including whirlpools on oceanfront decks and gas fireplaces. The friendly staff will attend to your every need. One of the West Coast's most renowned and romantic inns, it has been listed by Harry Shattuck among "a baker's dozen of world's (sic) most delectible hotels" and by Sunset Magazine as one of the 20 best Seaside Getaways on the West Coast.

Rates
3 Oceanfront Rooms $230/$265; 14 Oceanfront Suites, $245/$330. Number of Rooms: 16

Cuisine
Buffet-style breakfast featuring fresh-baked goods is served in our oceanfront dining room. Enjoy a morning repast while having one of the best views on the coast. We have a significant wine selection available with many fine restaurants nearby.

Nearest Airport
Portland International (PDX) - 2.5 Hours

Whale Cove Inn

www.whalecoveinn.com

2345 S. Highway 101, P.O. Box 56, Depoe Bay, OR 97341

Reservations 800-628-3409 • 541-765-4300 • Fax 541-765-3409

Member Since 2009

info@whalecoveinn.com

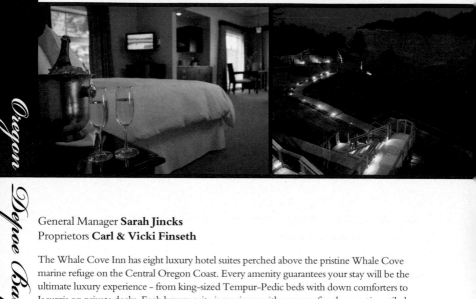

Oregon

Depoe Bay

General Manager **Sarah Jincks**

Proprietors **Carl & Vicki Finseth**

The Whale Cove Inn has eight luxury hotel suites perched above the pristine Whale Cove marine refuge on the Central Oregon Coast. Every amenity guarantees your stay will be the ultimate luxury experience – from king-sized Tempur-Pedic beds with down comforters to Jacuzzis on private decks. Each luxury suite is spacious, with cozy gas fireplaces, artisan-tiled showers with European water features, wet bars and flat-screen HDTVs. Every luxury suite offers panoramic views of Whale Cove and the Pacific Ocean – highlighted by orca whales in migration, bald eagles, and a front row seat for storm-watching, when the surf pounds the rocks at the mouth of the cove below. And there is no finer place to be for spectacular evening sunsets. As a quaint fishing village, Depoe Bay is home to many fine restaurants and a host of beach activities – from charter fishing for Chinook and Coho Salmon, Halibut, Albacore Tuna, Dungeness Crab, Rockfish and Ling Cod – to exploring tide pools, shopping or flying kites. Grey Whales can be seen 10 months of the year.

Rates

7 Signature Suites $395.00; 1 Owner's Suite $795.00 Other rates may apply for off season/holidays. Number of Rooms: 8

Cuisine

Breakfast is included, with an assortment of oven-baked pastries, fresh seasonal fruit, juices, and fresh roasted coffee. Dinner is served in the oceanfront dining room with progressive new American cuisine of Restaurant Beck. www.restaurantbeck.com

Nearest Airport

Portland International Airport (PDX) 2.5 Hours

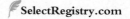 SelectRegistry.com

WildSpring Guest Habitat

www.wildspring.com
92978 Cemetery Loop, Box R, Port Orford, OR 97465
866-333-WILD • 541-332-0977 • Fax 541-332-0360
michelle@wildspring.com

Member Since 2006

Oregon

Port Orford

Innkeepers/Owners
Dean & Michelle Duarte

The great outdoors now comes with an equally great indoors. WildSpring Guest Habitat is a small, ecofriendly resort in Port Orford, overlooking Oregon's spectacular southern coast. On five acres of old Native American grounds, it offers luxurious accommodations in a naturally beautiful environment. Stay in elegant cabin suites built like small homes, filled with art and antiques, in a secluded forest. Relax in the Guest Hall, help yourself to hot chocolate, play a game or just gaze at the ocean on its lounging deck. Immerse in the open-air slate hot tub/spa and enjoy whale-watching by day or the Milky Way at night. Wander the walking labyrinth, find a hammock or secluded alcove and take a nap. Indulge in an in-cabin massage or pedicure. Make yourself popcorn, choose a movie (over 500 DVDs). Sleep to the sound of wind through the trees and wake up to deer outside your window. A short walk to an uncrowded beach for agates and driftwood, in a lovely small town with art galleries, hiking trails, birdwatching, historical sites and the most westerly lighthouse in the 48 states.

Rates
$198/$308 double, depending on the season and the cabin; $40/additional person. Open all year. Number of Rooms: 5

Cuisine
A breakfast buffet overlooking the ocean, including fresh fruit salad w/organic fruits, all sorts of treats & a special hot entree. We respond to dietary requests. Help yourself to refreshments, including fruit, juices, popcorn and chocolate any time.

Nearest Airport
United or Alaska Air connect to Crescent City CA, 1 hr S and North Bend OR, 1 hr N. Or Portland PDX, 4.5 hr drive.

Pennsylvania

"The Keystone State"

Famous for: Liberty Bell, Declaration of Independence, Articles of Confederation, Constitution, Gettysburg Address, Valley Forge National Historical Park, Poconos, Hershey Chocolate World, Amish Homestead, Steel, Pumpkins, Glass.

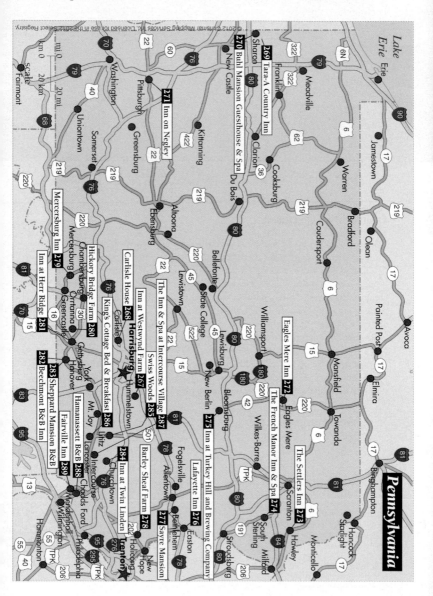

© 2012 Christus Mapping Services Inc. Licensed for use in the 2012 Select Registry

SelectRegistry.com

Inn at Westwynd Farm

www.westwyndfarminn.com
1620 Sand Beach Rd., Hummelstown, PA 17036
717-533-6764 • 877-937-8996 • Fax 717-835-0335
innkeeper@westwyndfarminn.com

Member Since 2011

Innkeeper/Owner
Carolyn Troxell

Luxury Abounds Near the Sweetest Place on Earth. The Inn at Westwynd Farm invites you to step into a world of casual elegance and relaxation. Tucked away on our horse farm overlooking Hershey, the Inn offers serenity found few other places. Enjoy carefully appointed rooms, beautiful gardens, lovely views, gourmet breakfasts and refreshments. Let us pamper you with comforting amenities accented by antiques, fireplaces, jacuzzis, and luxurious linens. The nuzzle of a horse, the soft purr of a sweet barn cat or perhaps a quiet glass of wine by the waterfall ensures any hint of care will drift away. Experience a bed and breakfast beyond your expectations midst rolling hills and horses, - just moments away from all that our region has to offer. Hersheypark, Chocolate World and the Giant Center, Hershey Theatre, Convention Center and Medical Center are minutes away. Amish Country, Civil War sites, antiquing, biking, canoeing, or shopping - whatever brings you here, the Inn is situated to be the perfect base for your activities or a respite from a too hectic schedule.

Rates
Rates change seasonally and range from $109 to $295 reflecting room amenities.
Number of Rooms: 10

Cuisine
American Gourmet featuring locally produced and farm fresh ingredients whenever possible. In addition to a full breakfast, complimentary beverages and refreshments are available throughout the day.

Nearest Airport
Harrisburg International - 15 miles away

Carlisle House

www.thecarlislehouse.com
148 South Hanover Street, Carlisle, PA 17013
717-249-0350 • Fax 717-249-0458
maryd@thecarlislehouse.com

Member Since 2011

Pennsylvania

Carlisle

Innkeepers/Owners
Alan and Mary Faller Duxbury

Located in Downtown Carlisle's National Register Historic District, the Carlisle House is in the heart of the most exciting restaurant area in South Central PA. While surrounded by living history, you will find an extraordinary combination of gourmet restaurants featuring Spanish Tapas, Crepes and Chocolate, Belgian, Thai, Japanese, Vietnamese, English, Chinese, Italian, or American cuisine. Relax in your room with amenities such as wired and wireless Internet access at the writing desk, long-distance phone service, Flat-screen TVs and a DVD library and in-room fridge with complimentary beverages. Enjoy a convivial breakfast featuring our renowned international-themed quiches, then embark on a day of antiquing, shopping, golfing, hiking the Appalachian Trail, fly-fishing on two of the world's top streams (the Letort and the Yellow Breeches) or indulge in a sybaritic spa experience. Schedule your visit for a class at the Kitchen Shoppe's culinary school, exhibits at historical museums, or one of Carlisle's world-famous auto shows. Come enjoy hospitality with history!

Rates
Open year round featuring well-appointed rooms and suites from $149 to $259. Private baths, several with whirlpools, soaking tubs, or jetted showers, individual A/C, HDTVs, wi-fi, luxurious linens, spa robes, and custom amenities. Number of Rooms: 10

Cuisine
Breakfasts are a social affair featuring our signature savory quiches, house-baked muffins or cake, fruit, cereals and juices, with freshly ground coffee and a selection of Twinings teas. Special needs accommodated. Walk to more than 20 restaurants.

Nearest Airport
Harrisburg 37 min; Balt/Washington 2hr; Philadelphia 2hr.20min; Washington Dulles 2hr; Washington Reagan 2hr.15min

Tara – A Country Inn

www.Tara-Inn.com
2844 Lake Road, Clark, PA 16113
800-782-2803 • 724-962-3535 • Fax 724-962-3250
Info@Tara-Inn.com

Owner **Donna Winner**
General Manager **Deborah DeCapua**

Inspired by the greatest movie of our time, Gone With the Wind, Tara is in essence an embodiment of the Old South. Tara, although located in the "North," offers you a lasting impression of Southern Hospitality and a chance to enjoy the luxuries of days gone by. Tara is a virtual museum of Civil War and Gone With the Wind memorabilia and antiques. Indulge in our magnificent guest rooms complete with fireplaces and Jacuzzis and enjoy the finest in gourmet or casual dining. Tara offers an extensive wine list and an expertly stocked lounge. Afternoon Tea is a daily opportunity for houseguests to mingle and enjoy. Take a leisurely swim in either our indoor or outdoor heated pools, or stroll through formal gardens overlooking the beautiful 450-acre Shenango Lake. Guests may enjoy massages in-house or pamper themselves at nearby Buhl Mansion Spa. Celebrating 26 years of award-winning dining and overnight accommodations, Tara is the ultimate in World Class Country Inns, devoted to guests who expect the exceptional and appreciate the best.

Rates
Gone With The Wind Getaway Packages (MAP) $350-$425. (B&B) $200-$350.
Corporate rates available. Number of Rooms: 27

Cuisine
Ashley's Gourmet Dining Room offers the finest in 7-course white-glove and candlelight service while Stonewall's Tavern boasts a casual atmosphere with a wide array of hearty dinner selections.

Nearest Airport
Pittsburgh, PA; Cleveland, OH

Buhl Mansion Guesthouse & Spa

www.BuhlMansion.com
422 East State Street, Sharon, PA 16146
866-345-2845 • 724-346-3046 • Fax 724-346-1702
Info@BuhlMansion.com

Pennsylvania

Sharon

Owner **Donna Winner**
General Manager **Laura Ackley**

Buhl Mansion Guesthouse & Spa, rated one of America's Top 10 Most Romantic Inns, offers the ultimate in luxury, pampering and unsurpassed hospitality. Listed on the National Register of Historic Places, this 1890 Romanesque castle is steeped in history and romance. After years of neglect and abuse, the opulent home of Steel Baron Frank Buhl is now lovingly restored and offers grand memories of a lifetime as guests experience the life of America's royalty in our lavishly appointed guestrooms with fireplaces and Jacuzzis. The full-service spa offers the epitome of indulgence with over 100 options of services from which to choose. The Spa Romance Package is the most popular, offering couples massages, facials, manicures, lunch and a bottle of champagne. Guests have complimentary access to the spa's sauna, steam room and monsoon showers. Indulge each morning with breakfast in bed or dine in the picturesque sunroom. The limo takes guests to Tara for gourmet or casual dining. Perfect for romantic getaways, indulgent spa escapes, exclusive executive retreats and castle weddings.

Rates
Castle Escape Packages: $350 King & Queen Rooms; $450 Royal Grand Rooms; $50 off 2nd night. "Castle for a Day" packages available for weddings, spa, golf or executive retreats. Number of Rooms: 10

Cuisine
Champagne & Welcome Tray in each room. Afternoon Tea served daily, Champagne Reception served Fri & Sat. Rates include 25% discount at Ashley's Gourmet Dining Room or Stonewall's Tavern both at Tara-A Country Inn (Limo provided on weekends).

Nearest Airport
Pittsburgh, PA; Cleveland, OH

SelectRegistry.com

The Inn on Negley

www.innonnegley.com
703 South Negley, Pittsburgh, PA 15232
412–661–0631 • Fax 412–661–7525
info@innonnegly.com

Member Since 2006

Pennsylvania

Pittsburgh

Proprietor
Elizabeth Sullivan

The Inn on Negley is a beautifully restored period home located in the heart of Pittsburgh's charming and historic Shadyside area. Each of our eight guest rooms are custom designed with period furnishings, elegant bathrooms, exquisite linens, and a careful attention to detail. To enhance the experience, every guest is gifted L' Occitane bath products upon arrival as well as at turndown. The Inn is just one block from Walnut Street and Ellsworth Avenue, which offers the finest and most unique shopping, dining, and entertainment experiences in Pittsburgh. Guests can linger and enjoy the tranquil atmosphere over refreshments while the innkeepers assist with plans to enjoy Pittsburgh. Additionally, our lovely Fernwood Tea room accepts appointments for English High Tea service offered each afternoon. Whether guests plan a full day of activities, business meetings, or an afternoon enjoying a splendid high tea service, The Inn on Negley can accommodate every preference.

Rates
King Suites: $205/$240. Queen Suites: $180/$190. Suites are beautifully appointed with private baths, luxurious linens, fireplaces, jacuzzi tubs, robes, slippers, high speed Internet, cable television & private phones w/ voicemail. Number of Rooms: 8

Cuisine
Room rate includes gourmet breakfast for two. Breakfast: onsite chef prepared baked goods, hot, sweet and savory gourmet entrees, fresh fruit, yogurt, homemade cereals and granola. Also includes afternoon pastires, iced tea, and evening wine.

Nearest Airport
Pittsburgh International (20 miles)

Eagles Mere Inn

www.eaglesmereinn.com
Box #356 29 Mary Ave, Eagles Mere, PA 17731
800-426-3273 • 570-525-3273 • Fax 570-525-3904
relax@eaglesmereinn.com

Member Since 1993

Pennsylvania

Eagles Mere

Innkeeper/Chef
Toby Diltz

Eagles Mere, 'the last unspoiled resort,' sits on a mountain with a pristine lake surrounded by giant hemlock, rhododendron, and mountain laurel. Restored in 2000, we are the last full service historic inn remaining from the 1800's. Incredible waterfalls, sunsets, hiking trails, birding, covered bridges, fishing, golf, tennis and swimming. Featured by numerous travel writers. Guests enjoy genuine hospitality and personal attention. We loan our bikes, XC skis and kayaks. If you want a quiet, relaxing place to spend time together while enjoying warm hospitality and gourmet meals, visit our web site or call for reservations. "The LAST UNSPOILED RESORT" now waits for you!

Rates
16 rooms/3 suites $179/$269 includes five course Gourmet Dinner and Breakfast for two. Number of Rooms: 19

Cuisine
Selected as a "Top Ten" Pennsylvania Inn, we continue the tradition of offering first-class cuisine while utilizing local products as much as possible. We serve a five-course meal which is included in the room rate, as well as a full country breakfast.

Nearest Airport
Williamsport Regional Airport (IPT)

The Settlers Inn at Bingham Park

🍴 🍴 🍴 ♈

www.thesettlersinn.com
4 Main Avenue, Hawley, PA 18428
800-833-8527 • 570-226-2993 • Fax 570-226-1874
settler@thesettlersinn.com

Member Since 1992

Pennsylvania

Hawley

Innkeepers/Owners
Grant & Jeanne Genzlinger

The Settlers Inn is a place to gather. Relax, play and rejuvenate at this carefully restored arts and crafts inn. Stroll the extensive grounds and discover colorful flower and herb gardens, a quiet reflecting pond, or sit along the banks of the meandering Lackawaxen River. Guestrooms are thoughtfully and simply appointed with your comfort in mind. Luxurious European linens, featherbeds, whirlpool tubs and fireplaces invite travelers to pamper themselves. High speed wireless internet, available at no additional cost, provides the flexibility to stay connected. The cornerstone of the inn is the award winning farm-to-table restaurant highlighting artisan breads and menus influenced by the seasons. The Dining Room and Chestnut Tavern reflect the style of William Morris which is carried throughout the building. After a day of hiking or cross-country skiing, bask in the warmth of the bluestone fireplace. Summer offers dining alfresco on the terrace overlooking the grounds as well as the Potting Shed, a gift shop in the garden.

Rates
21 Rooms and Suites, $165/$260 B&B. Open year-round. Number of Rooms: 21

Cuisine
Our award winning restaurant, rated AAA 4 Diamond, has a 20+ year tradition of working with local farmers and producers. It offers a comfortable and casual atmosphere for a romantic dinner for two or gathering place for friends and family.

Nearest Airport
Scranton (AVP), Allentown (ABE)

🍽️ 🍽️ 🍽️ 🍷

The French Manor Inn and Spa

www.thefrenchmanor.com
50 Huntingdon Drive, South Sterling, PA 18445
877-720-6080 • 570-676-3244
info@thefrenchmanor.com

Member Since 1991

Pennsylvania

South Sterling

Innkeepers/Owners
The Logan Family

An enchanting storybook stone chateau, the French Manor Inn and Spa is nestled on 45 acres overlooking the beautiful Pocono Mountains. Old world charm and elegant furnishings are seamlessly joined with all the modern conveniences. Le Spa Forõt at the French Manor is a Green Spa with indoor salt water pool, hot tub, fitness room, and offers fireside massages, spa facials, body wraps and nail services. Guests can enjoy luxurious suites with fireplace, Jacuzzi, and private balconies. Every guest is welcomed with complimentary sherry, cheese and fruit plate, and pampered with turndown service with Godiva chocolates. The four diamond award winning restauarnt features authentic & Nouvelle French cuisine served in the "Great Hall" where a 40-foot vaulted ceiling & magnificent twin fireplaces create a romantic setting. An excellent wine list compliments the dining experience. Travelers can also enjoy a cocktail or a causal meal in Hanna's Cafe or on the veranda in nicer weather. Enjoy miles of trails for hiking, mountain biking, picnicking, and snowshoeing. AAA ◆◆◆◆

Rates
5 Rooms, $190/$285 B&B; 14 Suites, $265/$375 B&B. All suites FP, most with whirlpool tub & balcony view. Number of Rooms: 19

Cuisine
Gourmet breakfast. Room service available. Nouvelle and authentic French cuisine for dinner. Spa Cuisine Lunch and picnic basket lunches available upon request. Cafe and Bar onsite. An extensive wine list is available and top-shelf liquors.

Nearest Airport
Scranton/Wilkes-Barre (AVP), Lehigh Valley International Airport (LVIA)

Inn at Turkey Hill and Brewing Company

🍽️   🍽️ 🍷

www.innatturkeyhill.com
991 Central Road, Bloomsburg, PA 17815
570-387-1500 • Fax 570-784-3718
info@innatturkeyhill.com

Member Since 2002

Pennsylvania

Bloomsburg

Innkeeper/Owner
Andrew B. Pruden

From romantic couples seeking a weekend diversion, corporate travelers looking for a tranquil place to rest, the inn is a casually elegant and comfortably appointed escape of charm and class. Among the rolling hills and farmlands of rural eastern Pennsylvania, The Inn at Turkey Hill is considered "an oasis along the interstate". Conveniently located just off Interstate 80, guests are treated to a hospitable atmosphere of towering trees and friendly, resident ducks waddling about the courtyard complete with a gazebo and pond. Rejuvenate yourself in one of our guest rooms attractively furnished with reproduction pieces or give in to the allure of a whirlpool bath and fireplace. An award winning restaurant located in the main house features creative, world class cuisine and acclaimed wine list. Also on the property is a renovated 1839 bank barn transformed into a brewpub and casual dining establishment. The Turkey Hill Brewing Company Pub and Grille features house-brewed beer in a unique and diverse environment.

Rates
14 Traditional rooms $129/$143; 2 Inn rooms $134/$148; 5 Stable Rooms $167/$201; Deluxe King $183/$223; King Supreme $200/$243. Number of Rooms: 23

Cuisine
Complimentary continental breakfast including hot entree. Afternoon refreshments. Fine dining nightly at the Inn and casual dining at The Brew Pub.

Nearest Airport
Wilkes-Barre

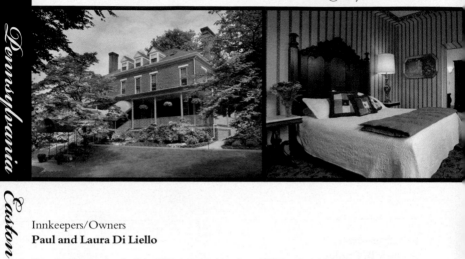

The Lafayette Inn

www.lafayetteinn.com
525 W. Monroe St., Easton, PA 18042
800-509-6990 • 610-253-4500 • Fax 610-253-4635
info@lafayetteinn.com

Member Since 2000

Innkeepers/Owners
Paul and Laura Di Liello

Our elegant mansion, built in 1895, is situated in a beautiful historic neighborhood near Lafayette College. Eighteen antique filled guest rooms welcome travelers visiting the Lehigh Valley's many attractions. The suites feature fireplaces and whirlpool tubs for that special getaway. The inviting parlor, wrap-around porch and tiered patio with fountain/waterfall call out to those longing to relax with a cup of coffee and a good book. A bountiful freshly prepared breakfast is served at individual tables in our bright sunroom or on the porch. Complimentary soft drinks, coffee, fresh baked goods and fruit are available all day. The entire Inn has free wireless high-speed internet access and a loaner laptop is available. Whether visiting the colors of the Crayola Factory with the kids, riding the historic, mule-drawn canal boats, hot air ballooning above the countryside, exploring underwater diving excitement, visiting area colleges or just lounging and rejuvenating, The Lafayette Inn makes a great base for your getaway. Welcome to our Inn!

Rates
18 Rooms (5 Suites) $125/$250. Antique-filled rooms with all the modern amenities, including TV/DVD, phones, WiFi. All private baths. Number of Rooms: 18

Cuisine
Full American breakfast daily, complimentary soft drinks, coffee, fruit, and pastries available all day. Excellent restaurants within walking distance. No liquor license.

Nearest Airport
20 minutes from Lehigh Valley International (ABE), 60 minutes from Newark (EWR) or Philadelphia (PHL)

SelectRegistry.com

Sayre Mansion

www.sayremansion.com
250 Wyandotte Street, Bethlehem, PA 18015
877-345-9019 • 610-882-2100 • Fax 610-882-1223
innkeeper@sayremansion.com

Member Since 2003

Pennsylvania *Bethlehem*

Proprietors
**Grant & Jeanne Genzlinger and
Carrie Ohlandt**

Timeless Elegance in a Distinguished Gothic Revival Mansion. The Inn offers luxury and comfort in nineteen guest rooms each preserving the architectural details of the Main House. In addition to the Main House, our classically restored Carriage House offers guests a home away from home atmosphere in their choice of three suites. Each suite provides a separate living room and bedroom allowing guests ultimate privacy. Amenities include: fine linens, private baths, high-speed wireless internet access, featherbeds, jacuzzi bathtubs, and flat screen TV's. Robert Sayre's Wine Cellar offers guests an opportunity to sample a selection of wine. Personal Service is the cornerstone of the guest experience. The Asa Packer Room, our unique conference center, is ideal for business meetings. Gatherings and special events are held in a pair of elegant parlors, each with its own fireplace. Century old trees adorn the two acres of picturesque grounds which provide a beautiful setting for weddings or large gatherings under our 30' x 60' tent.

Rates
22 rooms and suites, $160/$325 B&B. Open Year-Round. Number of Rooms: 22

Cuisine
Breakfast highlights artisan breads, home made pastries, house specialties including belgian waffles, quiche, and omelets. Excellent restaurants serving lunch and dinner are located within one mile of the Inn.

Nearest Airport
Lehigh Valley International Airport is a five minute drive.

The Inn at Barley Sheaf Farm

www.barleysheaf.com
5281 York Road (Rte 202), Holicong, Bucks County, PA 18928
215-794-5104 • Fax 215-794-5332
info@barleysheaf.com

Member Since 1982

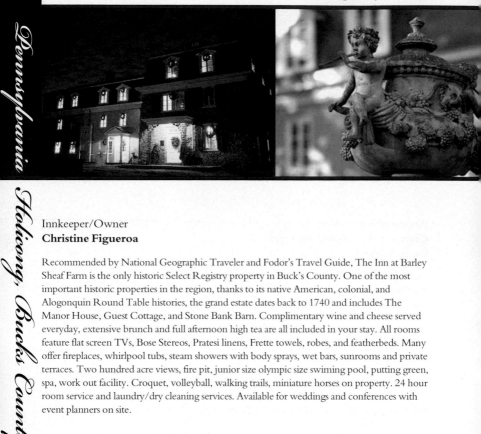

Innkeeper/Owner
Christine Figueroa

Recommended by National Geographic Traveler and Fodor's Travel Guide, The Inn at Barley Sheaf Farm is the only historic Select Registry property in Buck's County. One of the most important historic properties in the region, thanks to its native American, colonial, and Alogonquin Round Table histories, the grand estate dates back to 1740 and includes The Manor House, Guest Cottage, and Stone Bank Barn. Complimentary wine and cheese served everyday, extensive brunch and full afternoon high tea are all included in your stay. All rooms feature flat screen TVs, Bose Stereos, Pratesi linens, Frette towels, robes, and featherbeds. Many offer fireplaces, whirlpool tubs, steam showers with body sprays, wet bars, sunrooms and private terraces. Two hundred acre views, fire pit, junior size olympic size swiming pool, putting green, spa, work out facility. Croquet, volleyball, walking trails, miniature horses on property. 24 hour room service and laundry/dry cleaning services. Available for weddings and conferences with event planners on site.

Rates
16 luxurious suites, $275/$525 Open year round. Activities: Spa, New Hope shops, antiquing, museums, art galleries, Delaware River outdoor activities. Number of Rooms: 16

Cuisine
Full gourmet brunch, afternoon snack, dinners Friday and Saturday evenings, other nights by request. Wine and cheese in our Conservatory Dining Room from 4-6 PM.

Nearest Airport
Philadelphia Airport (PA) and Newark Airport (NJ)

Mercersburg Inn

www.mercersburginn.com
405 South Main St., Mercersburg, PA 17236
717-328-5231 • 866-MBURG-01 • Fax 717-328-3403
Lisa@mercersburginn.com

Member Since 1998

Owners
Jim & Lisa McCoy

In 1909, Ione and Harry Byron had a magnificent dream, to build a home that brought comfort and entertainment to those that entered. From that dream, the 24,000 sq. ft. Prospect, with 11 ft. ceilings throughout, was born. The mahogany-paneled dining room and the sun-filled enclosed porch invite our guests to a culinary experience that will not be soon forgotten. Large enough to ensure your privacy but still able to maintain the intimacy and service of a country Inn. The double-curving staircases lead you to our luxuriously appointed guest rooms. Draw yourself a nice warm bath in one of our antique soaking tubs, dry off with the softest of towels, slip on a fine robe, and drift away to sleep on your feather-bed. Awake in the morning to the smell of fresh baked morning goods, and our delicious 3-course breakfast. If the season permits, stroll through the flower and herb gardens that appoint the 5.5 acre property. If golfing, hiking, swimming, fly-fishing, or skiing are on your to-do-list, let our staff make the arrangements for you. We look forward to having you in our home.

Rates
$140/$395 3 w/fireplaces, 1 w/clawfoot whirlpool tub, 2 w/Jacuzzi and TV, 3 w/antique baths. Kings and Queens. Open year round except Christmas Eve and Christmas Day. Number of Rooms: 17

Cuisine
Enjoy our full gourmet breakfast. Fine dining and wines at Byron's, our fine dining restaurant. Seating 5:30 pm till 8:30 pm. Thurs-Sun. Reservations are recommended. Full bar service. Join us for a French Cooking Class or Wine Tasting/Pairing Dinner.

Nearest Airport
BWI, Dulles, Hagerstown Regional

Hickory Bridge Farm

www.hickorybridgefarm.com
96 Hickory Bridge Road, Orrtanna, PA 17353
717-642-5261 • Fax 717-642-6419
info@hickorybridgefarm.com

Member Since 1976

Pennsylvania

Orrtanna

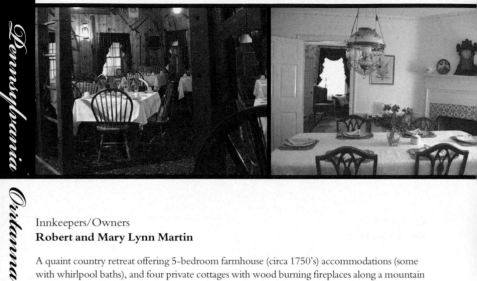

Innkeepers/Owners
Robert and Mary Lynn Martin

A quaint country retreat offering 5-bedroom farmhouse (circa 1750's) accommodations (some with whirlpool baths), and four private cottages with wood burning fireplaces along a mountain stream. Dinner is served in a beautiful restored Pennsylvania barn decorated with hundreds of antiques. All meals are farm-fresh and bountiful. Full breakfast is offered to overnight guests at the farmhouse and is taken to their room on Sunday morning. The farm is located 9 miles west of Gettysburg, Pennsylvania, on 75 beautiful acres-a wonderful place to relax while visiting Gettysburg or antiquing in the nearby area. Featured in Taste of Home magazine and National Geographic Traveler. Family owned and operated since 1977.

Rates
9 Rooms, Cottages and Farmhouse, $110.00/$165 B&B. Open year-round. Number of Rooms: 9

Cuisine
Fine country dining in a beautiful restored Pennsylvania barn. Friday, Saturday, and Sunday. banquets and parties served daily. No spirits are served; you may bring your own. Reservations Suggested!

Nearest Airport
Harrisburg

SelectRegistry.com

Inn at Herr Ridge

www.herrtavern.com

900 Chambersburg Rd., Gettysburg, PA 17325

800-362-9849 • 717-334-4332 • Fax 717-334-3332

info@herrtavern.com

Member Since 2004

Pennsylvania

Innkeeper/Owner

Steven Wolf

Gettysburg

The enchanting atmosphere of the Inn at Herr Ridge is unforgettable. Built in 1815 and nestled between the historic battlefields of Gettysburg and one of Pennsylvania's wooded treasures, Caledonia State Park on historic Rt 30. The Inn offers a rare experience to every guest who crosses the threshold, and is only minutes from town. Tastefully decorated, charmingly unique rooms await. Enjoy our roof top patio overlooking Seminary Ridge or step into your private Jacuzzi bath. Hungry? Relax while our chef creates a fabulous meal soon not to be forgotten. And don't forget the wine. Our Wine Spectator award winning wine list offers over 1000 selections, many of which are stored in our exquisite, windowed wine cellar. Our full-service bar also offers premium spirits. The main house of the Inn became the first Confederate hospital during the battle of Gettysburg. It is beautifully restored and listed in the National Register of Historic Places. If you are searching for a relaxing and romantic getaway, look no further. The fireplace is glowing & the wine is chilled. Come visit us!

Rates

$169/$359. Open year-round. All rooms have private baths, spa robes, pillowtop featherbeds, and gas fireplaces. Most rooms with two person jacuzzi tubs. Number of Rooms: 16

Cuisine

Bountiful breakfast consisting of daily baked muffins & cinnamon buns. House made granola and a hot breakfast created by the chefs. Fabulous innovative and seasonal influenced lunch and dinner menus. Private Dining and Banquet facilities.

Nearest Airport

Harrisburg (MDT), Baltimore (BWI)

The Beechmont Bed & Breakfast Inn

www.thebeechmont.com
315 Broadway, Hanover, PA 17331
800-553-7009 • 717-632-3013 • Fax 717-632-2769
innkeeper@thebeechmont.com

Member Since 2003

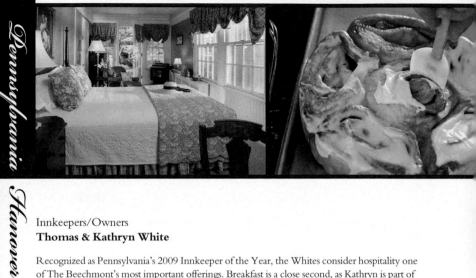

Innkeepers/Owners
Thomas & Kathryn White

Recognized as Pennsylvania's 2009 Innkeeper of the Year, the Whites consider hospitality one of The Beechmont's most important offerings. Breakfast is a close second, as Kathryn is part of Eight Broads in the Kitchen, a group of imaginative innkeepers who share recipes and local insights (www.eightbroads.com). Located on a tree-lined street of stately historic homes in a town just 14 miles east of Gettysburg, The Beechmont welcomes travelers with thoughtful extras that exceed your expectations. A well-stocked library, lovely gardens and patio offer a backdrop for relaxed conversation, while well-appointed guest rooms assure a comfortable stay and sweet dreams. Commemorate the 150th anniversary of the Civil War at the Gettysburg Battlefield and Museum. Explore President Eisenhower's farm. Search for bargains in antique malls, tour wineries, bicycle back country roads, savor fresh vegetables and fruits from farmers markets, dine at great restaurants, and get married in the garden. Come for the history, stay for the hospitality, return for the experience all over again!

Rates
$154 - 184. Corporate rates Mon-Thur. A/C, WIFI, guest internet station, cable TV, fireplaces, all baths with custom jetted showers and three updated in 2012. Four 2-room suites. Winter specials noted online. Number of Rooms: 6

Cuisine
Sumptuous breakfast served at the time you select. Start with freshly brewed coffee from Mukilteo Coffee roasters, then a made-from-scratch breakfast featuring locally grown produce and goods. Afternoon sweet treat. Excellent restaurants nearby.

Nearest Airport
75 min Baltimore Washington International (BWI) and Harrisburg (MDT); 90 min from Dulles; 2 hrs Philadelphia (PHL).

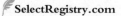 SelectRegistry.com

The Sheppard Mansion

101 101 ♀

www.sheppardmansion.com
117 Frederick St., Hanover, PA 17331
877-762-6746 • 717-633-8075 • Fax 717-633-8074
reservations@sheppardmansion.com

Member Since 2002

Pennsylvania

Hanover

Innkeeper/Owner
Kathryn Sheppard Hoar

Nestled in the heart of Hanover's Historic District stands a grand 3-story brick and marble Mansion surrounded by lush gardens. Built in 1913 by Mr. and Mrs. H.D. Sheppard, co-founder of The Hanover Shoe, the Mansion now operates as an elegant full service Inn and event facility. Full of the original furnishings and restored with modern amenities, the Mansion features bedrooms and suites with over-sized soaking tubs in the private marble baths–all for our guests' enjoyment. Days can be spent exploring nearby Gettysburg, antique hunting or touring Lancaster, Baltimore, Washington, DC. Want to relax instead? Have a massage and lounge around the house. Complete your pampered experience with an exquisite meal in our Dining Room, serving seasonal refined American cuisine Wednesday through Saturday nights. Check our website for lodging and dining packages. Our entire staff eagerly awaits the opportunity to be of service; whether for business or pleasure, the Sheppard Mansion is sure to be an unforgettable experience.

Rates
6 rooms and suites, King, Queen Beds, $140/$350 per night. 2 BR Guest Cottage on property available weekly. Corporate rates available. All rooms have private baths, A/C, WiFi, TV, Telephones and in-room coffee. Number of Rooms: 6

Cuisine
Full gourmet breakfast included. Fine dining offered Wed. thru Sat. nights features local produce in an ever-changing seasonal menu of refined American cuisine.

Nearest Airport
BWI - 1 hour, MDT - 1 hour

Inn at Twin Linden

www.InnAtTwinLinden.com
2092 Main St., Churchtown, PA 17555
866-445-7614 • 717-445-7619
info@InnAtTwinLinden.com

Member Since 2011

Innkeepers/Owners
Norm and Sue Kuestner

Imagine the luxurious ambience of a restored 1840's country estate - a gracious manor surrounded by 2 acres of beautiful gardens and stately trees. Farm-dotted valleys stretch as far as the eye can see while the "clip-clop" of horse-drawn buggies is heard echoing down the main street. These pleasures await you where discriminating guests are welcomed to relax and rejuvenate with exceptional accommodations and the finest cuisine. Guest rooms feature pillow-topped canopy beds, fireplaces and whirlpool tubs. Deluxe rooms offer the ultimate in privacy with a refined contemporary decor. Menus are created using seasonal, local farm produce and meats. The Inn overlooks scenic Amish and Mennonite farm valleys, yet is conveniently located to a wide range of activities from Amish farm tours, country auctions, and antiquing to wineries, museums, theatre, historic sites, state parks, and lots of shopping. Relax at day's end by wandering through moonlit gardens or sip sherry by the fire - then retire to turned-down beds with Belgian chocolates and a cordial at bedside.

Rates
6 tastefully appointed rooms $130-$199, 2 deluxe rooms with private entrances and grand view of scenic countryside $245-$275. Private Baths, Fireplaces, Whirlpool Tubs, Bath Robes, Crabtree & Evelyn Amenities, Cable TV, Free WIFI. Number of Rooms: 8

Cuisine
A full-course breakfast served in our garden-view dining room by candlelight. Refreshments available 24/7. Fine dining offered on Saturday evenings by reservation - prix-fix menu and BYOB. Dietary restrictions are accommodated with advance notice.

Nearest Airport
Lancaster (LNS) 18 mi., Philadelphia (PHL) 41 mi., Harrisburg (MDT) 43 mi., Lehigh Valley (ABE) 46 mi.

Swiss Woods

www.swisswoods.com
500 Blantz Road, Lititz, PA 17543
800-594-8018 • 717-627-3358 • Fax 717-627-3483
innkeeper@swisswoods.com

Member Since 1993

Innkeepers/Owners
Werner and Debrah Mosimann

Surrounded by meadows, gardens and woods, Swiss Woods is a quiet retreat on 35 acres in Lancaster's Amish country. Perfect for those who love quiet and all things nature. Our rooms feature patios or balconies, bordering on the gardens and are decorated with the natural wood furnishings typical of Switzerland. Fabulous breakfasts, complemented by our own blend of coffee and a wide assortment of quality teas, are served in a sunlit common room. Afternoons feature pastry and biscotti. Convenient to Lancaster's Amish community, famous farmers markets, greenhouses and quilt shops, Hershey is also just a short drive. After a day of antiquing, shopping or touring enjoy views of extraordinary gardens, landscaped with a wide variety of annuals and perennials. Take a relaxing hike through the woods, watch the huge variety of birds, or enjoy a drink on the garden swing with a good book and a sweet treat from our kitchen. Enjoy the evening around the outdoor chimenea in spring, summer and fall. In winter settle in to read next to the Inn's handsome sandstone fireplace. German spoken.

Rates
6 Rooms (2 with Jacuzzi, balconies, and high open beamed ceilings), all with patios or balconies. $165-$225 1 suite $205/$255. Additional guests in the Suite, $30 per person. Number of Rooms: 7

Cuisine
Inn breakfast specialties may include garden fritatta, freshly-baked breads from old world recipes, all created by one of the 8 Broads in the Kitchen. The afternoon boasts sweets on the sideboard such as caramel apple cake or fresh fig cake.

Nearest Airport
Harrisburg and Philadelphia. Lancaster Airport is close and has connection with BWI

The King's Cottage

www.kingscottagebb.com
1049 East King Street, Lancaster, PA 17602-3231
800-747-8717 • 717-397-1017 • Fax 717-397-3447
info@kingscottagebb.com

Member Since 1995

Pennsylvania

Lancaster

Innkeepers/Owners
Janis Kutterer and Ann Willets

Feel yourself unwind as you travel through Lancaster County's tranquil back roads in Amish Country. Enjoy world-class entertainment, savor Pennsylvania Dutch cooking, visit historic sites, stroll art galleries, enjoy intimate gourmet restaurants - all within minutes of the King's Cottage - your home away from home. Come enjoy our wonderful Lancaster Bed and Breakfast. Elegant, luxurious guest rooms with cozy fireplaces enhance relaxation and romance! Let us pamper you with our gourmet breakfast, afternoon goodies and even a massage that melts your cares away. Or immerse yourself in a decadent rose petal bath while you nibble on chocolate-covered strawberries. The possibilities for celebrating a special occasion or just plain spoiling yourself are endless at the King's Cottage. Our location offers the best of both worlds - being a mile and a half away from a buzzing art scene and fabulous restaurants, while just a few minutes from Amish Country! We have not forgotten our business traveler with 24-hour check-in, early breakfast, fax service & complimentary WiFi.

Rates
7 rooms (2 with whirlpool tub), 1 Honeymoon Cottage with whirlpool tub: $160/$295. Fireplaces, DVD, WIFI, Business rates available. Number of Rooms: 8

Cuisine
Gourmet breakfast, afternoon refreshments. Dietary restrictions accommodated with advance notice. Close to casual and fine dining. 24 hr. guest kitchen with ice, bottled water, snacks, hot beverages.

Nearest Airport
Harrisburg (MDT) 40 min, Philadelphia (PHL) 90 min, Baltimore (BWI) 120 min

SelectRegistry.com

The Inn & Spa at Intercourse Village

www.inn-spa.com
P.O. Box 598, 3542 Old Philadelphia Pike, Intercourse, PA 17534
800-664-0949 • 717-768-2626
info@inn-spa.com

Member Since 2005

Pennsylvania

Intercourse

Innkeepers
Kurt & Char Thomas

Winner of the "Top Ten Romantic Inns" Award. Enjoy elegance in a quiet village setting that entreats you to a place of peace, beauty and comfort. Travel through time as you enter the Historic 1909 Inn filled with period furnishings and antique treasures. Its refinement and sophistication deliver high-class accoutrements for those of discerning tastes. If upscale country is more your style, then reserve one of our Country Homestead suites with private entrance and over 400 sq. ft. of space to relax in and forget the world around you. Our suites include queen pillow top beds, private bath, jetted tub, steam shower, separate sitting area with love seat, gas-log fireplace, flat panel TV, wet bar and many other special treats. For divine romance and relaxation, find yourself engulfed in sumptuous grandeur in our Grand Suites complete with Jacuzzi for two, King pillow top bed, flat panel TV, gas-log fireplace. Arise to a full five course candlelit breakfast and indulge yourself in a delightful diversion at our onsite Day Spa, then relax and stroll thru the Historic Village.

Rates
Grand Suites w/King pillowtop bed, flat panel TV, fireplace, Jacuzzi, $269-$399, Homestead Suites w/Queen pillowtop bed, flat panel TV, fireplace, $169-$239, Historic Main House Rooms w/Queen pillowtop bed, flat panel TV, $149-$199. Number of Rooms: 9

Cuisine
Enjoy a nice 5 course candlelit breakfast, prepared by our chef and served on fine English china in our Victorian dining room. Walk to the village for lunch. Enjoy sodas, coffee, fruit, pretzels or a snack provided daily by our chef.

Nearest Airport
Harrisburg International 1 hr, Philadelphia International 1 1/2 hrs, Baltimore 1 1/2 hrs.

Hamanassett Bed & Breakfast

www.hamanassett.com
725 Darlington Road, P.O. Box 366, Chadds Ford, PA 19017
877-836-8212 • 610-459-3000
stay@hamanassett.com

Member Since 2005

Pennsylvania

Chadds Ford

Innkeepers/Owners
Glenn & Ashley Mon

A worthy destination in the Brandywine Valley, Hamanassett is a grand 1856 English country house on 7 acres where Southern hospitality and personal service is emphasized. Seven spacious bedrooms and suites, featuring en suite baths, hardwood floors, antique furniture, queen or king beds, TV/DVD with free movies, free WIFI & guest computer, and robes. Enjoy the billiards room, living room, and light-filled sun room, terrace or porch overlooking the koi pond with waterfall. Two private two story 2 bedroom cottages for those traveling with small children or for those who just want extra privacy. Cooking classes. Near Longwood Gardens, Winterthur, Wyeth Museum, Barnes Museum, Nemours, and Philadelphia. Only 20 minutes to Wilmington, DE. and one hour from Amish Country. Recommended by major publications including The New York Times "The elaborate breakfasts are a highlight." "Sets the standard for luxury in the Brandywine area" David Langlieb from his book "Philadelphia, Brandywine Valley & Bucks Co." Enjoy our user friendly front porch!

Rates
Rooms: $165/$265. Carriage House: $350/$500/nt. Cottage: $325.00/nt. Weekly/monthly rates available. Number of Rooms: 9

Cuisine
Full gourmet candlelight breakfast. Special diets accommodated if notified in advance. Guest pantry stocked with complimentary soft drinks and snacks, microwave oven, ice maker, refrigerator and home baked cookies available 24 hours.

Nearest Airport
Philadelphia International 17 miles, Baltimore Washington International 94 miles. See web site for directions.

Fairville Inn

www.fairvilleinn.com
506 Kennett Pike (Rte. 52), Chadds Ford, PA 19317
877-285-7772 • 610-388-5900 • Fax 610-388-5902
info@fairvilleinn.com

Member Since 1995

Innkeepers/Owners
Richard and Laura Carro

The Fairville Inn, located in the heart of the Brandywine Valley and listed on the National Register of Historic Places, echoes the pastoral scenes of Wyeth Family paintings. The allure of the Brandywine Valley, which reaches in all directions from Chadds Ford, comes from the enchanting landscape. World famous Longwood Gardens and distinguished museums, such as Winterthur, Hagley, and the Brandywine River ("Wyeth") Museum, are just minutes away. Leisurely travel the Brandywine Valley Wine Trail and sample the latest vintages of local wineries. Accented with barn wood, beams, and the occasional cathedral ceiling, the Inn is the embodiment of elegant comfort. Most rooms feature decks overlooking the gardens or the meadow rolling toward a serene pond. Each room in the Main House (ca. 1826), Carriage House, and Springhouse has a private bath, satellite TV, telephone (with voice mail and complimentary local and long-distance service), wireless Internet, and individually controlled heating/air conditioning. Most rooms have a canopy bed and many have fireplaces (seasonal).

Rates
11 Rooms ($170 - $225), 2 Deluxe Rooms ($265), and 2 Spacious Suites ($295). Open every day. (Rates are subject to change modestly.) Please visit our website for seasonal and other specials. Number of Rooms: 15

Cuisine
Full breakfast (Mon-Fri 7-9 am; weekends and holidays 8-10 am) of refreshing beverages, cereal, fresh fruit, yogurt, Inn-baked goods and a choice of three hot entrees. Afternoon tea served daily with cheese, crackers, fresh fruit, and Inn-baked goods.

Nearest Airport
Philadelphia International, about 28 miles.

Famous for: Jazz Festivals, Seaside Victorian Mansions, "Mile of History." Cliff Walks, Beaches, Sailing.

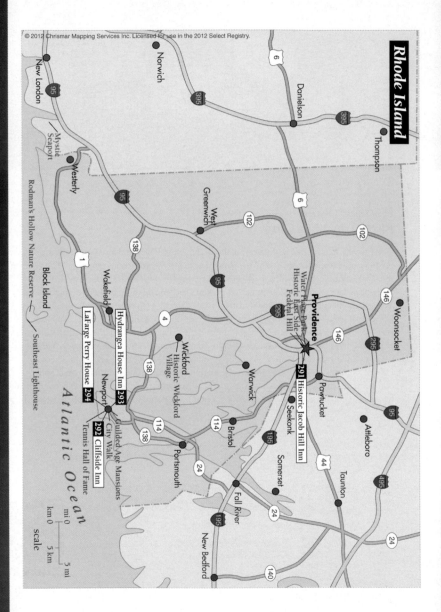

© 2012 Chrismar Mapping Services Inc. Licensed for use in the 2012 Select Registry.

Historic Jacob Hill Inn

www.Jacobhill.com
P.O. Box 41326, Providence, RI 02940
888-336-9165 • 508-336-9165
host@jacobhill.com

Member Since 2000

Innkeepers/Owners
Bill & Eleonora Rezek

Located on a peaceful country estate, just a 10 minute drive from downtown Providence, the Rhode Island Convention Center, Brown University and the Historic East Side. Built in 1722, Jacob Hill has a long history of hosting America's most prominent families, including the Vanderbilts. Recently updated rooms are spacious, all with private bathrooms; most have Jacuzzi tubs. King-and queen-sized canopied beds blend with hand-picked antiques, period wall coverings and Oriental rugs. The gleaming wood floors mirror the romantic flames from the original fireplaces. The elegant surroundings are complemented by the genuine warm hospitality that will make you feel at home. Awarded "Top 10 Most Romantic Inns," ZAGAT "Top U.S. Hotels, Resorts & Spas," TripAdvisor.com "Travelers' Choice Award," Inn Traveler "Best Guest accommodations," "Ten best Urban Inns" Forbes.com, "Room of the Year" North American Inns Magazine. Featured by the New York Times, Country Living Magazine, USA Today and many others.

Rates
12 unique guestrooms, w/private bathrooms $199/$459. Phones, TV, AC, Internet Access. Open year-round. Pool, tennis, ping pong, billiard room w/large plasma TV, meeting room, & gazebo to view the beautiful sunsets. Spa services. Number of Rooms: 12

Cuisine
Award-winning breakfast, complimentary beverages, chocolate chip cookies and cheese plate. Many fine restaurants nearby for lunch and dinner.

Nearest Airport
Providence T F Green

Cliffside Inn

www.cliffsideinn.com
2 Seaview Avenue, Newport, RI 02840
800-845-1811 • 401-847-1811 • Fax 401-848-5850
reservations@cliffsideinn.com

Member Since 1997

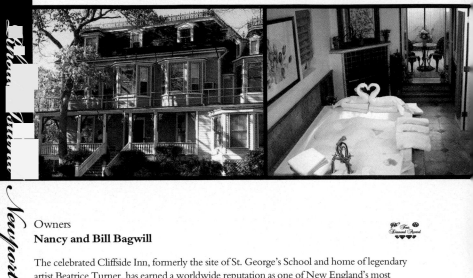

Owners
Nancy and Bill Bagwill

The celebrated Cliffside Inn, formerly the site of St. George's School and home of legendary artist Beatrice Turner, has earned a worldwide reputation as one of New England's most distinguished Bed and Breakfast luxury inns. Known for seamlessly blending today's finest deluxe amenities – whirlpools, steam baths, fireplaces, grand beds, fine Italian linens, iPod sound systems, wifi – with Victorian elegance and antiques, refined design, and stunning artwork. The Cliffside Inn is a magical hideaway. The grand Victorian Manor House and "coastal chic" Seaview Cottage are peacefully perched above the Atlantic Ocean and Newport's dramatic Cliff Walk. Whether you are looking for a relaxing escape or romantic getaway, guests enjoy warm hospitality and attentive service with a number of Cliffside special touches and epicurean delights. The regional wine bar features the best of the nearby vineyards, and signature in-room spa services are available.

Rates
7 Deluxe Suites/State Rooms $300/$500; 5 Deluxe Rooms $250/$425; 4 Classic Rooms $200/$400. Number of Rooms: 16

Cuisine
Multi-course breakfast. Afternoon tea featuring a seasonal menu of tea sandwiches, scones, tarts, and other sweets & savories is offered twice weekly. A manager's wine tasting reception on other days. Our signature Fondeles at turndown.

Nearest Airport
Providence, Boston

SelectRegistry.com

Hydrangea House Inn

www.hydrangeahouse.com
16 Bellevue Avenue, Newport, RI 02840
800-945-4667 • 401-846-4435 • Fax 401-846-6602
hydrangeahouseinn@cox.net

Member Since 2005

Rhode Island Newport

Innkeepers/Owners
Grant Edmondson & Dennis Blair

Enter a world of grace, elegance and style where the intimate charm of Hydrangea House is complemented by its prestigious Bellevue Avenue address where once lived the Vanderbilt's, the Astors and the Dukes. Its proximity to the magical gilded mansions, recreational harbor, historic sites, fine dining, and extraordinary shopping means you can walk to almost everything. All nine rooms and suites are individually decorated with a dramatic use of color, sumptuous fabrics and trims and elegant furnishings. Suites have the added luxury of a two-person spa tub, marble shower and steam bath and flat screen "mirror" television. All rooms offer plush robes, triple sheeting, high speed Internet, long distance and local calling, CD players and iPod hook-ups. Complimentary wine and cheese is served daily in the parlor or one of Hydrangea House's expansive porches, and don't miss a home-made cookie to make the night complete. AAA Four diamond award. Named "Top 10 Most Romantic Inn" in 2008 by American Historic Inns and ILoveInns.com. Winner of Yankee Magazine "Editors Choice" 2006 award.

Rates
$265/$475 year round. Year round packages available. Number of Rooms: 10

Cuisine
Expect to find more than the usual continental breakfast. We will serve you our own special blend of fresh ground House Coffee, home-baked breads & granola–as well as our incredible raspberry pancakes perhaps or seasoned scrambled eggs in puff pastry.

Nearest Airport
Providence Airport (PVD) 30 minutes.

La Farge Perry House

www.lafargeperry.com
24 Kay Street, Newport, RI 02840
877-736-1100 • 401-847-2223 • Fax 401-847-1967
reservations@lafargeperry.com

Member Since 2006

Innkeeper
Jennifer Balch

La Farge Perry House is a Victorian-era luxury inn located on a quiet street within walking distance to major attractions in Newport. The inn is named after the famed artist John La Farge, who lived in the house in the 1860's. Each of the inn's six distinctive rooms honor La Farge, his family, and ancestors. Four guestrooms feature queen-sized beds and two feature king beds. All rooms are adorned with luxurious private bathrooms, luxury bedding and amenities, and feature fresh flowers from the award winning gardens. Many rooms also feature Jacuzzi tubs, fireplaces, and large sitting areas. Common areas include a formal living room, French Provencal kitchen with sitting area and a fireplace, dining room with hand-painted panoramic murals of Newport, secluded balcony on the third floor, front porch with white wicker furniture, and Adirondack chairs in the award-winning backyard gardens.

Rates
Summer Rates range from $249 to $349 on weekdays and from $289 to $499 on weekends. Winter Rates range from $139 to $169 on weekdays and from $189 to $289 on weekends. Number of Rooms: 6

Cuisine
Breakfasts are cooked to order by our innkeeper with many choices, including Eggs Benedict on Sundays. The table is set daily with homemade jams, pastries, fresh fruit, and more. Seasonal afternoon refreshments are also offered.

Nearest Airport
Providence/TF Green, RI

South Carolina

"The Palmetto State"

Famous for: Congaree Swamp National Monument, Hilton Head Island, Myrtle Beach, Plantations, Charleston, Blue Ridge Mountains, Fort Sumter, Tobacco, Corn, Peaches, Cotton, Textiles.

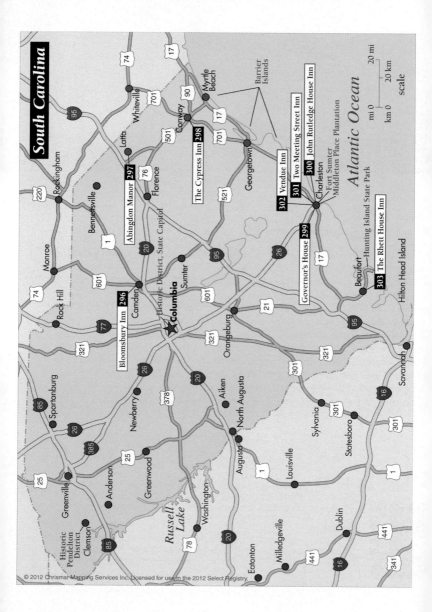

Bloomsbury Inn

www.bloomsburyinn.com
1707 Lyttleton Street, Camden, SC 29020
803-432-5858 • Fax 803-432-5858
info@bloomsburyinn.com

Member Since 2010

Innkeepers/Owners
Bruce A. and Katherine L. Brown

Sensational in Every Season! Bloomsbury, an award-winning property, is known for Southern hospitality, gourmet breakfasts and complimentary socials which include a walk through history with the owners. Located in the historic district, 3 miles off I-20, near fine shops/arts and great restaurants, Bloomsbury Inn, circa 1849, awaits you. Significant notoriety is derived from the writings of the famous diarist, Mary Boykin Chesnut, author of A Diary from Dixie. From the outside in, this beautifully appointed property offers old world charm with all the modern comforts. Sitting on two acres of manicured grounds, several garden sitting areas and the veranda offer peace and tranquility from the everyday stresses of life. Inside this lovingly restored antebellum home, with uncompromising attention to detail, we have created a warm and welcoming environment for all who traverse the leaded glass doorway. With large bed chambers, luxurious amenities and thoughtful touches, Bloomsbury will well-surpass your expectations. We have everything ready for your arrival–safe travels!

Rates
Enjoy gracious, oversized guest bed chambers, king and queen, with Italian tile private baths, featuring luxury amenities. $159.00 - $215.00 (inclusive rate: full gourmet breakfast, 5:30 pm social, wifi, top amenities, all taxes). Number of Rooms: 4

Cuisine
Delicious gourmet breakfasts, using local products...farm fresh eggs, homemade breads, real butter, aged cheeses, custom-blended coffee. Dining room or veranda; diet restrictions honored. Complimentary social: tea/wine and light hors d'oeuvres.

Nearest Airport
Columbia SC or Charlotte NC are easy drives. I-20, exit 98, N Hwy 521, right @ Chesnut St, left @ Lyttleton St

Abingdon Manor

www.abingdonmanor.com
307 Church Street, Latta, SC 29565
888-752-5090 • 843-752-5090
abingdon@bellsouth.net

Innkeepers/Owners
Chef Patty & Michael Griffey

The only establishment offering luxury accommodations and fine dining in the Carolinas and Georgia close to I-95, Abingdon Manor is the overnight destination for travelers on the East Coast. Halfway between NYC and Palm Beach, the Inn offers superior lodging, extraordinary cuisine and impeccable service. One of only a select few properties in South Carolina to be awarded a AAA 4-diamond rating annually for both the Inn and Restaurant, Abingdon Manor offers the amenities of a small luxury hotel in an opulent National Register mansion. Located in a quaint, quiet and safe turn of the century village, the Inn features 3 acres of landscaped grounds. For destination travelers, the Inn offers a variety of activities including cooking school weekends, historic touring, antiquing, nature-based activities and private country club golf. Food writers and critics consistently rank "The Dining Room at Abingdon Manor" as one of the best restaurants in the Carolinas. Abingdon Manor offers a refined, yet comfortable, atmosphere for the discriminating traveler. Abingdon Manor is a AAA Four Diamond and Mobil Three Star Inn and Restaurant.

Rates
$180/$215. All guestrooms offer ensuite bathrooms, cable TV, working fireplaces, individual temperature controls and wifi. Number of Rooms: 7

Cuisine
The award winning restaurant offers exceptional fine dining nightly. The one seating, pre-fixe meal is crafted daily using the freshest ingredients available and begins with cocktails at 7:00. A full breakfast is offered from 7:45 to 9:00 am.

Nearest Airport
Florence, Myrtle Beach

The Cypress Inn

www.acypressinn.com
16 Elm Street, Conway, SC 29526
800-575-5307 • 843-248-8199 • Fax 843-248-0329
info@acypressinn.com

Member Since 2001

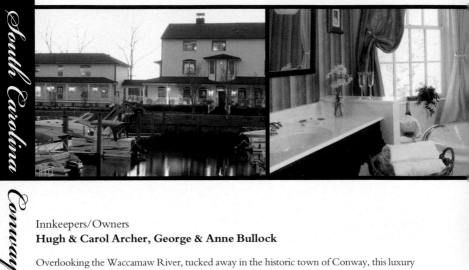

Innkeepers/Owners
Hugh & Carol Archer, George & Anne Bullock

Overlooking the Waccamaw River, tucked away in the historic town of Conway, this luxury inn is near, but distinctly apart from the golf mecca of Myrtle Beach. Located 2 blocks from the downtown area of Conway, the inn is within walking distance of charming shops, restaurants, art galleries and stately live oak trees. Eleven unique guestrooms offer comforts such as en-suite private baths with Jacuzzis, plush robes, individual heat/air, high speed internet (Wi-Fi). We also have an on-site massage therapist. The inn offers the privacy of a hotel with the personal service of a bed and breakfast. Enjoy the pristine beaches of the South Carolina coast or the peacefulness of an ancient river; an outstanding sculpture garden, or live theater shows. Many extras such as fresh flowers, chocolates and strawberries and a selection of fine wines are available. In addition to being a charming destination, the inn is great for those traveling north or south along the east coast and for the business traveler seeking a relaxing atmosphere. Meeting and banquet facilities are also available.

Rates
$145-$245 B&B. Open year-round. Corporate Rates. Number of Rooms: 12

Cuisine
A wonderful hot breakfast is served each morning. There are fine restaurants within walking distance. A small guest refrigerator is stocked with lemonade, sodas, bottled water. Complimentary wine and beer, cookies and other treats.

Nearest Airport
Myrtle Beach

Governor's House Inn

www.governorshouse.com
117 Broad Street, Charleston, SC 29401
800-720-9812 • 843-720-2070 • Fax 843-805-6549
governorshouse@aol.com

Member Since 2000

General Manager **Mary Kittrell**
Owners **Janice Gardner, Sue and Kevin Shibilski**

Governor's House is a magnificent National Historic Landmark (circa 1760) reflecting the Old South's civility and grandeur. Praised by one national publication as "Charleston's most glamorous and sophisticated inn," the former Governor's mansion is the perfect blend of historic splendor and romantic elegance. The mansion's original living rooms, dining room, nine fireplaces, Irish crystal chandeliers, and sweeping southern porches delight guests from around the globe. Harmonize these aristocratic pleasures with luxuries like whirlpool baths, wetbars, high speed Internet and individually controlled room environments, and the result is refined gentility. During the American Revolution, Governor's House was the home of Edward Rutledge, youngest signer of the Declaration of Independence. Today, the inn has been acclaimed as "a flawless urban hideaway" by Southern Living. Visit us online at: www.governorshouse.com

Rates
Governor's House offers 11 guest rooms and suites. Rates are $195-$560, depending on season, and include Southern breakfast, afternoon tea, wine and cheese, evening sherry, bicycles, WiFi, concierge services, and private parking. Number of Rooms: 11

Cuisine
Gourmet breakfast, Low-country afternoon tea. Wine and cheese is also served during the tea hour. Premiere restaurants nearby.

Nearest Airport
Charleston

John Rutledge House Inn

www.johnrutledgehouseinn.com
116 Broad Street, Charleston, SC 29401
800-476-9741 • 843-723-7999 • Fax 843-720-2615
kleslie@charminginns.com

Member Since 1992

Owner **Richard Widman**
Innkeeper **Kathy Leslie**

John Rutledge, one of the 55 signers of the Constitution of the U.S., built his home in 1763. Now exquisitely restored, it is one of only fifteen homes belonging to those signers to survive and the only one to now accommodate overnight guests. One may choose between the classic elegance of rooms and spacious suites in the grand residence or its two carriage houses. The Inn is located in the heart of the Historic District where you are just a few steps away from the famed "South of Broad" neighborhood. Antique and boutique shopping, museums and many other local attractions are just around the corner. Spa services and dinner reservations at acclaimed Circa 1886 Restaurant available nearby to our guests. Afternoon tea and evening port, sherry and brandy are offered in the Signers ballroom where patriots, statesmen and presidents have met. Wireless internet access, nightly turn-down service and breakfast are included with your room. A charter member of Historic Hotels of America, designated a National Historic Landmark. AAA◆◆◆◆

Rates
16 Rooms, $209/$365 and 3 Suites, $310/$435. Open year-round. Daily parking fee. 19 total rooms. Number of Rooms: 19

Cuisine
Breakfast served with daily hot item and expanded continental included. Afternoon tea and refreshments. Guests have a choice of having breakfast served in their room, in the courtyard or the Signers Ballroom.

Nearest Airport
Charleston International Airport 12 miles.

Two Meeting Street Inn

www.twomeetingstreet.com
2 Meeting Street, Charleston, SC 29401
888-723-7322 • 843-723-7322
innkeeper2meetst@bellsouth.net

Innkeepers/Owners
Pete and Jean Spell, Karen Spell Shaw

No other place is like Charleston, and in Charleston, no place is quite like Two Meeting Street Inn- the jewel in the crown of the city's historic inns. From the Inn's gracious Southern veranda- one of the most photographed porches in the South- guests enjoy layers of natural beauty. The Queen Anne Mansion was given as a wedding gift by a bride's loving father in 1890. The Inn features a carved English oak stairwell and Tiffany windows, as well as the Spell's collection of antiques and silver. Immediately surrounded by century-old live oaks amid lush gardens with a finely manicured lawn and cherry red azaleas, the inn overlooks Charleston's historic harbor, tip of the Battery; a few blocks away, world-class dining, modern boutiques, antique shops, art galleries, and historic museum houses await. Guests enjoy a hot Southern breakfast in the oval dining room and gracious afternoon tea on the veranda. Here, the pace slows and the mind rests. The inn invites you to discard your stress and relish the exquisite civility and romance of Charleston. We await your arrival.

Rates
9 Unique guest rooms with private baths. Tariffs $225 to $519. Besides breakfast and afternoon tea, our complimentary package includes concierge services, daily newspapers, hi-def cable television, wireless internet and parking. Number of Rooms: 9

Cuisine
Begin your day with Southern pecan coffee and a full, hot breakfast. Be rejuvenated with Lowcountry afternoon tea. Indulge in an enticing array of Key Lime Pound Cake, Plantation Brownies and Benne Wafers. An evening cream sherry ends your day.

Nearest Airport
Charleston International Airport 12 miles from downtown.

🍴 🍴 🍴 ♀

Vendue Inn

www.vendueinn.com
19 Vendue Range, Charleston, SC 29401
800-845-7900 • 843-577-7970 • Fax 843-577-2913
info@vendueinn.com

Member Since 2002

General Manager
Susie Ridder

Imagine a place where the genteel comfort of a bygone era has been perfectly preserved. Where the style is more sophisticated, the service, more gracious. A place that offers every convenience in an intimate setting that exceeds every expectation. You've found someplace very special at Charleston's Vendue Inn where comfort, cobblestone streets and genteel Southern hospitality await. Charleston, South Carolina is known for its warm hospitality, gracious living, vibrant history, and Southern charm. Experience it all at The Vendue Inn. In the heart of Charleston's Historic District, one block from the harbor and Waterfront Park, the Vendue Inn is nestled in what is known as the French Quarter. Guests consistently remark on the attentive personal service they receive; our staff's hospitality is warm even by Southern standards! The Vendue Inn is a luxury historic small hotel. Our friendly, caring, and experienced staff awaits your arrival.

Rates
66 Rooms, $129/$379; 15 Suites, $259/$699. Sixty-six beautifully appointed guest rooms and suites. Number of Rooms: 66

Cuisine
Complimentary Southern Family Breakfast. The Rooftop Bar and Restaurant serves lunch and dinner 7 days and features nightly live entertainment. The Library Restaurant is open Tuesday through Saturday from 5:00 PM until 10:00 PM.

Nearest Airport
Charleston

 SelectRegistry.com

The Rhett House Inn

www.rhetthouseinn.com

1009 Craven Street, GPS: 32.4329453,-80.6737595, Beaufort, SC 29902

888-480-9530 • 843-524-9030 • Fax 843-524-1310

info@rhetthouseinn.com

Member Since 1991

South Carolina

Beaufort

Owners
Steve & Marianne Harrison

The Rhett House Inn consists of the Thomas Rhett House, built ca. 1820 as a summer home for one of S.C.'s wealthiest planters and statesmen; The Cottage, built ca. 1864 as a combination school/store for freedmen; and The Suites at Newcastle Cottage, a beautiful 2-suite house adjacent to the inn, perfect for two couples, wedding family members, special occasions, etc. Listed in the National Register of Historic Places, the Rhett House contains 10 rooms; in 1996 the Cottage was renovated and transformed into 7 additional charming and historic rooms, with fireplaces, whirlpool baths, and individual decks/patios. Newcastle Cottage contains 2 beautiful suites, with a large living/dining area, gourmet kitchen, and screened veranda. The house and many of the rooms are decorated with English and American antiques, oriental rugs, fresh orchids, and spacious verandas. Situated in Beaufort's 300 year-old National Historic Landmark District, the Inn, Cottage, and Newcastle Cottage are the perfect base for your trip to the southern jewel that is Beaufort. AAA Four Diamond rated.

Rates
19 Rooms - 9 with fireplaces, 8 with whirlpool baths. Open 365 days/year. $180-$300.
Number of Rooms: 19

Cuisine
A stay at The Rhett House Inn includes a Full Southern Breakfast; afternoon teas, lemonade, and pastries; evening hors d'oeuvres and cocktail gathering; nightly homemade desserts; and picnic baskets to order.

Nearest Airport
Savannah/Hilton Head International Airport

Famous for: Cumberland Gap National Historic Park, Cumberland Caverns, Fall Creek Falls, Grand Ole Opry House, Great Smokey Mountains, Graceland, Guinness World Research Museum, Country Music Hall of Fame, Tennessee Valley.

© 2012 Christmas Mapping Services Inc. Licensed for use in the 2012 Select Registry

Butterfly Meadows Inn & Farm 305
Monteagle Inn 311
Whitestone Country Inn 306
Richmont Inn 307
Mayor's Mansion Inn 312
Christopher Place Resort 308
Berry Springs Lodge 310
Eight Gables Inn 309

Butterfly Meadows Inn & Farm

🍴 🍴 🍴

www.butterflymeadowsinn.com
6775 Bethesda Arno Road, Franklin, TN 37179
877-671-4594 • 615-671-4594
relax@butterflymeadowsinn.com

Member Since 2012

Tennessee

Franklin

Innkeepers/Owners
Darlene & Norman Bobo

Nestled atop a ridge and surrounded by 40 acres of woods and meadows, Butterfly Meadows Inn & Farm offers the perfect backdrop for stories to begin and to continue. The Inn is a new farmhouse reflecting a strong devotion to the culture and heritage of the area's history while incorporating modern amenities. Breathtaking, panoramic views and bountiful nature are paralleled by exceptional, personalized service & attention to detail. A cozy library is home to thousands of volumes and hundreds of DVDs. The rocking chair porch offers a peaceful place to enjoy an early morning cup of coffee, view amazing sunsets, or end an evening under a blanket of stars. Choose Butterfly Meadows Inn & Farm for a romantic getaway for two, as a rejuvenating group retreat, an inspiring business retreat, or a spectacular event site for a wedding or celebration. You're just minutes to historic Franklin & Nashville. This is an inviting place where the best of yesterday and today seamlessly intertwine for an experience like no other. Come visit and discover why our motto is Relax ~ Breathe ~ Create!

Rates
Range seasonally: $159-$259/night double. Accommodations wrap you in comfort & luxurious amenities: most w/king beds, private baths, fresh baked cookies, robes, fresh flowers, Wi-Fi, I-docks, fine bath products, turndowns & more. Number of Rooms: 7

Cuisine
A delectable gourmet breakfast will await you each morning. Our skilled culinary team can offer additional meal options for your entire stay. Our menus change seasonally and feature farm fresh produce and herbs from our kitchen garden.

Nearest Airport
Nashville International Airport-36 miles; Huntsville International Airport-98 miles

🍽️ 🍽️ 🍽️

Whitestone Country Inn

www.whitestoneinn.com
1200 Paint Rock Rd., Kingston, TN 37763
888-247-2464 • 865-376-0113 • Fax 865-376-4454
info@whitestoneinn.com

Member Since 2000

Tennessee

Kingston

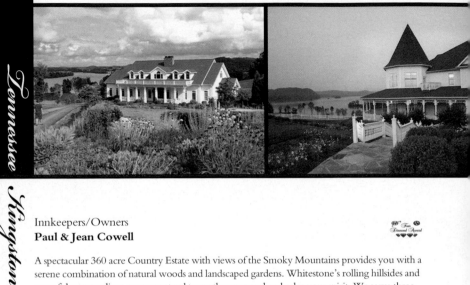

Innkeepers/Owners
Paul & Jean Cowell

A spectacular 360 acre Country Estate with views of the Smoky Mountains provides you with a serene combination of natural woods and landscaped gardens. Whitestone's rolling hillsides and peaceful surroundings are guaranteed to soothe your soul and calm your spirit. We serve three lavish meals a day and you can nibble on home baked cookies and other delectable treats anytime. Many of our rooms are equipped with the sensuous delight of waterfall-spa showers and private decks. You will be surrounded by 5,400 acres of wildlife-waterfowl refuge and 39,000 acre Watts Bar Lake with opportunities for birding, fishing, kayaking, canoeing, paddle-boating or just rocking on our many porches and swinging in our hammocks. This is the perfect place for vacations, retreats, meetings, weddings or honeymoons. Whitestone Country Inn is one of only seven AAA, four-diamond properties in Tennessee, and was named one of the '10 Most Romantic Inns in America!' Discover a Sanctuary for your Soul.

Rates
22 Rooms/Suites, $165/$325 per night. Each room and suite has fireplace, king bed, spa tub, TV/DVD, free Wi-Fi, and refrigerator. Number of Rooms: 22

Cuisine
The very best classic cuisine. Enjoy elegant meals in one of our three dining rooms, two overlooking the lake. For between-meal snacks, sample from the cookie jars in our kitchen.

Nearest Airport
Knoxville, Mcghee/Tyson airport

The Richmont Inn of the Great Smokies

🍴 🍴🍷

www.richmontinn.com
220 Winterberry Lane, Townsend, TN 37882
866-267-7086 • 865-448-6751 • Fax 865-448-6480
innkeeper@richmontinn.com

Member Since 1997

Innkeepers/Owners
Jim & Susan Hind

Escape to the Great Smoky Mountains and refresh your body and soul. Relax in our secluded mountain top setting with breathtaking views, privacy and quietness, 18th century English antiques and French paintings, amenities such as spa tubs, private balconies, wood-burning fireplaces, candlelight desserts, and a gourmet breakfast. Main lodge is styled as an Appalachian cantilevered barn, an icon of the Smokies. New Chalet with luxurious suites, ideally suited for small business groups, family socials or a romantic rendezvous. Open air Chapel-in-the-Woods and wedding services for small groups, private and memorable. Special Weekend Rendezvous and three night Rose and Romance Packages available. Ten minutes to National Park and Cades Cove. Rated "Top Inn" by Country Inns and awarded grand prize by Gourmet Magazine for our signature dessert. "...may be the most romantic place in the Smokies" - Southern Living. "A wonderful place to recharge your batteries" -Country Magazine "Romantic getaway" -HGTV

Rates
9 Rooms, $170/$200, 1 Luxury Suite $200/$220, Chalet Luxury Suites $250/$275; King beds/spa tubs/fireplace/balconies/fridge. Number of Rooms: 14

Cuisine
Full French and Swiss style breakfasts. Also complimentary gourmet desserts, flavored coffees by candlelight and afternoon tea. Classic four course Swiss fondue dinners by reservation. Fine Champagnes, wines, and imported beers.

Nearest Airport
Only 30 mins. from McGhee Tyson (Metro Knoxville) airport.

Christopher Place

www.christopherplace.com
1500 Pinnacles Way, Newport, TN 37821
800-595-9441 • 423-623-6555
stay@christopherplace.com

Member Since 2000

Tennessee

Newport

Innkeeper/Owner
Marston Price

Secluded in the scenic Smoky Mountains on a 200-acre private estate, Christopher Place, an Intimate Resort, is the ideal Inn for a romantic, relaxing getaway. An elegant setting is coupled with friendly, unpretentious service and unspoiled, panoramic views. The hosts know your name and greet you with a warm smile. You can fill your days with activities, or with none at all, as the Inn is centrally located to most of the sights and attractions of the Smokies and offers many resort amenities of its own. Rooms and Suites are spacious and romantically appointed. Casual fine dining with an extensive wine list completes your romantic retreat. Special requests are encouraged. Voted the area's Best B&B. Named one of the 10 most romantic inns in America; one of the 12 best locations for a fantasy B&B wedding; and a winner of BedandBreakfast.com's Best of the South! We invite you to sit back, enjoy, and overlook nothing but the Smoky's.

Rates
4 Rooms, $175; 4 Suites, $275/$330. Suites offer double whirlpools, woodburning fireplaces, private dinning, cable TV, and scenic views. Number of Rooms: 9

Cuisine
Hearty mountain breakfast served at your leisure. Picnics and back-pack lunches. Intimate 4-course candlelit dinners by reservation at tables set for two in our exquisite dining room overlooking the mountains.

Nearest Airport
Knoxville

Eight Gables Inn

www.eightgables.com
219 North Mountain Trail, Gatlinburg, TN 37738
800-279-5716 • 865-430-3344 • Fax 865-430-8767
eightgablesinn@aol.com

Member Since 2002

Tennessee

Gatlinburg

Owners
Lee Bennett & Guy Jacobs

Eight Gables Inn, The Smoky Mountains' Premier Country Inn, offers 21 luxurious rooms and suites. All rooms have private baths, cable TV, feather top beds, plush bathrobes, telephones, personal amenities and several feature the warmth of fireplaces and whirlpool tubs. Our rates include a full served breakfast, and evening dessert. Conveniently located on the drive between Gatlinburg and Pigeon Forge, our peaceful setting lends itself to a casual elegance and relaxing charm. Eight Gables is easily accessible to all the area attractions including the Smoky Mountain National Park. Knoxville and the airport is just 30 miles away. We are also on the trolley route. AAA Four Diamond rated.

Rates
10 Rooms $125/$145; 9 Deluxe Suites $150/$175. Diamond Suites $175/$205, TV/VCR/CD, complementary designer coffees, teas, sodas and bottled water, bath robes, most with King beds, fireplaces, Jacuzzi. Number of Rooms: 21

Cuisine
Full seated service breakfast, and evening dessert.

Nearest Airport
Knoxville TN, McGee Tyson

¡Ø¡ ¡Ø¡ ¡Ø¡

Berry Springs Lodge

www.berrysprings.com
2149 Seaton Springs Road, Sevierville, TN 37862
888-760-8297 • 865-908-7935
stay@berrysprings.com

Member Since 2005

Tennessee

Sevierville

Innkeepers/Owners
Patrick & Sue Eisert

Perched on a 33 acre secluded scenic ridge top in the Great Smoky Mountains, this lodge offers the perfect picture of solitude and romance. Take a leisurely walk down to the bass or catfish ponds and try your luck. Ride bikes, play horseshoes, relax in a hammock or just sit back and enjoy the beautiful views of the Smoky Mountains from your rocking chair on the main deck of the lodge. With this remote setting, one would not guess the lodge is within a 15-minute drive of most area destinations, including Gatlinburg, Pigeon Forge, Sevierville and the "Great Smoky Mountain National Park" Awards and Accolades 2012 Trip Advisor: "#1 Rated B&B in TN" 2006 USA Today: "10 great places to settle into for fall viewing" 2005 Blue Ridge Country: "Tennessee's Berry Springs Lodge Gives the Gift of Trees" 2004 Arrington's Inn Traveler: "Best Scenic Mount View" 2003 Arrington's Inn Traveler: "Best Inn for Rest and Relaxation" 2001 Better Bed and Breakfasts: "Enjoy the Best of Both Worlds at Berry Springs Lodge"

Rates
9 rooms. $135/$215, 2 Suites $175/$235. Includes breakfast and evening desserts.
Open year-round. Number of Rooms: 11

Cuisine
Country gourmet breakfast. Lunch and dinner picnic baskets are available upon advanced request. Local restaurants within 15 minutes. Nightly signature desserts.

Nearest Airport
Knoxville

Monteagle Inn & Retreat Center

www.monteagleinn.com
204 West Main Street, P.O. Box 39, Monteagle, TN 37356
888-480-3245 • 931-924-3869 • Fax 931-924-3867
suites@monteagleinn.com

Member Since 2006

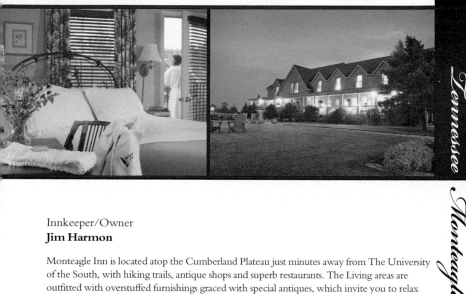

Innkeeper/Owner
Jim Harmon

Monteagle Inn is located atop the Cumberland Plateau just minutes away from The University of the South, with hiking trails, antique shops and superb restaurants. The Living areas are outfitted with overstuffed furnishings graced with special antiques, which invite you to relax and experience the mountaintop. The Inn's large living room with 4 distinct sitting areas encourages you to curl up on one of the oversized sofas with a good book. A welcoming fire in the cool months adds to the total relaxation. Picturesque balconies, a spacious front porch and garden courtyards provide private outdoor relaxation hide-a-ways. Crisp white linens welcome you to relax and enjoy your bedroom with hot cookies and flavored teas. The spacious dining room is filled with light and color from windows on 3 sides while Provencal linens grace the windows and tables. Brightly-patterned Italian urns, bowls and dishes serve as a backdrop for your gourmet breakfast specialties. Monteagle Inn is the perfect place for your getaway and business retreats, family reunions and wedding functions.

Rates
All of the rooms have spacious private baths and are furnished with luxurious white bed and bath linens including coverlets; fluffy towels, the most comfortable pillows. Wireless DSL is available throughout the Inn. $160/$265. Number of Rooms: 13

Cuisine
Extensive herb & vegetable gardens help create acclaimed "mountain gourmet" breakfast.New Orleans Praline French Toast, Mays Eggs Bearnaise, Garden Fresh Frittatas & Herb Roasted Sweet Potato Fries are just a few bountiful items prepared each morning.

Nearest Airport
Chattanooga–45 miles– Nashville-85 miles

Mayor's Mansion Inn

www.mayorsmansioninn.com
801 Vine Street, Chattanooga, TN 37403
423-265-5000 • Fax 423-265-5555
info@mayorsmansioninn.com

Member Since 1996

Tennessee

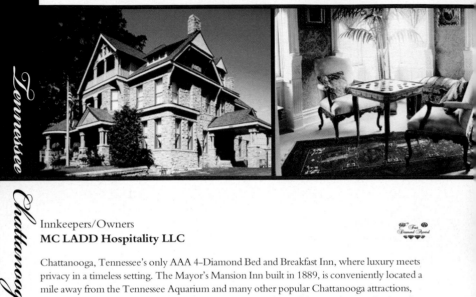

Chattanooga

Innkeepers/Owners
MC LADD Hospitality LLC

Chattanooga, Tennessee's only AAA 4-Diamond Bed and Breakfast Inn, where luxury meets privacy in a timeless setting. The Mayor's Mansion Inn built in 1889, is conveniently located a mile away from the Tennessee Aquarium and many other popular Chattanooga attractions, many within walking distance from the Inn. Boasting 11 beautiful guest rooms and suites, the Mayor's Mansion Inn offers peaceful outdoor spaces, delicious breakfasts, weekend appetizer hour and a level of service unlike any other. Allow our friendly staff to recommend a special restaurant, local event or attraction during your stay. Named "one of the best inns in the South" by National Geographic Traveler Magazine, this historic Victorian Romanesque-style Inn offers Southern charm blended with the luxury of modern amenities. Our unique and elegant spaces are also available for weddings, private dinners, corporate retreats and meetings. The Mayor's Mansion Inn has been honored by the National Trust for Historic Preservation and located in the Fort Wood Historic Neighborhood.

Rates
$130-$295.Seasonal, Corporate, Group rates available. Number of Rooms: 11

Cuisine
Start your morning with a 3-course breakfast served in our elegant Tiffany Dining Room or "en suite". Hors d'ouerves Friday & Saturday evenings. Find more than 60 restaurants in a 2 mile radius of the the Inn or order from over 20 restaurants nearby.

Nearest Airport
Chattanooga Metro Airport-13 miles, Nashville Intl-135 miles, Atlanta Intl-125 miles

Texas

"The Lone Star State"

Famous for: The Alamo, San Antonio Missions National Historic Park, Enchanted Rock, Big Bend National Park, Padre Island National Seashore, Marfa Lights, Guadalupe Mountains National Park, Lyndon B. Johnson Space Center.

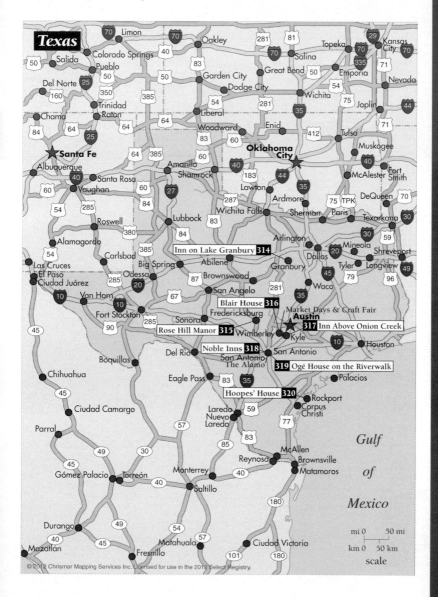

Inn on Lake Granbury

www.innonlakegranbury.com
205 West Doyle Street, Granbury, TX 76048
877-573-0046 • 817-573-0046
info@innonlakegranbury.com

Member Since 2006

Texas Granbury

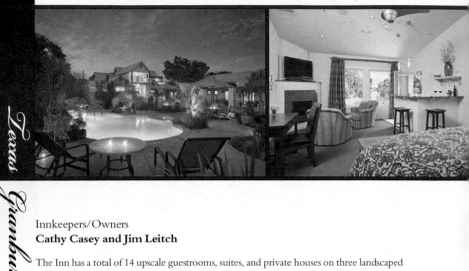

Innkeepers/Owners
Cathy Casey and Jim Leitch

The Inn has a total of 14 upscale guestrooms, suites, and private houses on three landscaped acres directly on beautiful Lake Granbury. Each luxurious room, suite or house has an oversized king or queen bed, fabulous guest robes, private showers (some with steam showers and heated bathroom floors), some with jetted tubs, some with lake views, and all with wireless Internet access. Our newest addition to the Inn is a wonderfully spacious lake house in the southwest corner of the property with floor to ceiling glass doors and windows overlooking the lake. Experience our flagstone encased saltwater pool with tanning ledge and waterfall or sit on the swing under 200 year old oak trees for a spectacular view of the lake. Walk less than three blocks to the historic square for shopping and fine dining. Complimentary appetizers and beverages are served every afternoon along with a full breakfast each morning.

Rates
$215/$295 per night Sunday-Thursday and $235/$345 per night Friday and Saturday. Group rates available for corporate/business retreats. Wedding package pricing also available upon request. Number of Rooms: 14

Cuisine
Rates include a full gourmet breakfast and appetizers and complimentary beverages including wine each afternoon. Lunch and dinner for group stays upon request.

Nearest Airport
Dallas Fort Worth Airport

Rose Hill Manor

www.rose-hill.com
2614 Upper Albert Road, Near Fredericksburg, TX 78671
877-767-3445 • 830-644-2247
rosehill@ktc.com

Member Since 2006

Innkeepers/Owners
Robert & Patricia VanderLyn

Rose Hill Manor is the only place in Texas where you can stay at a AAA Four Diamond inn with a fine dining restaurant and walk to a winery and tasting room. Our graciously appointed and spacious accommodations offer all the amenities required by the Four Diamond standard. Enjoy the celebrated cuisine of the on-site gourmet restaurant, where great meals are creatively prepared and wines are poured from a thoughtfully chosen cellar highlighted by fine vintages from around the world and premium liquor. Nestled in the heart of the Texas wine country, Rose Hill is located only fifteen minutes from the historical town of Fredericksburg, Texas and serves as an excellent base for exploring the region's best wineries, historical architecture, shopping and museums. Rose Hill has received critical acclaim for both the lodging and restaurant in Gourmet Magazine, Wine Spectator, Victoria Magazine, The Dallas Morning News, and Texas Highways. Come escape to an oasis of tranquility, Texas hill country style!

Rates
1 Queen Suite, $155/$249. 3 King Suites, $155/$249. 8 King Cottages, $155/$249.
Number of Rooms: 12

Cuisine
Complimentary multiple-course breakfast to overnite guests at private tables. On-Site upscale gourmet restaurant with outstanding wine list, each Wednesday through Sunday night - open to both our guests and the general public.

Nearest Airport
Either the San Antonio or Austin airport ~ 1 hour away. Airport for small planes in Fredericksburg - 15 minutes.

Texas

Near Fredericksburg

Blair House Inn

www.blairhouseinn.com
100 W. Spoke Hill Drive, Wimberley, TX 78676
877-549-5450 • 512-847-1111
info@blairhouseinn.com

Member Since 1998

Texas

Wimberley

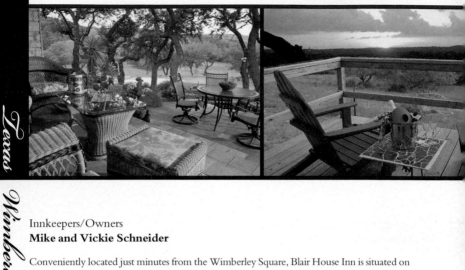

Innkeepers/Owners
Mike and Vickie Schneider

Conveniently located just minutes from the Wimberley Square, Blair House Inn is situated on 22 peaceful acres featuring breathtaking hill country vistas. Meticulous service, warm hospitality, delectable food and luxury amenities provide the ultimate in comfort. This inviting inn is light and airy and features one of the best art galleries in Wimberley. A pool and whirlpool spa set in the hillside allows for spectacular views while relaxing. Blair House also provides spacious and attractive common areas including a living room with a fireplace, a television/game room, a library, plus a front porch with beautiful sunset views and a patio by the herb garden. Guests can enjoy a massage, use the sauna, hike the grounds, venture out on one of the bicycles or just nap in a hammock. Rated third nationwide as "Best Evening Cuisine" and "Best B&B for Relaxing and Unwinding," by Inn Traveler™ Magazine and the "Best Breakfast in Texas" - Southern Living™.

Rates
3 Rooms, Main House, $150/$170. 5 Suites, $215/$248. 4 Individual Cottages, $289/$345. Open year-round. Number of Rooms: 12

Cuisine
Full 3-course gourmet breakfast, evening dessert, 5-course fixed menu gourmet dinner on Saturday evenings. Complimentary beverages.

Nearest Airport
Austin/San Antonio

SelectRegistry.com

Inn Above Onion Creek

www.innaboveonioncreek.com
4444 W FM 150, Kyle, TX 78640
800-579-7686 • 512-268-1617 • Fax 512-268-1090
info@innaboveonioncreek.com

Member Since 2003

Innkeeper **Amy Dolan**
Owners **John and Janie Orr**

Tucked away on 100 acres at the end of our mile-long driveway, the Inn Above Onion Creek awaits you with 15-mile hill country views. While you may feel a million miles away from everything, the Inn is conveniently located near great wineries on the Texas Wine Trail, excellent shopping, and many popular hill country attractions. Each night's stay includes a three-course dinner and full hot breakfast, fresh flowers in your room from our garden and all the homemade cookies you can eat! Each of the twelve rooms features classic antique pieces, luxurious linens, fireplace, wireless internet, flat panel television and DVD player. Relaxing by the pool, sitting on a porch to read your favorite book, or taking a hike on our miles of hiking trails are appealing ways to enjoy a day at the Inn. Our Spa offers relaxing massages, body and skin treatments for those looking for a more pampering stay. Come see why the Inn Above Onion Creek has 100's of glowing reviews. We're destined to become your favorite getaway.

Rates
12 rooms, incl. 3 suites, 2 cottages: $199/$499. Rates include Dinner and Breakfast with each night's stay. Each room has fireplace & porch, 6 with whirlpool tub. Special discounted rates for small meetings and retreats. Number of Rooms: 12

Cuisine
3-course dinner served at 6:00 each evening. Full hot breakfast with freshly squeezed orange juice served from 8:30-10:00 each morning. Dinner and Breakfast with each night's stay. Complimentary coffee, tea, cold drinks, and homemade cookies always!

Nearest Airport
Austin Bergstrom

Noble Inns

www.nobleinns.com
107 Madison Street, San Antonio, TX 78204
800-242-2770 • 210-223-2353 • Fax 210-226-5812
stay@nobleinns.com

Member Since 2001

Texas

San Antonio

Owners
Don & Liesl Noble

Don and Liesl Noble, sixth-generation San Antonians, invite guests to experience the rich history and ambiance of San Antonio. Noble Inns comprise The Jackson House (JH) and Aaron Pancoast Carriage House (PCH), two 1890s-era historic landmarks, located four houses apart in the King William Historic District. Both provide Victorian elegance with modern luxuries and superior amenities for the discerning business or leisure traveler, and are just off the Riverwalk near all downtown sites, including the Alamo, convention center and Alamodome. All rooms include private marble bath, gas fireplace with antique mantel, antique furnishings and elegant fabrics, complimentary high-speed internet (wired and/or wireless), color cable TV, private phone w/voice mail, custom guest robes, and central air conditioning. Gardens feature two pools and heated spa. Two-person whirlpool tub in bath, canopy bed, DVD player w/ complimentary DVD library are available in certain suites and rooms. Complete your experience by booking transportation in our classic 1960 Rolls Royce Silver Cloud II.

Rates
7 Rooms, $179/$269; 2 Suites, $239/$299. Inquire about special group and corporate rates, discounts, and last minute specials. Number of Rooms: 9

Cuisine
The Jackson House features a delicious full breakfast, afternoon refreshments, evening sherry and port. Aaron Pancoast Carriage House features full breakfast for adult groups at the Oge House and expanded continental breakfast for groups w/children.

Nearest Airport
San Antonio International - 9 mi./13 min. via expressway to downtown.

SelectRegistry.com

The Ogé Inn on the Riverwalk

www.nobleinns.com
209 Washington St, San Antonio, TX 78204
800-242-2770 • 210-223-2353 • Fax 210-226-5812
stay@nobleinns.com

Member Since 1994

Owners
Don & Liesl Noble

Boasting 1.5 landscaped acres directly on the famous RiverWalk in the King William Historic District, this 1857 Antebellum Mansion is one of Texas' historic architectural gems. With its grand verandas and spacious rooms, it is known for its elegance, quiet comfort and luxury. Furnished in European and American antiques, all rooms have been recently redecorated and feature a king or queen bed w/down featherbed, private bath w/tub and shower, flat-panel TV w/cable and DVD player, DVD library access, phone, custom robes and guest refrigerator. Delicious full breakfast served at private tables in the dining room or on front veranda. Most rooms have fireplace and/or porch. All suites feature luxurious granite baths with double Jacuzzi tub and separate shower, multi-room stereo system w/CD player, fireplace and porch (one w/private Riverwalk balcony). Conveniently located downtown near the Alamo, convention center, Alamodome, shopping, dining and entertainment. Amenities for business travelers include complimentary high-speed Internet, in-room desk, and flexible breakfast options

Rates
7 Rooms and 3 Suites on 3 floors, $229/$449. Inquire about special corporate and group rates, as well as specials and last minute discounts. San Antonio's only 4 diamond inn. Number of Rooms: 10

Cuisine
Delicious full breakfast, afternoon refreshments including home-made cookies, evening sherry and port.

Nearest Airport
San Antonio International - 9 mi./13 min. via expressway to downtown.

Hoopes' House

www.hoopeshouse.com
417 N. Broadway, Rockport, TX 78382
800-924-1008 • Fax 361-790-9288
hoopeshouse@sbcglobal.net

Member Since 2010

General Manager
Paula Sargent

Built in the 1890's, the historic Hoopes' House in Rockport, Texas has been meticulously renovated and restored to its original splendor. The sunny yellow inn commands a panoramic view of Rockport Harbor and is within walking distance of museums, shops, galleries and restaurants. The main house consists of four charming guest rooms, each with a private bath. For those wanting a more private experience, a new wing houses four additional guest rooms, each beautifully appointed. The grounds feature a pool, a hot tub and a gazebo. Elegant but casual, the Hoopes' House combines modern luxury with old world charm. Hardwood floors, 12 foot ceilings, intricately carved fireplaces, crown molding, fine art and antiques recall another time... another era. Relax with a good book in the parlor. Enjoy the Gulf breeze under the gazebo. Linger over morning coffee in the sun-room. Listen to the call of the gulls on the porch. Delight in the pleasures of a slower time.

Rates
Range from $110.00 to $175.00 per night. Check web site for each room rate, full facility available for $1,400/night. Closed Christmas week. No pets allowed. Children 12 years and older. Number of Rooms: 8

Cuisine
Breakfast is served each morning from 9 am to 10 am in either the formal dining room, gazebo or sun-room. Breakfast fare includes pineapple casserole, fresh fruit, blueberry pancakes and cream cheese bread pudding for starters.

Nearest Airport
Located 35 miles north of Corpus Christi

Vermont

"The Green Mountain State"

Famous for: Maple Syrup, Dairies, Lakes, Forests, Mountains, and Skiing.

Forty Putney Road Bed & Breakfast

www.fortyputneyroad.com
192 Putney Rd, Brattleboro, VT 05301
802-254-6268 • 800-941-2413
innkeepers@fortyputneyroad.com

Member Since 2011

Vermont

Brattleboro

Innkeepers/Owners
Tim & Amy Brady

A comfortable yet elegant 6 room inn, overlooking the water and yet just a short walk to vibrant downtown Brattleboro, Vermont filled with shops, cafes, galleries, restaurants and pubs. We are not your typical B&B. We have a small pub on site with over 30 local craft beers. Every Saturday night our guests can enjoy a fun and informative craft beer tasting including a selection of locally made craft brews and cheeses while learning about the brewing process and beer styles. Every morning we serve a full 2 course gourmet breakfast made with fresh and local ingredients. Relax in the hot tub, or play a game of pool by the fire. Every room has its own private bathroom. Several rooms have fireplaces and private entrances. Of course we have free WiFi, every room has a flat panel TV, DVD player, complimentary snacks and beverages all day and so much more.

Rates
Rates range from around $159 to $299, depending on the particular room and time of year. We occasionally offer specials and last minute deals, so be sure to connect with us on facebook.com/vermontinn or call for more details. Number of Rooms: 6

Cuisine
All of our rates include a Full Two Course Gourmet Breakfast served daily anytime from 8 - 9:30am. From baked blueberry french toast to bacon wrapped asparagus to fresh vegetable frittata... Every day is different and delicious.

Nearest Airport
Bradley International Airport - Hartford / Springfield (BDL)

Rabbit Hill Inn

www.rabbithillinn.com
48 Lower Waterford Road, PO Box 55, Lower Waterford, VT 05848
800-76-BUNNY • 802-748-5168 • Fax 802-748-8342
info@rabbithillinn.com

Member Since 1990

Vermont

Lower Waterford

Innkeepers/Owners
Brian & Leslie Mulcahy

Even in these fast-paced, continuously connected times, there are still a few places in the world where one can escape to unwind and spend some "adult-only" time with that special someone. Named One of the World's Top 100 Hotels by Travel+Leisure Magazine, Rabbit Hill Inn offers all the luxuries that one would come to expect - fireplaces, double spa tubs, fine bath amenities, and more; yet what sets Rabbit Hill apart from just any nice place to stay is the warmth, comfort, and personal caring provided by its long-time hands-on innkeepers and wonderful staff. Dining at the Inn is truly outstanding. Sophisticated, locally sourced food at an intimate, candlelit table adds to a most romantic evening - comfortable and always unpretentious. A myriad of seasonal activities — everything from adrenaline pumping adventurous pursuits to relaxing in-room massage is available year-'round. Zagat Guide said it best: "...this just might be the most romantic place on the planet...!" Free wifi available; non-smoking.

Rates
Including breakfast, afternoon tea, turndown service, and gratuity for staff - Classic: $199/$239 peak; Superior w/fireplace: $259/$299 peak; Luxury w/whirlpool & fireplace: $335/$399 peak. Number of Rooms: 19

Cuisine
Full country breakfast and afternoon tea and pastries included. Dinner features a frequently changing, multi-course, modern and innovative menu. Beer, wine, and spirits available in our Snooty Fox Pub.

Nearest Airport
Manchester, NH (MHT)-2 hours; Burlington, VT (BTV)-2 hours; Logan Int'l (BOS)-3 hrs.

The Inn at Weston

www.innweston.com
630 Main St, PO Box 66, Weston, VT 05161
802-824-6789
theinnatweston@comcast.net

Member Since 2012

Vermont Weston

Wine Spectator

AWARD OF EXCELLENCE

Innkeepers
Robert & Linda Aldrich

Escape to the heart of the Green Mountains where warmth and hospitality greet you at the door! The Inn at Weston is located in the quintessential Southern Vermont Village of Weston. Relax and unwind in one of our 13 graciously appointed guestrooms-some with whirlpools for two and walk-in sauna/steam showers. Several have their own deck, almost all have fireplaces and all have private bath. Stroll to the town green with gazebo, shops, galleries and museum. Sit by the waterfall of the Old Mill, attend services at the Weston priory or visit our two clapboard New England churches. Visit during Winter and ski one of four local mountains-Magic, Stratton, Bromley and Okemo. All winter sports are nearby. In summer, take in a performance at the award winning Weston Playhouse Theater, bike, hike and picnic in the beautiful Green Mountains. Have a superb dinner in our casually elegant dining room or on our orchid filled deck and gazebo and ask George to play your favorite melody on our grand piano. Tour our onsite orchid greenhouse. We look forward to greeting you!

Rates
Traditional rooms-$185-$205. Luxury rooms-$225-$325. $50 more per night during holidays and foliage. 2 night minimum some weekends. Seasonal packages and specials online. Number of Rooms: 13

Cuisine
Full country breakfast and afternoon tea with home made pastry included. Dinner is Vermont contemporary cuisine using local ingredients. Wine Spectator awarded wine cellar. Large Oregon Pinot Noir selection. Cozy pub with wood burning fireplace.

Nearest Airport
Albany, New York-1.5 hours. Hartford, Ct-2 hours. Boston, Ma-3 hours.

SelectRegistry.com

The Inn at Round Barn Farm

🍽 ♀

www.theroundbarn.com
1661 East Warren Road, Waitsfield, VT 05673
802-496-2276 • Fax 802-496-2276
lodging@theroundbarn.com

Member Since 2000

Vermont

Waitsfield

Innkeepers/Owners
AnneMarie DeFreest & Tim L. Piper

We invite you to our elegant, romantic Bed & Breakfast Inn, located amidst 245 acres of lush green hills, flower-covered meadows, graceful ponds, and extensive perennial gardens in Vermont's Green Mountains. This four season retreat in the Sugarbush/Mad River Valley has offered an escape for lovers of the arts, history, and the outdoors since 1987. The interior of the Inn is memorable; the restoration impeccable. The Inn offers wireless throughout. The Inn's 12 guest rooms are individually decorated while maintaining refurbished wide-board pine floors covered in oriental rugs, beautiful wallpapers in a palette of rich tones, decorative accents and attention to the details that matter. In winter, our meadows and woodlands are covered in a blanket of snow. Snowshoe trails and snowshoes are available for our guests to experience the magic of our Vermont winter wonderland. In the summer enjoy concerts, theater, our very own three week opera festival in June and a variety of outdoor activities. Our Innkeepers (and freshly baked cookies) await your arrival at the Inn.

Rates
Rates $175/$335. Tempur-Pedic beds, down comforters, whirlpool tubs, steam showers, green products, gas fireplaces, individual heat and A/C. Number of Rooms: 12

Cuisine
As founding members of the Vermont Fresh Network and having our own certified organic garden, our breakfasts and hors d'oeuvres are prepared with seasonal/local ingredients. Dinner is enjoyed at one of 15 area restaurants.

Nearest Airport
43 Minutes from the Burlington International Airport (BTV)

🍽 🍽 ♀

Swift House Inn

www.swifthouseinn.com
25 Stewart Lane, Middlebury, VT 05753
866-388-9925 • 802-388-9925 • Fax 802-388-9927
info@swifthouseinn.com

Member Since 2005

Vermont

Middlebury

Innkeepers/Owners
Dan & Michele Brown

A historic 20-room former governor's mansion, the Swift House Inn is Middlebury's only in-town Country Inn, and offers the essence of New England warmth. Large, comfortable rooms provide modern amenities in period decor. The Inn's three buildings are on four acres with extensive lawns and gardens. Enjoy a casual dinner in the bar, on the deck, or in Jessica's Restaurant. Relax, sip a glass of wine by the fireplace, or ponder your favorite book. Every window frames a picture of country tranquility, yet shops, museums, and Middlebury College are a short walk away. The Town Hall Theater and College bring numerous world class performing artists to the area with performances most weekends. Enjoy hiking the Trail Around Middlebury or in the nearby Green Mountains. Bike the Champlain Valley, fly fish our numerous rivers and creeks, or participate in water activities on nearby lakes Champlain and Dunmore. Downhill and cross country ski areas are just a short drive. Bring your bike, golf clubs, fly rod or just come to relax. After a busy day enjoy the sauna or steam shower.

Rates
20 Rooms in three buildings. Main House $129-$199, Gate House $129-$169, Carriage House $229-$299, rates vary by season. Many rooms with fireplaces and whirlpool tubs. All rooms have individual heat and A/C controls, satellite TV Number of Rooms: 20

Cuisine
Full Breakfast from 7:30 to 9:30. Dinner in Jessica's is served 4 nights a week winter/spring and 5 nights summer/fall; changing menu prepared with many local Vermont products. Full bar service and extensive wine list, Wine Spectator Award

Nearest Airport
Burlington International Airport, 35 miles Albany Airport 112 miles

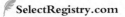
SelectRegistry.com

West Hill House Bed & Breakfast

🍽️

www.westhillbb.com
1496 West Hill Road, Warren, VT 05674
802-496-7162
innkeepers@westhillbb.com

Member Since 2009

Vermont

Warren

Innkeepers/Owners
Peter & Susan MacLaren

Nestled in the serene setting of the Green Mountains, this beautiful 1850s home on a quiet country road is surrounded by gorgeous perennial gardens and offers a peaceful retreat from the rush of everyday life at any time of year. The B&B is located beside Sugarbush's ski resort and its Robert Trent Jones, Sr. championship golf course, 7 miles from the Mad River Glen ski area, and the Catamount Ski Trail crosses our property. Also for the warmer months we are perfectly located for hiking the Long Trail, kayaking, biking and many other summer activities. Year round you will enjoy the many attractions and activities of central Vermont. Just minutes away, the shops, artisans and marvelous restaurants of Warren and Waitsfield await you. Our classic Vermont B&B offers comfort, hospitality and delicious breakfasts. The guest rooms have gas fireplaces, A/C, free phone calls and WiFi. The well-appointed ensuite bathrooms all feature Jacuzzis and/or steam showers. An ideal spot for elopements, weddings up to 80 guests, business retreats, and most especially a place to come and relax.

Rates
Open year round. $140-$265 per night double occupancy including breakfast. Taxes and fees add 13%. Each room or suite has a king or queen bed and each ensuite has either a Jacuzzi tub, steam shower or both. Number of Rooms: 9

Cuisine
Our sumptuous breakfast starts with fruit juice, home made bread or muffins & a fruit dish. A tantalizing hot entree gives your taste buds a morning treat. Hot beverages, home-made cookies and honor bar are always available. Single Malt bar in evening.

Nearest Airport
Burlington International (BTV) is a beautiful 45 mile drive from the B&B.

The Maple Leaf Inn

www.mapleleafinn.com
PO Box 273, 5890 Vermont Route 12, Barnard, VT 05031
800-516-2753 • 802-234-5342 • Fax 802-234-6456
innkeeper@mapleleafinn.com

Member Since 2002

Vermont

Barnard

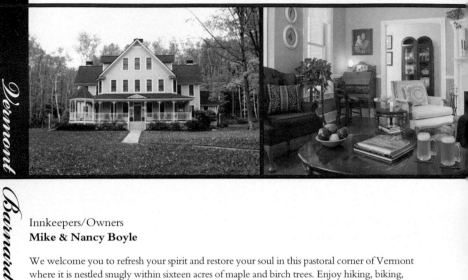

Innkeepers/Owners
Mike & Nancy Boyle

We welcome you to refresh your spirit and restore your soul in this pastoral corner of Vermont where it is nestled snugly within sixteen acres of maple and birch trees. Enjoy hiking, biking, golfing, cross-country skiing, and snow-shoeing on the trails nearby, or go fishing, canoeing and kayaking at nearby Silver Lake. Fantastic restaurants are a short drive away. Each luxurious, light-filled guest room has its own personality and charm with crisp linens, comfy duvets and handmade quilts. Individually controlled central heating/air-conditioning, heated bathroom tile floors and a pillow library all add to your personal comfort. Wood-burning fireplaces are set daily for your convenience and a collection of romantic videos awaits your viewing. Snacks, sodas, coffee, tea and bottled water are available at any time. Complementary wine and beer are served every day. Memorable gourmet breakfasts are prepared fresh each morning and served at candlelit tables for two.

Rates
$150/$290 B&B. Spacious guest rooms with king beds, luxurious private baths w/ whirlpools, WIFI. Number of Rooms: 7

Cuisine
A gourmet three-course breakfast is served at candlelit tables. Light afternoon refreshments are served in the parlor at check-in. Complimentary coffee, tea, sodas and snacks available. Dinners available upon request. Beer & wine available for sale.

Nearest Airport
Burlington, VT; Manchester, NH; Boston, MA

Fox Creek Inn

www.foxcreekinn.com
49 Dam Road, Chittenden, VT 05737
800-707-0017 • 802-483-6213 • Fax 802-483-2623
innkeeper@foxcreekinn.com

Member Since 1998

Innkeepers/Owners
Jim and Sandy Robertson

Just the way you have always pictured a Country Inn. Here is the Vermont you have been searching for. There are a myriad of activities: hiking, biking and water sports in summer and downhill alpine and cross country skiing in winter. Relax in front of one of our fireplaces or sit on the front porch with a glass of wine listening to the sounds of the creek; these are the times when memories are made. Once the home of William Barstow, you can easily imagine the family entertaining their friends, the Fords, Firestones, and his partner, Thomas Edison. We strive to keep the tradition of entertaining alive. Fox Creek is an Inn full of charm and casual elegance and with a gentle pace that permits you to relax and enjoy the moment. Complimentary coffee, tea and soft drinks are always available.

Rates
All rooms with private baths most with fireplaces & spa tubs. Rooms are double or single occupancy, our suite sleeps 3. Inn is not appropriate for young children. Room 8 is pet friendly. Rates: $175-$285 B&B $215-$325 high season. Number of Rooms: 8

Cuisine
A gourmet breakfast is served every morning using fresh and local ingredients. A four course dinner, table d'hote is available by advance reservation, Select a wine from our wine cellar and enjoy our quaint pub that features single malt scotch.

Nearest Airport
Rutland Regional Airport with shuttle service from/to Boston; Burlington,VT. Manchester, NH. Albany, NY

Crisanver House

www.crisanver.com
1434 Crown Point Road, Shrewsbury, VT 05738
800-492-8089 • 802-492-3589 • Fax 802-492-3480
Member Since 2005
info@crisanver.com

Vermont

Shrewsbury

Innkeepers/Owners
B. Michael & Carol Calotta

"This grand country retreat, in south central Vermont on 120 acres away from the everyday hubbub, has a natural charm. Discriminating guests escape to relax, enjoy fine dining and breathtaking fresh air and mountain high views that wow the senses for an enhanced special experience. Our high quality boutique inn is completely renovated and painstakingly appointed in upscale chic, for a perfect destination with its eclectic mix of classic linens, down duvets, oriental rugs, original artworks accentuated by our recent conservatory with a surrounding porch. A wood burning fireplaced living room is graced by a baby grand piano. Lovely gardens, bucolic meadows and woodlands allow guests to walk trails without leaving the property complimented by a 20x40 pool and teahouse, tennis, shuffleboard, pond, bocce and snowshoeing. Excellent shopping, museums, theater, abundant golf, microbreweries and artisan cheese makers are nearby. Bed & Breakfast Diamond Collection, Listed "1,000 places to see in US and Canada" Trip Advisor Certificate of Excellence

Rates
4 Deluxe Rooms Main House $145-$265, 2 Suites Main House $245-$395, 3 Cottage Deluxe Rooms $205-$375. Number of Rooms: 9

Cuisine
Epicurean dining featuring the freshest of local offerings and our garden harvest. Complimentary served full country breakfast. Afternoon tea. Prix fixe candlelight dinner by reservation. Fine European wines. Many restaurants nearby.

Nearest Airport
Rutland Regional - 10 minutes; Albany, Hartford, Burlington International - each 2 hours

Stone Hill Inn

www.stonehillinn.com
89 Houston Farm Road, Stowe, VT 05672
802-253-6282 • Fax 802-253-7415
stay@stonehillinn.com

Member Since 2002

Owners/Innkeepers
Linda and George Fulton

Relax. Quiet, secluded, and barely visible fifty feet above the Mountain Road. Surrounded by woods on 9.5 acres; feels like an island of calm. Here luxury is defined by both the thoughtfulness of your accommodations and opportunities for intimacy — intimacy of life and love. Shhhh. You are in the presence of timelessness. Yet, Stowe, its restaurants, fly fishing among five local streams, spectacular hiking, stand-up paddleboarding, kayaking, canoeing, vista-laden golf and the best skiing in New England are just minutes away. Feel your shoulders unfold as you sink into your bubbling, fireside Jacuzzi for two–every room has one. Fall asleep in your king-size bed warmed by your fireplace and accompanied by a movie from our 200+ collection. (Free popcorn!) Ahhhh. Your massages are an hour from now in your room. No wonder we received a perfect score in Select Registry's inspection, or that we received Trip Advisor s 2012 Traveler s Choice award as one of the top 25 inns/B&B s in all of the US!

Rates
$299-$400 (varies by season). Visit Stone Hill Inn.com for exact seasonal rates and seasonal packages. Number of Rooms: 9

Cuisine
Like the powdered sugar on your orange-pecan waffle, sun dabbles the two of you during your three-course breakfast within a cathedral of 40 windows. Nine rooms; nine tables. Hors d'oeuvres at the 5:30 PM social hour. Water, coffee, tea and sodas are complimentary.

Nearest Airport
Burlington, VT (45 min). Morrisville (10 min) has a small airport for private aircraft.

The Inn at Ormsby Hill

www.ormsbyhill.com
1842 Main Street, Historic Route 7A, Manchester , VT 05255
802-362-1163 • 800-670-2841 • Fax 802-362-5176
Member Since 1996 stay@ormsbyhill.com

Vermont

Manchester

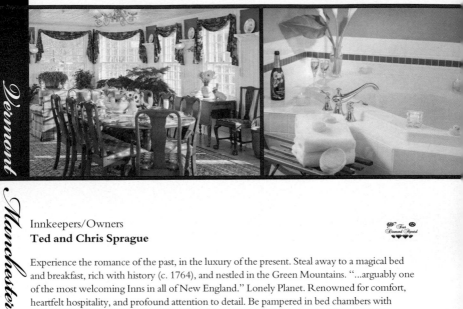

Innkeepers/Owners
Ted and Chris Sprague

Experience the romance of the past, in the luxury of the present. Steal away to a magical bed and breakfast, rich with history (c. 1764), and nestled in the Green Mountains. "...arguably one of the most welcoming Inns in all of New England." Lonely Planet. Renowned for comfort, heartfelt hospitality, and profound attention to detail. Be pampered in bed chambers with canopies, fireplaces, air-conditioning, digital flat-screen televisions, and endless amenities. Luxurious bathrooms with Jacuzzis for two; some with two-person steam saunas and views of the fireplace. "...the elegance of the bed chambers and public rooms is matched by the sumptuousness of the Inn's breakfast offerings." Three times an Editors' Pick – Yankee Magazine. If our lavish rooms and nationally-acclaimed breakfasts aren't enough to take your breath away, our spectacular views of the Taconic and Green Mountains will. Proud recipients of the AAA Four Diamond Award for the past thirteen years - a Manchester Inn exclusive. One enchanting evening with us and you'll understand why.

Rates
8 Rooms and 2 suites, all with fireplace and Jacuzzi for two, $205/$425 B&B. Open year-round. Number of Rooms: 10

Cuisine
"Expect truly memorable and bountiful breakfasts!" - Andrew Harper's Hideaway Report.
"...a breakfast that'll knock your socks off..." - Yankee Magazine's Travel Guide.
"...perhaps the best breakfasts in Vermont," says New England Travel.

Nearest Airport
Albany, New York (1 hour 15 minutes). Hartford, Connecticut (2 hours 15 minutes).

SelectRegistry.com

The Inn at Manchester

www.innatmanchester.com

3967 Main Street, P.O. Box 41, Manchester , VT 05254

802-362-1793 • 800-273-1793 • Fax 802-362-3218

innkeepers@innatmanchester.com

Member Since 2008

Innkeepers/Owners
Frank & Julie Hanes

Unforgettable personality and unlimited possibilities await you at one of Vermont's most inviting getaways, The Inn at Manchester. Tucked away in the breathtaking landscape of the Taconic and Green Mountains in Vermont's cultural haven, Manchester - where there's something for everyone year round. Golf, skiing, hiking, fishing, shopping, theatre or art, Manchester and the Mountains has something for every taste. As always, there is no rule you ever have to leave the Inn! Unwind beside the hearth in the living room, or over a game of chess in the cozy den. Maybe take a stroll around our beautiful grounds, a dip in the pool, or just relax in a rocker on the porch. Then drop in for a cocktail in the Nineteenth Room, our fully licensed pub - one of the places where guests gather to relax and socialize. We look forward to welcoming you to the Inn at Manchester, a Gem in the Green Mountains.

Rates
Our rates run from $155 to $295. Number of Rooms: 18

Cuisine
We pride ourselves on a full traditional breakfast that is guaranteed to start your day off in the right way! Try our famous cottage cakes with hot apricot sauce or a savory omelet. Also, sneak into our guest pantry and help yourself to refreshments.

Nearest Airport
Albany, New York (Approximate time: 1 1/2 hours)

West Mountain Inn

www.WestMountainInn.com
144 West Mountain Inn Road, Arlington, VT 05250
802-375-6516 • Fax 802-375-6553
info@WestMountainInn.com

Member Since 1984

Vermont

Arlington

Innkeepers/Owners
The Carlson Family

A Vermont country retreat you can call your own! Luxurious rooms, splendid meals, refreshing outdoor pursuits, relaxing afternoons and convivial evenings - that is what a visit to the West Mountain Inn is. Set high on a mountainside overlooking the historic village of Arlington and Green Mountains beyond, the century-old West Mountain Inn has welcomed guests for over thirty years. Visitors to the Inn are surrounded by fantastic views & 150 acres of gardens, lawns, woodlands and meadows. Without having to leave the Inn's property, guests can hike or snowshoe on miles of trails, flyfish, swim or canoe in the famous Battenkill River and relax in the Adirondack chairs on the front lawn. The Inn's wood-paneled dining room provides a perfect setting for the lavish country breakfasts and sumptuous 5-course dinners created daily by our award-winning chef. The Inn also offers private dining rooms & a wonderful antique barn for the unique celebration of weddings, birthdays, anniversaries, reunions or business retreats. Mobil ☆☆☆, Fodor's "Choice," Frommers "Highly Recommended".

Rates
12 Rooms, 3 Suites, 3 Townhouses $155/$340 B&B, $255/$420 MAP. Service charges included in all rates. Number of Rooms: 20

Cuisine
A lavish country breakfast and splendid 5-course dinner are prepared daily. Seasonal menus focus on local VT products and organic produce. Weddings and rehearsal dinners a specialty. Full bar, premium beers and exceptional wine list.

Nearest Airport
Albany, NY - 1 Hour. Hartford, CT/Manchester, NH/Burlington, VT - all 2 1/2 hours.

F SelectRegistry.com

Four Columns Inn

www.fourcolumnsinn.com
P.O. Box 278, 21 West Street, Newfane, VT 05345
800-787-6633 • 802-365-7713 • Fax 802-365-0022
innkeeper@fourcolumnsinn.com

Member Since 2000

Vermont
Newfane

Innkeepers/Owners
Bruce & Debbie Pfander

The Four Columns Inn was lovingly built in 1832 by Pardon Kimball to replicate the childhood home of his southern wife. Today that home is an elegant country inn with 15 delightfully refurbished guest rooms, each featuring a queen or king-sized bed, private bath, individual heat-a/c, period antiques, high-speed wireless internet, complimentary phones, and afternoon treats. Gas fireplaces are the focal point in 11 rooms, and the deluxe, grand, and luxury rooms deliver extra large bathrooms with spa tubs and separate showers. Select rooms also offer TV/DVD players plus a huge library of complimentary dvd's. A hearty country breakfast is included for all house guests. Evening dining by reservation. Situated on the historic Newfane Village Green, unchanged since the 1830s, the property includes an inviting stream, ponds and exquisite gardens, all nestled at the base of its own private mountain. Guests enjoy a lovely outdoor pool, or nearby hiking, biking, horseback riding in summer, plus world-class skiing, snowshoeing, or snowmobiling in winter...all only a short drive away.

Rates
$195-375 sgl or dbl; $220-400 Holidays/Foliage; +9% Vt tax. 2 night minimum stay weekends, holidays, foliage. All rates per night with full breakfast included. Seasonal specials & packages available online. www.fourcolumnsinn.com Number of Rooms: 15

Cuisine
Named in Boson Magazine's "Top 20 Destination Restaurants in New England" (April 2011), Chef Greg Parks and team deliver on their well-earned reputation for creative regional cuisine. Wood-burning fireplace in winter. Reservations. Full bar, wine list.

Nearest Airport
Bradley-Hartford CT, 1.5 hours Logan-Boston MA, 2.5 hours JFK-New York NY, 3.5-4 hours

Deerhill Inn

www.deerhill.com
14 Valley View Road, P.O. Box 136, West Dover, VT 05356
800-993-3379 • 802-464-3100 • Fax 802-464-5474
innkeeper@deerhill.com

Member Since 1999

Vermont

West Dover

Innkeepers/Owners
Ariane Burgess and Scott Kocher

On a peaceful hillside above the historic village of West Dover, Deerhill Inn looks across the beautiful Mount Snow Valley to Vermont's tranquil Green Mountains. It's a special place with a warm welcome where guests return again and again to relax deeply and reconnect. Beautifully decorated guest rooms feature jetted tubs, fireplaces and TV/DVD players; spacious decks and balconies have Mountain and garden views. A pretty pool nestles in the flower-filled gardens. Sitting and dining rooms are comfortable, elegant and welcoming with log fires in winter and wonderful views. All-seasons Southern Vermont offers hiking, biking, golfing, fishing, canoeing, kayaking and lake boating in the summer; skiing, snowboarding, snowshoeing, husky-mushing, snowmobiling and sleigh-rides in the winter – all within easy reach of the inn. With shopping and antiquing year-round, museums, historic houses, theaters, concerts and driving tours to Vermont's farms and villages, there is plenty to enjoy. Then come home to the inn for a deep and restful sleep under Vermont's starry skies.

Rates
$131-$293 (Spring) $145-$325 (Base) $145-$335 (Winter) $165-$355 (Foliage & Holidays). Value-add, celebration & holiday packages and seasonal offers - see our website www.deerhill.com. Number of Rooms: 13

Cuisine
Made-to-order country breakfast & afternoon tea. Delicious American Country Cuisine with fresh local ingredients & Wine Spectator-awarded wine list. Comfortable dining rooms with spectacular views of Vermont's Green Mountains and cozy full-service bar.

Nearest Airport
Albany, NY - 1.5 hours; Bradley Hartford, CT - 2 hours; Logan Boston, MA - 3 hours; JFK NYC, NY - 4 hours

Hermitage Inn

www.hermitageinn.com
25 Handle Road, PO Box 2210, West Dover, VT 05356
(877) 464-3511 • (802) 464-3511 • Fax 802-464-3575
info@hermitageinn.com

Vermont

West Dover

General Manager
Steven O'Hern

Welcome to an exquisite retreat where traditional Vermont hospitality meets 21st century luxury, both formal and casual. Upon arrival, guests enter an elegant 18th century Vermont farmhouse with soft music and lights, enchanting art at every turn, a warm fireplace, and an equally warm staff that addresses you by name. With the rustic delights of southern Vermont at your doorstep, you'll feel at home the way home should be. Spring, summer and fall activities include fly-fishing in our stocked trout pond, hiking and bicycling miles of trails through and beyond our own trails, and garden tours. Off-site activities include the Clay Shooting School, golf courses, and water activities. In winter, at the inn, our guests can enjoy cross-country skiing, snowshoeing, ice-skating, tubing, a sauna and hot tubs, and downhill skiing at Mount Snow. We also have a full fitness room, spa facilities, and a game room. We host special culinary events in our exhibition wine cellar. We warmly welcome you to enjoy the epitome of Vermont country luxury, a sublime escape from everyday life.

Rates
Superior: $195-$224 Deluxe: $224-$253 Queen: $253-$282 King: $282-$310 Carriage House: $310-$340 Number of Rooms: 19

Cuisine
The Hermitage is a culinary experience to relish, featuring fresh Vermont ingredients in innovative fare. Enjoy fine dining in our Main Dining Room or lite fare in our pub and tavern. Extensive wine list. Full Vermont breakfast included with your stay.

Nearest Airport
Albany, NY: 1 hour 45 minutes Hartford, CT: 2 hours

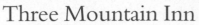

Three Mountain Inn

www.threemountaininn.com
3732 Main Street Route 30/100, P.O. Box 180, Jamaica, VT 05343
800-532-9399 • 802-874-4140
stay@threemtn.com

Member Since 1982

Vermont

Jamaica

Innkeepers/Owners
Ed & Jennifer Dorta-Duque

The Three Mountain Inn, located in the small, unspoiled village of Jamaica, Vermont is a perfect choice to spend a few days of rest and relaxation. Peacefully set among Vermont's Green Mountains, the Inn overlooks the woodlands and trails of the Jamaica State Park and is just minutes away from Stratton, Bromley and Magic Mountain Ski areas. Our individually decorated rooms feature luxurious linens, relaxing robes, period pieces, fabulous queen or king featherbeds, private baths, air conditioning and WiFi. Most have fireplaces while some have private decks, whirlpool tubs and TV/DVDs. With its wide-planked pine walls and multiple fireplaces, the Three Mountain Inn has an abundance of history and a sense of luxury. Whether you enjoy a romantic dinner in our Dining Room, relax by one of the many fireplaces, indulge in our incredible three-course breakfast, or explore the various outdoor possibilities; the Three Mountain Inn will revive your senses.

Rates
$199 to $360, Seasonal Packages available. Visit www.threemountainn.com. Number of Rooms: 10

Cuisine
Offering an elegant dining experience, showcasing contemporary Vermont Fresh Cuisine.

Nearest Airport
Hartford, CT (1.5 hours); Albany, NY (1.5 hours)

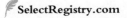

Virginia

"The Old Dominion"

Famous for: Blue Ridge Mountains, Mount Vernon, Monticello, Arlington National Cemetery, Skyline Drive, Manassas National Battlefield Park, Colonial Williamsburg, Jamestown Settlement, Virginia Beach, Yorktown, Chesapeake Bay.

Chestnut Hill Bed & Breakfast

www.chestnuthillbnb.com
236 Caroline Street, Orange, VA 22960
888-315-3511 • 540-661-0430 • Fax 540-661-4212
info@chestnuthillbnb.com

Member Since 2010

Virginia

Orange

Innkeeper/Owner
Kathleen Ayers

Built in 1860, the award-winning Chestnut Hill is located in the center of Virginia's wine country and has been skillfully renovated to preserve the master craftsmanship of this renowned historic home. As a result of the extensive six-year renovation combined with being professionally decorated, Chestnut Hill provides guests with an opportunity to appreciate the past while enjoying the luxuries and comforts of the present. Each room offers a private bath with hairdryers, quality toiletries, pillow-top beds dressed in triple-sheeted superior quality cotton linens, lush cozy spa robes, HD flat-screen televisions, and Wi-Fi Internet access. Two guestrooms, Alexander Daley's Master Suite and Ask Anna, feature hot tubs. Extra special touches may include fresh-cut flowers, bottled flat or sparkling water, and homemade tea-time treats & confections. Our savory fusion breakfast, evening wine & cheese tasting, all-day complimentary beverages, access to our outdoor cinema, and unparalleled customer service are always standard offerings during your stay at Chestnut Hill.

Rates
Six luxurious guest rooms with private baths. Fireplaces and hot tubs available. Prices include a full two-course gourmet breakfast served each morning and wine & cheese tasting each afternoon. Prices range from $179 - $295. Number of Rooms: 6

Cuisine
Our two-course fusion breakfast varies from sweet one day to savory the next, sometimes a combination of each. We are always prepared to accommodate special dietary needs. Join us for a glass of Virginia wine during our afternoon wine & cheese tasting.

Nearest Airport
Richmond International Airport, Washington Dulles Airport & Reagan National Airport.

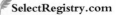 SelectRegistry.com

The Doctor's Inn Virginia

www.thedoctorsinnvirginia.com
406 W. Stuart Drive, Galax, VA 24333
276-238-9998 • 276-237-0144
stay@thedoctorsinnvirginia.com

Member Since 2012

Virginia Galax

Owner **Ron Stamey**
Innkeeper **Margo Crouse**

Listed on the National Register of Historic Places: the Doctor's Inn Virginia has achieved a Tripadvisor rating of 5 stars by its guests and therefore has been awarded a Certificate of Excellence for the Year of 2011. The Colonial Revival style house, built in 1913, is located in a small city of Galax, VA., and just 10 miles from I-77. We are within walking distance from downtown, the Rex Theater, Chestnut Creek School of the Arts, the New River Trail and Felts Park and only 7 miles from the beautiful Blue Ridge Parkway. Enjoy our elegant simple pleasures: Egyptian cotton lines, luxurious robes, widescreen TV, wireless Internet access, air conditioning, ceiling fans, queen and full rooms with cashmere blankets. Interesting artifacts from around the world mix with elegance from the past. We offer lots of books, periodicals, and various games. We provide snacks and beverages for the midnight munchies. Our warm hospitality and relaxing front porch brings our guests back for more. One visit at the inn and you appreciate the "Elegant Simplicity Prescribed by the Doctor"

Rates
In season, June - October $149 Off season, November - May $139 Check out our winter two night specials. Number of Rooms: 4

Cuisine
Gourmet breakfasts served on fine china and linens. Mouthwatering quiche, fruit smoothies, home made scones, made fresh each day and a perfect way to start your morning. Menu changes daily.

Nearest Airport
Greensboro, NC 1.5 hours

Inn at Onancock

www.innatonancock.com
30 North Street, Onancock, VA 23417
757-789-7711 • 866-792-7466 • Fax 757-789-7712
krisandlisa@innatonancock.com

Member Since 2012

Virginia

Onancock

Innkeepers/Owners
Lisa and Kris LaMontagne

The Inn at Onancock is located on Virginia's Eastern Shore just a few steps from the historic downtown and 3 blocks from the deep-water wharf. Enjoy our get-away-from-it-all style in laid back luxury. You may find it difficult to choose from among five spacious guest rooms, each with 10' ceilings and spa-style en suite baths, in settings inspired by favorite worldwide destinations. Antiques and oriental carpets were carefully selected to further create the ambience of these faraway places. You'll be comfortable in all seasons with gas fireplaces in some of the guest rooms and central air and ceiling fans throughout. Sleep in utmost comfort on feather-topped beds dressed with 1,000 thread count luxury linens. Melt away stress in two-person air jet tubs surrounded by spa décor. The experience is completed with fluffy white towels, towel warmers, cozy robes and luxury toiletries made especially for The Inn.

Rates
Rates vary by room and season. There is a multi-night discount for each night beyond a single night. A minimum stay of two nights is required for holidays and special events. Number of Rooms: 5

Cuisine
Breakfasts feature unique entrees, Lisa's famous granola, homemade breads and pastries, locally roasted private blend coffee and an assortment of yogurt, juices and teas. WineDown Hour offers select wines and distinctive hors d'oeuvres.

Nearest Airport
Salisbury Ocean City Wicomico Airport (SBY), Norfolk International (ORF)

SelectRegistry.com

Inn at Riverbend

www.innatriverbend.com
125 River Ridge Drive, Pearisburg, VA 24134-2391
540-921-5211 • Fax 540-921-2720
stay@innatriverbend.com

Member Since 2005

Virginia

Pearisburg

Innkeepers/Owners
Janet & Jimm Burton

Relax, refuel, refresh at Inn at Riverbend situated on 13 acres overlooking the New River, the oldest river in the United States. Built in 2003 and designed to provide panoramic views of the mountains and river from the Great room, TV room and each guestroom; spacious decks and terraces provide plenty of space to enjoy spectacular views, bird watch and even spot deer in the lower meadow. The distant sound of the train sets the tone for a restful sleep. Perfect for romantic getaways, outdoor enthusiasts, retreats & family gatherings, and small intimate weddings. All rooms feature private baths, Comphy microfiber sheets, robes, satellite TV, WiFi, DVD and CD Players w/MP3 connections & Lather amenities. Enjoy afternoon refreshments, freshly baked cookies, and a sumptuous breakfast each morning. 3-course dinners available on Mondays with 72 hour notice. We are located two miles from the Appalachian Trail. Let us help plan a guided wine tour, a hike, a trip down the river, or pack a picnic for the Cascades Waterfalls!

Rates
$185/$259. Two night min. for all weekends and holidays. Corp and military rate available. Number of Rooms: 7

Cuisine
3 course gourmet full plated breakfast included with Riverbend Blend roasted coffee, assorted Stash teas and juices. Complimentary 24 hour beverage bar. Monday dinner w/advance reservation.

Nearest Airport
Roanoke-ROA

Brierley Hill Bed & Breakfast

www.brierleyhill.com
985 Borden Road, Lexington, VA 24450
800-422-4925 • 540-464-8421 • Fax 540-464-8925

Member Since 2007

relax@brierleyhill.com

Innkeepers/Owners
Ken & Joyce Hawkins

Brierley Hill offers the best of both worlds...spectacular views of the Shenandoah Valley and Blue Ridge Mountains and only minutes from the center of historic downtown Lexington, Virginia. Our individually decorated rooms – named for the Pati Bannister print that graces each – feature private baths, fireplaces (gas or electric), 350+ count linens, TV/DVD combinations, wireless Internet access and CD / MP3 / radio alarm clocks. The suites additionally offer whirlpool tubs with bathrobes, refrigerators and separate sitting areas. Both the main house and Magnolias cottage feature central air conditioning / heat for our guests' comfort. The common area consists of two rooms where you can meet other guests or just curl up with a good book. These rooms have a television, snack area, 24-hour hot beverage machine, refrigerator and a guest computer with high-speed Internet access. Guests are welcome to stroll through the award-winning gardens and enjoy our panoramic views of the Shenandoah Valley.

Rates
$139 / $329 (Dec 1 - Mar 31), $189 / $379 (Apr 1 - Nov 30), open year round. Number of Rooms: 6

Cuisine
Full 3-course country breakfast, snacks available in common area. Excellent restaurants in downtown Lexington.

Nearest Airport
Roanoke (1 hr.)

SelectRegistry.com

Fort Lewis Lodge

www.fortlewislodge.com
603 Old Plantation Way, Millboro, VA 24460
540-925-2314 • Fax 540-925-2352
info@fortlewislodge.com

Member Since 1990

Virginia

Millboro

Innkeepers/Owners
John and Caryl Cowden

Centuries old, wonderfully wild, uncommonly comfortable. A country inn at the heart of a 3200-acre mountain estate. Outdoor activities abound with miles of river trout and bass fishing, swimming, extensive hiking trails, mountain biking, and magnificent vistas. Fort Lewis is a rare combination of unpretentious elegance and unique architecture offering a variety of lodging choices where every room has a view. Three "in the round" silo bedrooms, four hand-hewn log cabins with stone fireplaces, and Riverside House are perfect for a true country getaway. Evenings are highlighted by contemporary American-style cuisine served in the historic Lewis Gristmill. This is destination dining where the emphasis falls firmly on the cuisine - the kitchen never ceases to impress. Like most country inns, we trade in a change of pace, romance and exceptional fare. But over the years, we've come to understand that Fort Lewis has an asset that very few others have. Our wilderness - the mountains, forests, fields and streams and all the creatures that call this their home.

Rates
13 Rooms, $215/$230 MAP; 3 Family Suites, $230 MAP; 4 Log Cabins, $270/$310 MAP. The Modified American Plan allows you to be our guest for both a memorable dinner and breakfast the next morning. Open April-mid Nov. Number of Rooms: 20

Cuisine
Dinner and breakfast are included in the daily tariff. Evening meals offer a vibrant mix of fresh tastes, just plucked vegetables and interesting menus. The aroma of hickory smoke rising from the grills will leave you yearning to hear the dinner bell.

Nearest Airport
Roanoke, VA (1.5 hrs.); Charlottesville, VA (1.75 hrs.); Staunton, VA (1hr.); Hot Springs (1/2 hour)

Sugar Tree Inn

www.sugartreeinn.com
145 Lodge Trail, Vesuvius, VA 24483
800-377-2197 • 540-377-2197
innkeeper@sugartreeinn.com

Member Since 1998

Virginia

Desvvius

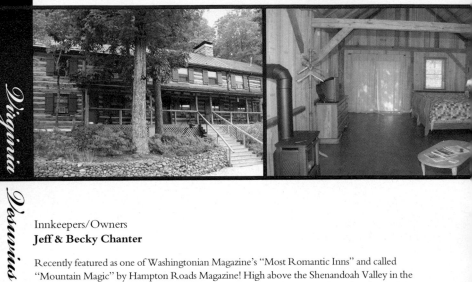

Innkeepers/Owners
Jeff & Becky Chanter

Recently featured as one of Washingtonian Magazine's "Most Romantic Inns" and called "Mountain Magic" by Hampton Roads Magazine! High above the Shenandoah Valley in the Blue Ridge Mountains (but only 6 miles from I-81) and less than a mile from the Blue Ridge Parkway, is our haven of natural beauty. Set on twenty-eight wooded acres at 2800 feet, Virginia's Mountain Inn is a place of rustic elegance, peace, and tranquility. Enjoy our 40-mile views, which are complemented by spring wildflowers, cool summer nights and brilliant fall colors. Each elegantly rustic room has a wood-burning fireplace, incredibly comfortable bed, private bath, coffee maker, CD player, and is decorated with a colorful country quilt. A full breakfast is served in our glass-walled dining room and you can savor our fine evening dining by reservation.

Rates
1 Luxury Cabin, $248; 9 Rooms, $148/$198; 2 Suites, $178 & $198; Creek House w/2 bedrooms, bath & full kitchen, $178. Number of Rooms: 13

Cuisine
A full country breakfast is served daily. Nicely prepared three course dinners with a choice of entrees available Friday and Saturday. Casual fare most busy weekdays.

Nearest Airport
Roanoke, Charlottesville

Frederick House

www.frederickhouse.com
28 North New Street, Staunton, VA 24401
800-334-5575 • 540-885-4220 • Fax 540-885-5180
stay@frederickhouse.com

Member Since 1997

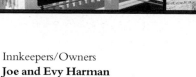

Virginia *Staunton*

Innkeepers/Owners
Joe and Evy Harman

Frederick House is a small, full service, historic, bed and breakfast hotel in seven separate buildings across from Mary Baldwin College in downtown historic Staunton, the Shenandoah Valley's oldest city. Five historic guest houses contain twenty three guest rooms or suites accommodating up to fifty seven guests and conference facilities for groups up to twenty five. Two furnished apartments are available for overnight or extended stays. Reception and Chumley's, the breakfast room at Frederick House open each morning from 7:30-10:00, are located in a vine covered building adjacent to one of three Frederick House parking lots. Breakfast includes a choice of beverages, hot or cold cereals, homemade granola and yogurt, whole grain waffles with real maple syrup, apple raisin quiche, ham and cheese pie, and strata. Special dietary requests can be met when requested. The restaurant at Frederick House, Ailoli, in an historic building adjacent to reception, serves contemporary Mediterranean cuisine.

Rates
12 Rooms, $109/$189; 11 Suites, $153/$279. Ask about our many packages.Open year-round. Number of Rooms: 25

Cuisine
15 Restaurants available within walking distance; Fine Dining, Seafood, Steaks, Pizza American, Italian, Mexican, Ribs, Gourmet Deli, Southern Home Cooking, Indian, Coffee Shops, Homemade Ice Cream, Homemade Chocolate Candy.

Nearest Airport
Shenandoah Valley Regional Airport or Charlottesville Albemarle Regional Airport

Foxfield Inn

www.foxfield-inn.com
2280 Garth Road, Charlottesville, VA 22901
434-923-8892 • 866-369-3536
stay@foxfield-inn.com

Member Since 2011

Virginia

Charlottesville

Innkeepers/Owners
Dan & Kathryn Bundy

At Foxfield Inn we treat you to a unique blend of luxury and ease in a warm, relaxing environment. We are located in the rolling horse country just minutes away from the Blue Ridge Mountains and from Charlottesville. There are many award winning wineries nearby for you to sample their wines before returning to one of the five gracious bedrooms at Foxfield Inn. Each of the rooms offers a calming retreat from the hustle and bustle of daily life. For your romantic getaway, stay in one of our rooms with a fireplace and two-person Jacuzzi tub. Relax on the patio overlooking the fishpond and park-like grounds, or relax in the outdoor hot tub while gazing at the stars. You might want to take a stroll down the country lane next to the inn, which meanders past pastures, wooded fields, and ponds. Be sure to keep an eye out for deer and birds in the fields. Come join us at Foxfield Inn for rejuvenation with grace and casual elegance.

Rates
$175-280, 4 rooms with fireplaces and Jacuzzi tubs, all have handcrafted Queen beds made by a local artisan. Wireless Internet available throughout the inn. Open year-round. Number of Rooms: 5

Cuisine
We believe that breakfast should be a culinary and creative experience. Join us for a three course breakfast using locally sourced ingredients. Complimentary beverages, wine and cheese offered in the afternoon. Cookies and fruit always available.

Nearest Airport
Charlottesville/Albemarle Airport or Richmond International

Prospect Hill Plantation Inn

www.prospecthill.com

Box 6909, 2887 Poindexter Rd., Louisa Co, Charlottesville, VA 23093

800-277-0844 • 540-967-0844 • Fax 540-967-0102

Info@prospecthill.com

Member Since 1979

Virginia

Charlottesville

Innkeepers/Owners
The Sheehan Family since 1977

Award-winning country inn on historic 1732 plantation complex located just 15 miles East of Charlottesville, VA. Romantic candlelight dining daily with 12 rooms, suites and cottages featuring breakfast-in-bed, working fireplaces, double Jacuzzi baths (in 8 rooms), outdoor swimming pool, and gazebo on over 40 acres of beautiful grounds in the serenity of the countryside near Jefferson's "Monticello". Nearby are many excellent wineries and other historic sites. B&B rates from $195 and also offering weekend dinners that includes pre-dinner wine reception and candlelight dining at private table for two. Guests have the choice breakfast-in-bed served on a tray to their room or in our dining room. Corporate, meeting, MAP package and other special rates available. Go to www.prospecthill.com for descriptions, rates, virtual tours of all rooms, sample menus to get an idea why so many romantics choose Prospect Hill for their getaway. Selected many times over the past 33 years as one of America's most romantic getaways. Uncle Ben's "10 Best Country Inns" award three times.

Rates
12 rooms/suites from $195 - $395 B&B. Number of Rooms: 12

Cuisine
Elegant Continental-American four course price-fixe dining by candlelight Fri & Sat evenings at 8 pm for $39 to $59pp. Wine and snacks in room on arrival, predinner wine reception, full country breakfast-in-bed (or served in dining room).

Nearest Airport
Charlottesville-Albemarle or Richmond International

🍽 🍽♉

Silver Thatch Inn

www.silverthatch.com
3001 Hollymead Drive, Charlottesville, VA 22911
800–261–0720 • 434–978–4686 • Fax 434–973–6156
info@silverthatch.com

Member Since 1986

Virginia

Charlottesville

Innkeepers/Owners
Jim and Terri Petrovits

This historic inn began its life as a barracks built in 1780 by Hessian soldiers captured during the Revolutionary War. As wings were added in 1812 and 1937, it served as a boys' school, a tobacco plantation, and a melon farm. It has been providing gracious lodging in antique-filled guest rooms and elegant candlelit dining since the 1970s. Relax and unwind in our intimate pub. Enjoy contemporary cuisine from our menu and wines from a list which has consistently won the Wine Spectator Award of Excellence, the Wine Enthusiast Award of Unique Distinction, and the inaugural Virginia Cellar Master 5 Stem award.

Rates
$175/$210 B&B. Open year-round. Number of Rooms: 7

Cuisine
Breakfast for house guests; Dinner served Wednesday - Sunday, specializing in contemporary cuisine, featuring local produce when available and eclectic sauces. Open to the public. Great English Pub, outstanding selection of wine and spirits.

Nearest Airport
Charlottesville/Albemarle Regional Airport, 2 miles.

The Inn at Vaucluse Spring

🍽 🍽 ♀

www.vauclusespring.com
231 Vaucluse Spring Lane, Stephens City, VA 22655
800-869-0525 • 540-869-0200 • Fax 540-869-9546
mail@vauclusespring.com

Member Since 2000

Virginia

Stephens City

Innkeepers/Owners
Barry & Neil Myers

Your place in the country. Set amidst 100 scenic acres in the rolling orchard country of the Shenandoah Valley, this collection of six guest houses is the perfect romantic getaway. Experience the elegance of the gracious 200 year old Manor House or the charm of an 1850s log home. For the ultimate in peace and privacy, stay in the Mill House Studio at the water's edge, the Gallery Guest House with views of the meadow, or the Cabin by the Pond. Relax beside Vaucluse Spring's cool, crystal clear waters. Weekends, experience the finest Contemporary American Cuisine in a relaxed atmosphere. For the ultimate foodie experience, arrange for a midweek Private Chef Dinner. Enjoy the pool in summertime or roam the pasture and woods year round. Ideally located between the historic sites of Winchester and the outdoor activities near Front Royal and the Shenandoah National Park's Skyline Drive. Acclaimed by guests for warm hospitality and fabulous food, the Inn has received TripAdvisor.com's Travelers Choice Award for Top 10 Best Inns and B&B's in the U.S.

Rates
12 Rooms/Suites: $165/$260 B&B. 3 Private cottages: $280/$320. Beautifully furnished, queen or king beds, all have fireplaces, 14 with Jacuzzis, most have water, mountain, or meadow views. Number of Rooms: 15

Cuisine
Contemporary American Cuisine, Friday and Saturday nights by advance reservation. Private Chef Dinners available Tuesday through Thursday nights by special arrangement. Wine and beer available. Full 3-course breakfast served daily.

Nearest Airport
Dulles International and Winchester Regional

L'Auberge Provencale

www.laubergeprovencale.com
13630 Lord Fairfax Highway, Boyce, VA 22620
800-638-1702 • 540-837-1375 • Fax 540-837-2004
celebrate@laubergeprovencale.com

Member Since 1988

Virginia

Boyce

Innkeepers/Owners
Chef Alain & Celeste Borel

Experience a touch of Provence in the Shenandoah Valley. L'Auberge Provencale is a destination for the discerning traveler & gourmand. Zagat and USA Today rated L'Auberge Provencale as one of the top 100 hotel dining rooms in the country. Indulge yourself in one of the guest rooms or suites at our quintessential French Country Inn. We feature cheerful yet elegant decor with faux walls, French fabrics and antiques to create an atmosphere of a true "Auberge," blending French country comfort with modern luxury. Dine evenings at the main manor house at Mt. Airy (circa 1753) in one of the three intimate dining rooms. Orchards, flower, vegetable and herb gardens supply the best and freshest for our cuisine. The inn is designated "Green" by the state of Virginia & supports sustainable local farming. Our Villa La Campagnette offers a swimming pool, luxury suites and privacy. The two inns offer a special experience for discerning guests with exquisite food and courteous, attentive service. If you can't go to France, visit L'Auberge Provencale.

Rates
8 Charming Rooms, $165/$275; 6 Romantic Suites, $295/$325. Fireplaces, Aroma Therapy Steam Showers, Flatscreens, Wireless Internet, Jacuzzi Tubs, Virginia Garden Tour Gardens and Majestic Views. Number of Rooms: 14

Cuisine
Enjoy elegant, romantic dinners with Provencale flair. Featuring fresh, local produce, meats, fruits and herbs. Dinner served six days, closed Tuesdays. Multi-course breakfast of one's dreams, gourmet picnics. Wine Spectator Award of Excellence.

Nearest Airport
Washington Dulles, National, and Winchester Regional

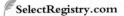

The Ashby Inn & Restaurant

🍽️ 🍽️ 🍽️ 🍷

www.ashbyinn.com
692 Federal Street, Paris, VA 20130
540-592-3900 • 866-336-0099 • Fax 540-592-3781
info@ashbyinn.com

Member Since 1988

Owners **Jackie and Chuck Leopold**
Innkeepers **Star and Neal Wavra**

This 1829 inn finds its character in the historic village of Paris and its heart in the kitchen. Guests are treated to a meal that offers the creative, progressive, farm to table cuisine of Chef Tarver King, an award winning wine list featuring Virginia wine and genuine hospitality in a relaxed setting. Four distinct dining rooms feature fireplaces, cozy booths, and an inviting sun porch. Summer dining on the covered terrace overlooking the lawn attracts a wide Washington following. Guest rooms furnished in period pieces, half with fireplaces and balconies, offer bountiful views stretching beyond the formal perennial gardens to the hills of the Blue Ridge. Located in the heart of Virginia's wine country, guests have a variety of activities to choose from. Within just minutes from the inn, one will find over half a dozen wineries, ample hiking at Sky Meadows State Park and boutique shopping in Middleburg. The Ashby was named a top 10 "On the Rise" restaurant to watch by Washingtonian Magazine and was given the Award of Excellence by Wine Spectator in 2011.

Rates
Six historic guest rooms at the Main Inn, $155-245 & four junior suites with wood-burning fireplaces and private balconies with views of the hillside at the School House, $275-295, plus tax. Includes a full breakfast and free wi-fi. Number of Rooms: 10

Cuisine
A full farmstead breakfast is included for our inn guests. Lunch and Dinner are available Wednesday-Sunday offering modern farm fare with Brunch on Sunday. Wine list and full bar available. Voted "Best Overall" by Open Table Diner's Choice Awards.

Nearest Airport
Winchester Regional Airport (16 miles), Washington/Dulles International Airport (36 miles)

🍽 🍽 🍷

Inn at Warner Hall

www.warnerhall.com
4750 Warner Hall Road, Gloucester, VA 23061
800-331-2720 • 804-695-9565 • Fax 695-9566
info@warnerhall.com

Member Since 2006

Virginia

Gloucester

Innkeepers / Owners
Troy & Theresa Stavens

Old world charm and new world amenities create the perfect balance between luxury and history in this beautifully restored romantic waterfront retreat. Established in 1642 by George Washington's great, great grandfather, Warner Hall beckons guests to relax and enjoy. Comfortable elegance, fabulous food and attentive, friendly service are the essence of Warner Hall. Spacious guest rooms combine sumptuous antiques, fabrics and art with modern conveniences. Many rooms offer fireplaces, Jacuzzis or steam showers – all have spectacular views. Experience Chef Eric Garcia's delicious cuisine paired with a bottle of fine wine. Explore the historic triangle of Williamsburg, Yorktown and Gloucester, or simply relax at the Inn's charming boathouse. Ideally situated at the head of the Severn River surrounded by 500 acres of fields and forest, Warner Hall resonates with tranquility and southern hospitality. National Register of Historic Places. Recommended by the Washinton Post, Southern Lady, Travel + Leisure, Hampton Roads Magazine, Virginian Pilot and Free Lance Star.

Rates
$195/$250 Sun.-Thurs. $220/$275 Fri-Sat. Number of Rooms: 11

Cuisine
Extraordinary breakfasts included. Chef's Tasting Dinners Fri./ Sat., or by special reservation. Cocktail and wine bar. Gourmet supper baskets Sunday-Thursday. Box lunches daily.

Nearest Airport
Nearest Airports Richmond / Norfolk

 SelectRegistry.com

Hope and Glory Inn

www.hopeandglory.com
65 Tavern Road, P.O. Box 425, Irvington, VA 22480
800-497-8228 • 804-438-6053 • Fax 804-438-5362
inquiries@hopeandglory.com

Member Since 2008

Virginia
Irvington

Innkeepers/Owners
Dudley & Peggy Patteson

TOP 100 IN THE WORLD - Twice "TOP 10 IN THE U.S." - Four times. Frommer's, Fodor's and Moon Travel Guides have awarded the Hope and Glory Inn their highest rating. The only inn in Virginia with this honor. An historic (1890) and very mega stylish schoolhouse, eclectically styled and hopelessly romantic, with quaint Garden Cottages surrounded by flowers rarely seen in Virginia gardens today. Unique in so many ways - a moon garden, which only blooms in the evening; and, an outdoor garden shower (Breakers Hotel circa 1940) with a claw foot tub in a most private setting. Additional accommodations can be found within walking distance in the Hope and Glory's Vineyard. Four Carpenter Gothic cottages called "tents" modeled after Oak Bluffs on Martha's Vineyard. Retreats are delightfully held here with today's technology in a creative environment and totally wireless. The inn also offers fine dining in its Dining Hall, cruises aboard its vessel; a hip pool; massage treatments in our special spa space; tennis courts; golf and chic shops in a classy Chesapeake Bay waterfront town.

Rates
Schoolhouse Rooms - $175-$290; Garden Cottages - $255-$345; Vineyard Tents - $310-$695. Number of Rooms: 25

Cuisine
We offer the best of fine dining in our Dining Hall. Our dinners are four courses and prix fixe. The menu changes daily and with the seasons. We have America's only Crab Cruise; and, offer wine tastings in the Hope and Glory's vineyard.

Nearest Airport
Newport News / Williamsburg (PHF) 55 min.; Richmond (RIC) 65 min; Norfolk (ORF) 90 min.; Dulles (IAD) 3 hrs

Wedmore Place

www.wedmoreplace.com
5810 Wessex Hundred, Williamsburg, VA 23185
866-WEDMORE • 757-941-0310 • Fax 757-941-0318
info@wedmoreplace.com

Member Since 2007

Virginia

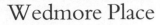

Williamsburg

Founders & Managers
The Duffeler Family

Wedmore Place is an elegant European Country Hotel, in the midst of a 300-acre winery farm located just 3 miles from Colonial Williamsburg. Whether for business or pleasure, the hotel offers a highly luxurious and relaxing atmosphere. The decor of each room is inspired by the culture and traditions of 28 different European provinces. Each is furnished and decorated in the style of the province after which it is named; all rooms have wood burning fireplaces, 10" ceilings and king-size beds. Exquisite dining is available in the Cafe Provencal, where fine French inspired Mediterranean cuisine is served daily. The dining room overlooks the pool terrace, offering guests a romantic and relaxed setting. Guests at the hotel can also make use of the massage facilities, fitness room and British Club style Library. No stay is complete without a walk next door to The Williamsburg Winery for a tour and wine tasting and shopping in the retail store. See what our guests are saying on Trip Advisor.

Rates
Traditional Rooms-$165-$205,Classic Rooms-$190-$245, Superior Rooms-$235-$345, 3 Suites: from $300-$625Weekend rates - Friday and Saturday Holiday Rates may apply. Number of Rooms: 28

Cuisine
Fine French Inspired Mediterranean Cuisine. Chef Tim feels that presentation and atmosphere of the restaurant are as important as the quality and freshness of its ingredients. That's why having access to the on-site 2 acre garden and local meats and seafood's is the key to a great meal.

Nearest Airport
Newport News/Wmbg Airport (PHF), 26 Miles; Richmond, VA (RIC), 50 Miles; Norfolk, VA (ORF), 65 Miles

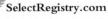

Goodstone Inn & Restaurant

🍽️ 🍽️ 🍽️ 🍷

www.goodstone.com
36205 Snake Hill Road, , Middleburg, VA 20117
877-219-4663 • 540-687-3333 • Fax 540-687-6115
information@goodstone.com

Member Since 2008

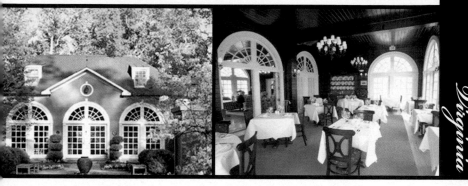

Virginia

Middleburg

General Manager
Mark Betts

Nestled in the heart of Virginia's wine and hunt country, Goodstone Inn & Restaurant is a luxurious, romantic country inn, one hour from Washington, DC. The historic property features six distinctive dwellings: the Carriage House, the Dutch Cottage, the Manor House, the French Farm Cottage, the Spring House and the Bull Barn. Goodstone provides superb cuisine, an impressive wine cellar featuring an extensive selection from Virginia and around the world, an elegant afternoon English Tea and full country breakfast along with facilities for weddings, corporate and social events. Recreational opportunities include spa treatments at Goodstone Spa, use of an outdoor pool nestled within Wisteria-covered ruins of the estate's original mansion, an all-season Jacuzzi, trails, biking, canoeing, stables for boarding guests' horses and superb Middleburg shopping. Conde Nast Johansens named Goodstone "2011 Most Excellent Inn" in North America. Open Table diners voted Goodstone as a winner of "2011 Best Restaurants in the USA."

Rates
Guest room rates range between $255-$840 and include a full country breakfast, afternoon tea service and variety of activities on Goodstone's 265 acre estate. Number of Rooms: 18

Cuisine
With years of culinary expertise, Executive Chef William Walden offers a refined approach to French cuisine with traditional and classical preparations, using the finest, fresh ingredients from Goodstone's herb and vegetable gardens.

Nearest Airport
Dulles International Airport: approx. 40 minute drive / Reagan National Airport: approx 1 hour, 9 minute drive

The Oaks Victorian Inn

www.theoaksvictorianinn.com
311 East Main St., Christiansburg, VA 24073
540-381-1500 • 800-336-6257 • Fax 540-381-3036
stay@theoaksvictorianinn.com

Member Since 1993

Virginia

Christiansburg

Innkeepers/Owners
Linda and Bernie Wurtzburger

Listed on the National Register of Historic Places; The Oaks is the only B&B In the Mid-Atlantic Region to receive the prestigious Four Diamond AAA award for 17 consecutive years. This Queen Anne Victorian is located in the small town of Christiansburg, near Roanoke just 2 miles off I-81; 3 miles from Blacksburg, home of Virginia Tech. Whether you are planning to elope, a "romantic getaway," a reunion, a historic trip to the New River, Roanoke and Shenandoah Valleys or the majestic Blue Ridge Parkway or Virginia wineries, come and enjoy the glorious setting in relaxed elegance. Fireplaces and beautiful private baths with Jacuzzis for romantics. Each room has wireless Internet, flat screen televisions, DVD players and refrigerators with complimentary beverages. Beautiful surroundings, luxurious guest rooms, a dedication to detail, warm hospitality and memorable breakfasts are the hallmark of The Oaks. The region provides the best in bike trails, hiking, antiques, live music, boating and golf...or just relax on the world class wrap-around porch.

Rates
5 Rooms, 1 Cottage, $129-$209 Low Season, $149-$229 High Season. Football games and Graduation rates slightly higher. Corp. rates Sun. through Thurs., Single Traveler Only. Open year-round. Number of Rooms: 6

Cuisine
Full breakfast by candlelight, excellent restaurants for dinner nearby.

Nearest Airport
Roanoke, 30 miles

SelectRegistry.com

Washington

Famous for: Mount St. Helens, Redwoods, Olympic National Park, Grand Coulee Dam, Space Needle, Pike Place Market, Puget Sound, San Juan Islands, Mount Rainier, Kettle Falls, Cascade Mountains, Apples, Jets, Hi-Tech.

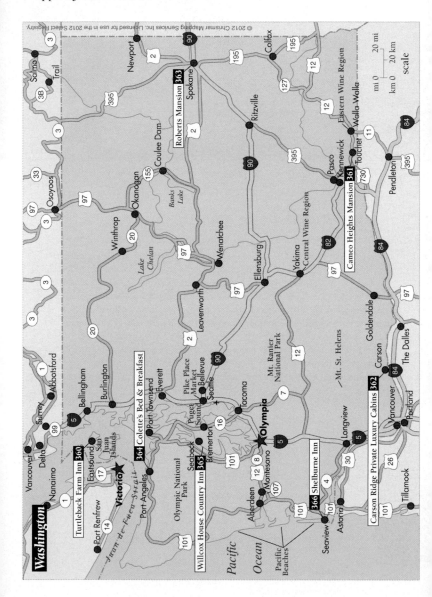

© 2012 Chrismar Mapping Services Inc. Licensed for use in the 2012 Select Registry

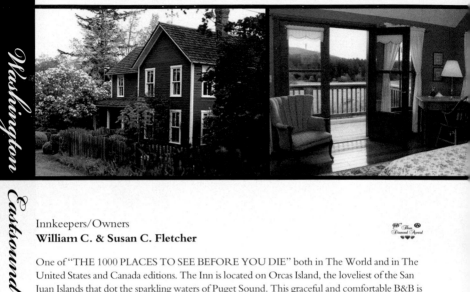

Turtleback Farm Inn and Orchard House

www.turtlebackinn.com
981 Crow Valley Road, Eastsound, WA 98245
800 376-4914 • 360 376-4914 • Fax 360 376-5329
info@turtlebackinn.com

Member Since 1991

Washington

Eastsound

Innkeepers/Owners
William C. & Susan C. Fletcher

One of "THE 1000 PLACES TO SEE BEFORE YOU DIE" both in The World and in The United States and Canada editions. The Inn is located on Orcas Island, the loveliest of the San Juan Islands that dot the sparkling waters of Puget Sound. This graceful and comfortable B&B is considered one of the most romantic places in the country. Highlighted by a spectacular setting, Turtleback is a haven for those who enjoy breathtaking scenery, tasteful accommodations and award-winning breakfasts. The Island offers unique shopping with artisan studios and craft and specialty shops offering a remarkable selection of personal and gift items. Orcas is known for it's many fine dining establishments and also for the varied outdoor activities available; whale watching, birding, bicycling, sea- kayaking, miles of hiking trails, sailing, fresh and salt water fishing, golf and summer lake swimming. A guest is only limited by time not interests. Turtleback Farm Inn is the perfect spot for the discriminating traveler to experience a step back to a quieter time.

Rates
11 Rooms -$125-$260 B&B. Open year-round. Children 8 and older are welcome in both buildings. Infants and toddlers are welcomne in The Orchard House. Pets are welcome in some rooms. Number of Rooms: 11

Cuisine
Full breakfasts featuring locally grown products when available. Freshly baked treats, complimentary sherry, Picnic baskets prepared. Luncheons and dinners can be provided from private parties. BYOB

Nearest Airport
Eastsound - 4 miles No. SEA-TAC Airport is 90 miles from the ferry landing at Anacortes. Ferry trip approx 1 hr.

Cameo Heights Mansion

www.cameoheightsmansion.com
PO Box 47, 1072 Oasis Road, Touchet, WA 99360
509-394-0211 • 509-302-0390 • Fax 509-394-8815
info@cameoheights.com

Member Since 2011

Washington

Touchet

Innkeepers/Owners
Alan and Deanne Fielding

Cameo Heights Mansion is a luxury bed and breakfast near Walla Walla, in the heart of Washington wine country. Situated in a quiet country setting, it features seven spacious suites with private baths, air-jetted tubs, gas fireplaces, and sumptuous fine dining. The most common compliment from our guests is: "You have thought of everything." (You imagine it and we surely have it in your suite.) The common area includes a large hospitality room with snacks, ping pong, games, and an adjacent theatre room with a world class sound system and over 200 DVD's and Blu-rays. Spectacular describes the view of the Walla Walla river valley with the rolling Tuscan hills in the background. Stargazing from the hot tub, swimming or sun tanning poolside in the desert heat, roasting s'mores, tetherball, horseshoes, hiking, and veranda dining at sunset are just a few of the recreational pleasures of the Mansion! Ranked Top 10 in U.S. for 2011-2012 by BedandBreakfast.com and Top 10 Best of the West in 2009 and admitted to Diamond Collection in 2012.

Rates
6 River view and Orchard view rooms $229-269; 1 limited view room $199. Winter discounts available. All rooms have the same amenities–everything imaginable. Number of Rooms: 7

Cuisine
Morning begins with "Wake-Up-Service" of coffee and danish at 8AM followed by a full country breakfast at 9AM. For your ultimate pleasure and convenience, we also offer the option of exquisite evening dining at our on-site restaurant, "The Vine."

Nearest Airport
Pasco (PSC), Walla Walla (ALW)

Carson Ridge Private Luxury Cabins

carsonridgecabins.com
1261 Wind River Road, Carson, WA 98610
509 427 7777 • 877 816 7908
info@carsonridgecabins.com

Member Since 2012

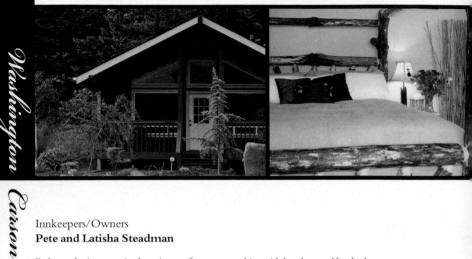

Washington

Carson

Innkeepers/Owners
Pete and Latisha Steadman

Relax and rejuvenate in the privacy of your own cabin, with hand-carved log bed, hydrotherapy spa tub for 2, spacious walk-in shower, open beamed ceilings and large windows that capture spectacular Columbia River Gorge views. Sip champagne in front of a roaring fire, curled up in a comfy leather chair. Read a book or gaze at the stars, rocking in the swing on your private porch. Stroll around the landscaped gardens or take a hike to visit one of thousands of nearby waterfalls. Soothe your tired muscles with an in-cabin massage or fragrant soak in your private spa tub. Thoughtful extras enhance your stay, from bathrobes, Gilchrist & Soames products, bath salts and candles to mini-kitchenette, iPod dock, satellite TV, DVDs, games and books. No wonder Carson Ridge has been named "Top 10 Most Romantic Inns in the Country," "Editors Pick of Best Inns to Celebrate Romance," "Best in the West". At Carson Ridge the setting, the cabins and personalized spa services blend perfectly to create an atmosphere of utter relaxation and escape. What are you waiting for?

Rates
Winter $150 - $365 Summer $245 - $415. Number of Rooms: 10

Cuisine
Enjoy breakfast in the dining room or in comfort of your cabin. Savor hot entrées, such as crème brulee french toast and a bacon, cheese & tomato quiche, or enjoy the lighter options including homemade granola, fresh baked bread and seasonal fruits.

Nearest Airport
Portland International (PDX) 45 minutes drive through the Columbia River Gorge, past Multnomah Falls.

 SelectRegistry.com

Roberts Mansion

http://www.robertsmansion.com
1923 W. 1st Ave., Spokane, WA 99201
509.456.8839
events@ejrobertsmansion.com

Member Since 2012

Washington

Spokane

Innkeeper
Megan Thompson

Take a step back in time and enjoy Victorian elegance, modern amenities, and Northwest hospitality. Upon arrival to Roberts Mansion, guests are greeted with hot tea, fresh pastries, and welcomed by an old oak tree trimmed with a chandelier. Light filters through the canopy of leaves, dappling the emerald grass below and creating a wonderful place to enjoy breakfast or a cup of tea. The gardens and landscaping at the Mansion have been lovingly maintained and represent the Victorian era with numerous sitting areas, arches, walkways, beautiful flower beds, and even a "secret garden" which lends itself to special tea parties and occasions with a wonderful flair. Although only five minutes from downtown Spokane, the Mansion feels completely obscured from the outside world, and the secret garden is a haven for weary travelers seeking peace and quiet. Indulge in Spokane's array of outdoor recreation and numerous attractions. Come visit the elegance and style of the 1800s while enjoying today's comfortable and relaxing conveniences.

Rates
The Mansion offers four suites each with their own private bath, and one separate suite complete with full kitchen and living room. You will love the high ceilings, bay windows, custom made draperies, and elegant decor. $140 - $200. Number of Rooms: 5

Cuisine
Begin your morning with a fresh pot of coffee, luscious pastries, and the finest seasonal fruit. Indulge in the chef's specially prepared breakfast entrees and treat yourself to an after breakfast crepe.

Nearest Airport
The Spokane International Airport is only five minutes away.

Colette's Bed & Breakfast

www.colettes.com
339 Finn Hall Road, Port Angeles, WA 98362
877–457–9777 • 360–457–9197 • Fax 360–452–0711
colettes@colettes.com

Member Since 2003

Innkeepers/Owners
Dae & Clif Todd

Colette's is a breathtaking 10 acre oceanfront estate nestled between the majestic Olympic Range and the picturesque Strait of Juan de Fuca. This unique area is the gateway to Olympic National Park, a world of stunning coastline with booming surf, wave-manicured beaches, and sweeping vistas in every direction. Each perfect day at Colette's starts with a gourmet multi-course breakfast. Luxurious King Suites with magnificent oceanfront views, romantic fireplaces, and indulgent Jacuzzi spas for two rejuvenate guests at the end of the day. Stroll through Colette's 10 acre outdoor sanctuary which includes enchanting gardens, towering cedars and lush evergreen forest. Fodor's Pacific Northwest - "Top Choice" for the Olympic Peninsula - considered the very best. Karen Brown's Guide Pacific Northwest- "Top Pick". Best Places to Kiss Pacific Northwest "Utopian Oceanfront Hideaway".Voted "Greatest Value" Award by Karen Brown's Pacific Northwest Exceptional Places to Stay. Selected as one of the "Top 10 Romantic Inns" by I Love Inns. Fine Gardening Magazine/June 2011 – "Front Cover"

Rates
Luxury King Suites $195/$395. Number of Rooms: 5

Cuisine
Our chef has created an exciting variety of culinary delights. Enjoy your multi-course, gourmet breakfast served with a panoramic view of the Strait of Juan de Fuca and the San Juan Islands.

Nearest Airport
Seattle and Port Angeles

SelectRegistry.com

Willcox House Country Inn

www.willcoxhouse.com
2390 Tekiu Rd. NW, Seabeck, WA 98380
800-725-9477 • 360-830-4492
willcoxhouse@silverlink.net

Member Since 1993

Innkeepers/Owners
Cecilia and Phillip Hughes

The Willcox House Country Inn is surrounded by the forest and overlooks the sparkling waters of Hood Canal. Located between Seattle and the Olympic mountains, this 1930's mansion offers guests peace and tranquility. From your private table in the dining room enjoy the spectacular view of the water and the Olympic Peninsula. The inn is furnished with antiques and period pieces for relaxation and comfort. Relax by the fire in the great room, play a game of pool in the game room or watch a movie in the theater. The terrace and the library are great places to enjoy a glass of wine in the afternoon. Five guest rooms, all with private baths, overlook the water and the Olympic mountains. Beautiful gardens host a champion Japanese maple tree and two fish ponds. Walk the oyster laden saltwater beach looking for driftwood and wildlife. Golfing, birding, and hiking are nearby. The combination of Native American, Scandinavian, Military, and world class garden attractions make Kitsap County an easy-to-tour destination rich in history and diversity.

Rates
Guest rooms have different amenities (fireplace $259, double spa tub $239, balcony $229) $169/$259 B&B. Open year-round. Number of Rooms: 5

Cuisine
Breakfast, afternoon wine and cheese included. The three course dinner is available by reservation only. All dining is private table. Extensive wine list. Beer is available. Complimentary hot beverages.

Nearest Airport
Seattle (SEA) Interstate 5 south to Tacoma; Hwy 16 to Bremerton; web site for specific mileage to inn 1&1/2 hours

Shelburne Inn & China Beach Retreat

www.shelburneinn.com or www.chinabeachretreat.com
P.O. Box 250, 4415 Pacific Hwy, Seaview, WA 98644
800-INN-1896 • 360-642-2442 • Fax 360-642-8904
innkeeper@theshelburneinn.com

Member Since 1988

Washington

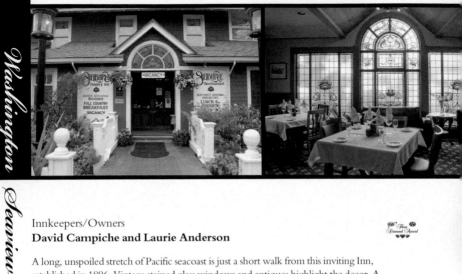

Seaview

Innkeepers/Owners
David Campiche and Laurie Anderson

A long, unspoiled stretch of Pacific seacoast is just a short walk from this inviting Inn, established in 1896. Vintage stained glass windows and antiques highlight the decor. A sumptuous breakfast is complimentary. Spa services available in the Shelburne Spa—manicure, pedicure and various massage therapies. The restaurant and pub offer musical entertainment at various times throughout the year. Innovative cuisine and a discriminating wine list have brought international recognition. Wireless Internet. Outdoor activities abound, including The Discovery Trail which parallels the majestic Pacific Ocean. Explore the western end of the Lewis & Clark trail from China Beach Retreat and its Audubon Cottage near Cape Disappointment State Park and two 100-plus-year-old lighthouses. Selected as one of the 'West's Best Small Inns' by Sunset Magazine. Featured in Martha Stewart Living magazine, The New York Times, 'a perfectly restored, impeccably run stronghold of antiques, fireplaces and stained glass for which the word "gem" is overused but unavoidable,' AAA Three Diamond-rated.

Rates
12 Rooms $139/$179 B&B; 2 Suites $199 B&B. Off-site waterside B&B; two Rooms $199 B&B; 1 Suite $229 B&B. Audubon Cottage: $289 B&B. Group Rates for Business Retreats and lodging/dining packages available Sun - Thurs, Oct - June. Number of Rooms: 18

Cuisine
Gourmet Regional Cuisine features the best seasonal and local ingredients. Restaurant and Pub offer breakfast, lunch and dinner featuring fine NW wines, microbrewed beer and liquor. Innkeepers' Breakfast served daily and offers creative preparations.

Nearest Airport
Astoria, Oregon

West Virginia

"The Mountain State"

Famous for: Appalachian Mountains, Monongahela National Forest, White Sulphur Springs, Harper's Ferry National Historical Park, Smoke Hole Caverns, Apple Butter Festival, Grave Creek Burial Mounds, Country Music, Coal, Oil, Gas.

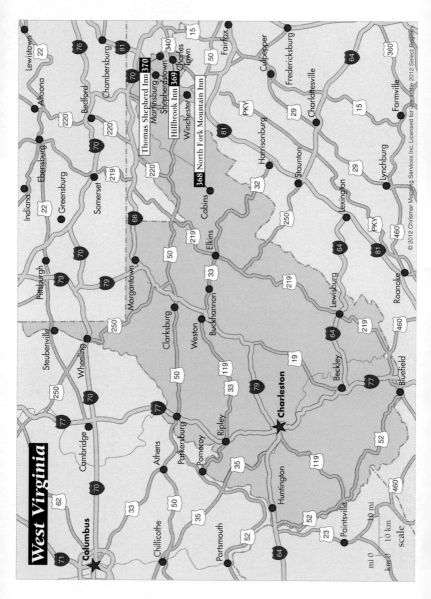

North Fork Mountain Inn

www.northforkmtninn.com
P.O. Box 114, 235 Canyon View Lane, Smoke Hole Road, Cabins, WV 26855
304-257-1108
info@northforkmtninn.com

Member Since 2007

Innkeepers/Owners
Ed & Carol Fischer

We invite you to come and enjoy the natural beauty of the area in a quiet, relaxing atmosphere. Enjoy a gourmet breakfast as you start your day. Spend the day hiking in the Monongahela Forest or enjoying a spectacular view of the mountains & valleys from a rocker on the Inn's front porch. It is like taking a journey back in time to a simpler, slower paced world. Located only three hours from the Washington DC area. The Inn is located 7.6 miles up a paved mountain road with a view of Smoke Hole Canyon and six different mountains. The three story log Inn is of white pine construction with native field stone fireplaces. Each guest room is uniquely decorated with rustic elegance. Guest common areas include comfortable chairs & sofas, book & movie libraries, DirecTV, billiard table, microwave, refrigerator, and board games. Excellent fishing nearby. Enjoy fine dining with award winning chef & master sommelier. Finish your day relaxing in the hot tub under a blanket of stars. Massages available on site. Conference area available for weddings, family gatherings or meetings.

Rates
7 Rooms, $140/$190. Two suites with king bed & loft, $245. Separate 1 Bedroom Cabin with full kitchen, $180. Gourmet breakfast included. Children under 12 welcome in the suites or cabin. Pets allowed in cabin. Number of Rooms: 10

Cuisine
Gourmet breakfast included. Fine dining w/wine tasting on Saturday evening, casual dining on other evenings, gourmet picnic baskets available for lunch or dinner. Ed is a master sommelier and an award winning chef in the Great American Seafood Cookoff.

Nearest Airport
Grant County Airport for small planes; nearest large airport is Washington Dulles

Hillbrook Inn

www.hillbrookinn.com
4490 Summit Point Road, Charles Town, WV 25414
800.304.4223 • 304.725.4223
info@hillbrookinn.com

Member Since 2012

Innkeepers/Owners
Christopher and Carissa Zanella

Picture a European style country house hotel cascading down a limestone ridge on eight levels, with 2000 panes of glass flooding the interior with light. Imagine the rich patina of old wood, the gleam of polished brass, the deep jewel tones of oriental carpets. Imagine, too, Flemish oils, African masks, a library lined with books, a relaxing spa and a fine dining restaurant on the premises. Add the flicker of candles and the warmth of a fire. A love seat. An intimate table for two. A quiet place to be alone together. Gardens bursting with color, a meandering stream and ducks on the pond. The gold of autumn. The beauty of a winter storm. And dinner. Three, Five or Seven spectacular courses. Fragrant herbs from the kitchen dooryard; vegetables from a nearby farm. A truly Romantic Getaway in West Virginia. Sophisticated yet unpretentious. Elegant and eclectic!

Rates
Rooms: $149-$369. Each room offers an eclectic range of style. All rooms offer private baths, iPad™, Keurig™ Coffee Pots, and the various amenities today's traveler enjoys. Please see web-site for package and spa information. Number of Rooms: 10

Cuisine
Indulge in a sumptuous dining experience. We use only the freshest ingredients and take pride in creating daily pre-fixe menus utilizing the dietary needs and restrictions of our guests. Gourmet Breakfast Daily~ Reservations Required for Dinner/Lunch

Nearest Airport
Dulles (IAD) 1hr; Baltimore (BWI) 1hr 15min

Thomas Shepherd Inn

www.thomasshepherdinn.com

300 W. German Street, P.O. Box 3634, Shepherdstown, WV 25443

888–889–8952 • 304-876-3715

info@thomasshepherdinn.com

Member Since 2006

Innkeepers/Owners
Jeanne Muir & Jim Ford

We invite you to stay in our bed & breakfast inn, with six 'inviting, well kept and beautifully decorated' guest rooms with private baths, central air and wi-fi, all located on the 2nd floor. Built in 1868, the inn offers gracious hospitality to guests for over 25 years. Relax in front of the living room fireplace or on the back porch overlooking the garden; start your day with a generous homemade breakfast. Room amenities include comfy robes and bedside chocolates. Shepherdstown, a hidden gem for weary urbanites, is less than two hours from Washington, DC or Baltimore. The town has a vibrant cultural scene, ranging from premiere plays at the Contemporary American Theater Festival to independent movies at the Opera House to music and crafts festivals featuring local and nationally-known artists. A variety of locally-owned shops and restaurants fill the historic buildings on nearby German Street. Rich U.S. history is only minutes away at Antietam Battlefield or Harpers Ferry. Biking, hiking and rafting abound along the C&O Canal Path, the Potomac and the Shenandoah Rivers.

Rates
$170-$210 Friday/Saturday/Sunday; $135-$180 Monday thru Thursday, not including taxes, double occupancy. Two night minimum stay required on Saturdays and holidays. Not suitable for pets or children under 12. No smoking inside Inn. Number of Rooms: 6

Cuisine
Full hot homemade breakfast daily w/fruit, entree, meat, baked goods; early beverage service w/signature spice biscotti. Hot beverages available all day; afternoon snacks. Walk to many locally-owned fine dining and casual restaurants on German Street.

Nearest Airport
BWI and Dulles airports - 70 miles. Parking beside and behind the Inn on Duke Street (corner of German Street).

SelectRegistry.com

Wisconsin

"The Badger State"

Famous for: Wisconsin Dells, Apostle Islands, National Lakeshore, Lake Superior, Mirror Lake State Park, House on the Rock (a 1940s retreat built on a 60-foot rock outcropping overlooking a 450 ft drop), Dairy, Beer, Cranberry Fest.

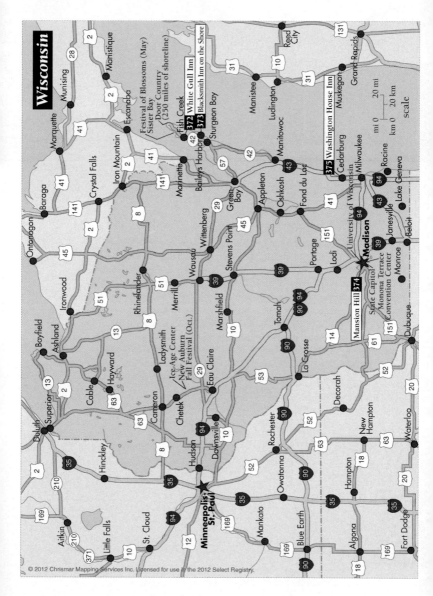

🍽 🍽 🍽 ⚲

White Gull Inn

www.whitegullinn.com
4225 Main Street, P.O. Box 160, Fish Creek, WI 54212
800-625-8813 • 920-868-3517 • Fax 920-868-2367
innkeeper@whitegullinn.com

Member Since 1979

Wisconsin

Fish Creek

Innkeepers/Owners
Andy & Jan Coulson

Established in 1896, this white clapboard Inn is tucked away in the scenic bayside village of Fish Creek on Wisconsin's Door Peninsula. Antiques, fireplaces and meticulously restored and exquisitely decorated rooms, suites and cottages provide a warm and romantic atmosphere. Several suites feature double whirlpool baths. Renowned for award winning breakfasts, sumptuous lunches and candlelit dinners, the Inn is famous for its traditional Door County fish boils, featuring locally caught Lake Michigan whitefish cooked outside over an open fire. With its back to a bluff and its face to the bay of Green Bay, Fish Creek today is a stroll around village with historic buildings housing numerous art galleries, shops and restaurants. A natural harbor filled with majestic yachts in summer separates the village from Peninsula State Park, Wisconsin's largest and most beautiful park. Within a few minutes of the inn, guests will find spectacular sunsets, theater, music festivals, antique stores and every imaginable recreational activity, from golf and fishing to wind surfing and kayaking.

Rates
6 Rooms, $165/$240; 7 Suites, $240/$295; 4 Cottages (1, 2 and 4 bedroom), $250/$480. Open all year. Number of Rooms: 17

Cuisine
Full breakfast included. Lunch served daily.Dinner from the menu Monday, Tuesday, Thursday in summer, Saturday through Thursday in winter. Traditional Door County fish boils featuring local Lake Michigan whitefish served other evenings.

Nearest Airport
Austin Straubel Field, Green Bay (75 miles)

Blacksmith Inn On the Shore

www.theblacksmithinn.com
8152 Highway 57, Baileys Harbor, WI 54202
800-769-8619 • 920-839-9222
relax@theblacksmithinn.com

Member Since 2002

Innkeepers/Owners
Joan Holliday and Bryan Nelson

Awaken to waves lapping the shore as the morning light glistens on the water. Linger over breakfast. Kayak the harbor. Hike the nearby Ridges Wildlife Sanctuary. Laze in your hammock. Bike a sleepy backroad to Cana Island Lighthouse. Bask in your whirlpool as you take in the warm glow of the fire. Stroll to village restaurants and shops. Serene water views, private balconies, hammocks, in-room whirlpools, fireplaces, fine linens, down pillows, satellite TV/DVD/CD, DVD library, wireless internet, ipod hook-up, in-room refrigerators and a bottomless cookie jar! Door County offers art galleries, antiquing, music, theater, lighthouses and miles and miles of shoreline. Adults Only.

Rates
Late May-Oct. Rooms $245/$295, Cottage $255/$445; Late Oct.- Late May, Rooms $145/$235, Cottage $155/$295. Number of Rooms: 16

Cuisine
Guests enjoy a homemade continental breakfast from the balcony overlooking the harbor. "There is nothing simple about the view that beckons each guest every morning," Jill Cordes, Food Network.

Nearest Airport
Green Bay (GRB)- Hwy 172 E. 8 mi. to Hwy 43 N. 5 mi. to Hwy 57 N. 63 mi. (90 min. drive)

Mansion Hill Inn

www.mansionhillinn.com
424 N. Pinckney Street, Madison, WI 53703
800-798-9070 • 508-255-0172 • Fax 920-478-5860

Member Since 1997

General Manager
Tania Worgull

Elegance, luxury and charm await you at The Mansion Hill Inn. The Inn's warm hospitality has made it a favorite of business and leisure travelers alike. Lovingly restored and lavishly decorated, Mansion Hill Inn is located in Madison. A masterpiece of Romanesque Revival style built in 1857, it abounds in fine architectural detail and period furnishings. Each of the ten guest suites and rooms are individually and exquisitely decorated to provide the best of antique ambiance and contemporary amenities. Many rooms have marble fireplaces and balconies as well as views of the State Capitol building. The Inn is conveniently located on a quiet corner in the heart of downtown Madison and boasts luxurious accommodations, amenities, and a convenient location. We're close to the campuses of the University of Wisconsin, Madison Area Technical College, Edgewood College and within walking distance of State Street. Valet parking is complimentary.

Rates
Ten Beautiful Guest Rooms including 2 Suites, 4 Grand Standard Rooms and 4 Standard Rooms, ranging from $200 to $400 on special event weekends. Number of Rooms: 10

Cuisine
Many fine restaurants within walking distance. Continental-plus breakfast in our Breakfast Parlour. On-site bar featuring wine and local beers.

Nearest Airport
Dane County Regional Airport

 SelectRegistry.com

Washington House Inn

www.washingtonhouseinn.com
W62 N573 Washington Avenue, Cedarburg, WI 53012
888-554-0515 • 262-375-3550 • Fax 262-375-9422
info@washingtonhouseinn.com

Member Since 2007

Innkeeper
Wendy J. Porterfield

Listed on the National Register of Historic Places, Washington House Inn successfully blends the charm and romance of days past with the amenities and conveniences expected by today's discriminating travelers. 34 rooms with luxury bedding include whirlpools (single and double), steam baths, antiques, fireplaces, flat-screen TVs and free in-room Internet. Guests are invited to enjoy a complimentary evening wine and cheese tasting featuring award-winning wines from local Cedar Creek Winery, and a sampling of Wisconsin cheeses. For a little extra pampering, the inn offers sauna and on-site massages. Located in the heart of Cedarburg's Historic District, the Inn offers elegant lodging within walking distance of shopping, dining and entertainment options, including the Ozaukee Interurban Trail (30 miles of paved trail for hiking or biking), making the Washington House Inn the place to stay in Historic Cedarburg. Within a 15 minute drive are five golf courses. The Inn is also perfect for small groups such as wedding parties, family re-unions, small meetings and business retreats.

Rates
Open year round. $125-$345 Friday/Saturday. $100-$275 Sunday-Thursday. Number of Rooms: 34

Cuisine
Enjoy our expanded continental breakfast buffet. Thoughtfully prepared for you each morning by staff bakers and served in our Gathering Room, or if you prefer, delivered to your guest room.

Nearest Airport
General Mitchell International

Wyoming

"The Equality State"

Famous for: Yellowstone National Park, Grand Teton National Park, Devils Tower National Monument, National Elk Refuge.

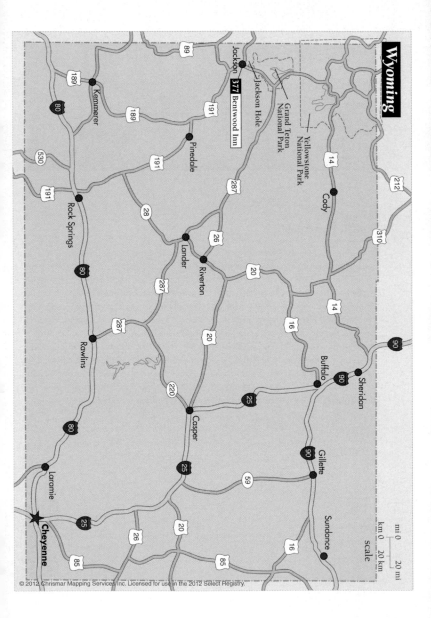

SelectRegistry.com

Bentwood Inn

www.bentwoodinn.com
P.O. Box 561, 4250 Raven Haven Road, Jackson, WY 83001
307-739-1411 • Fax 307-739-2453
info@bentwoodinn.com

Member Since 2008

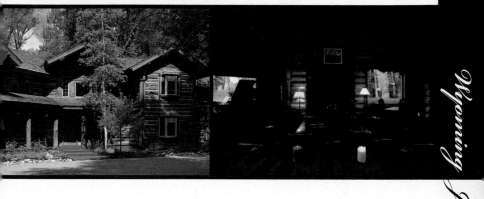

Wyoming Jackson

Innkeepers
Lee & Deborah Clukey

The Bentwood Inn is a luxury bed and breakfast in Jackson Hole, nestled in majestic old-growth cottonwoods on 3 acres of solitude. The Bentwood is 5 miles from down town Jackson, Jackson Hole Mountain Resort, and the south entrance to Grand Teton National Park. The Snake River is about a quarter mile away. This welcoming, intimate lodge highlighted by the Great Room with its three-story river rock fireplace, was built in 1995 with 200 year old logs salvaged from the Yellowstone Park fire of 1988. The Bentwood boasts 6,000 sq.ft. of Western eclectic decor with five guest rooms each featuring a fireplace, king bed, jetted tub, quality linens, towels and robes, cable TV and private balcony or deck. A gourmet breakfast launches the Bentwood magic for a day of wildlife viewing and activity in the parks on the hills and trails, or being pampered and shopping in Jackson. In late afternoons, guests share the day's experiences and bond while enjoying cheese, appetizers and refreshments on the expansive decks in the summer, or in front of the fire in the Great Room on cooler days.

Rates
Room rates vary by season. Please visit our website to view our "Rates At A Glance" page. Number of Rooms: 5

Cuisine
At the Bentwood Inn we strive to prepare innovative menus. Unique presentations with creative twists on old breakfast favorites will satisfy the appetite of the most discerning guests. Enjoy fresh baked goods and fresh fruit every day.

Nearest Airport
Jackson Hole Airport: 18 miles. Idaho Falls Airport: 85 miles, Salt Lake City Airport 250 miles.

Canada

SELECT REGISTRY represents the finest inns, B&Bs, and unique small hotels North America has to offer. We are proud to include among our members a number of exceptional Canadian properties. To our Canadian guests, we say, "Our innkeepers stand ready to welcome you during your travels, whether it is to the States or within Canada." To our American guests, we say, "Why not see what Canada has to offer?"

In these uncertain times, when crossing oceans is worrisome, nothing beats the exhilarating feeling of visiting an exciting new country in the security and comfort of your own car. Yes, for many millions of Americans, Canada is just a short drive away—and yet it is a whole new world!

Le SELECT REGISTRY représente plusieurs auberges, cafés–couettes et petits hôtels des plus distingués en Amérique du Nord. Nous sommes fiers de pouvoir compter parmi nos membres plusieurs des plus beaux établissements canadiens. À tous les voyageurs, canadiens-français, nous vous souhaitons de merveilleux sejours dans les auberges de prestige du SELECT REGISTRY.

There are the breathtaking vistas, mountain wildlife, Asian food and totem poles of British Columbia, the "foodie" paradise of the Niagara Peninsula (Canada's Napa Valley) and the Eastern Townships of Quebec, replete with friendly wineries and raw milk cheeses. There are festivals galore, museums, parks and world-class shopping in Toronto and Montreal as well as the fascinating culture of the Province of Quebec where French-Canadians take food and fun very, very seriously.

Many travelers have experienced all four seasons of the Northland (the winters are sunnier and less cold than you think). Traveling east to west, it would be hard to declare a regional winner. Some Canadians modestly claim to be the most hospitable of innkeepers, and a critic can't easily challenge that assertion.

Superb food, wine and service can be expected at the Canadian inns of the SELECT REGISTRY. Understated luxury, too. But above all, they offer you an exclusive glimpse of the best of Canada: its forests, crystalline lakes, affordable golf and skiing and cosmopolitan, secure and friendly cities. The Northland beckons!

British Columbia

"The Pacific Province"

Famous for: Canadian Rockies, Ferries, Vancouver Island, Spiral Railway Tunnels, Butchart Gardens.

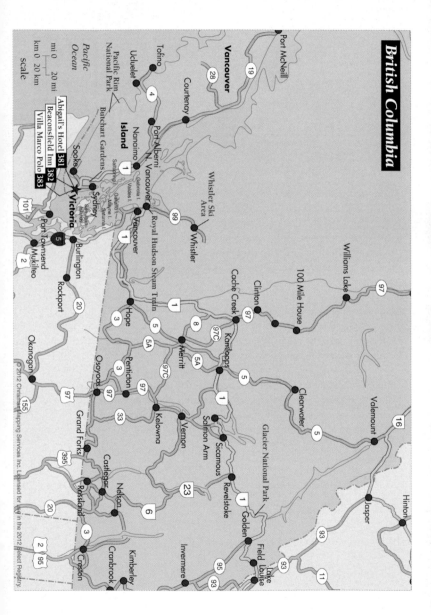

SelectRegistry.com

Abigail's Hotel

www.abigailshotel.com
906 McClure Street, Victoria, BC Canada V8V 3E7
800-561-6565 • 250-388-5363 • Fax 250-388-7787
innkeeper@abigailshotel.com

Member Since 2000

British Columbia

Victoria

Innkeeper/Owner
Ellen Cmolik

This unique and romantic boutique bed and breakfast hotel is conveniently nestled at the end of a tranquil cul-de-sac surrounded by quaint English gardens and friendly residential homes. Intimately housed in a 1930's heritage Tudor mansion, Abigail's blends the romance and charm of the past with all the comforts and conveniences of the present. Each of the 23 beautifully appointed guestrooms has its own characteristic and flair. Many rooms feature marvelous soaker baths, down duvets, rich linens and wood-burning fireplaces. Complimentary appetizers are served each evening in our Library Lounge which guests can pair with local award winning BC wine & champagne. Abigail's is walking distance to Victoria's must-see ocean or city tours, galleries, museums, and restaurants. Each morning the hotel fills with the irresistible aroma of freshly prepared baked goods, and gourmet breakfasts, interactively presented by Abigail's Executive Chef. Wireless internet service, local calling, coffee and tea 24 hours a day and parking are all-inclusive during your stay with us.

Rates
$172/$349 CDN. Seasonal discounts available. Open year-round, reservations available 24 hrs. Number of Rooms: 23

Cuisine
Our famous gourmet breakfast is served each morning in the sunny breakfast room and complimentary evening appetizers served every evening in our fireside library. Licensed premises.

Nearest Airport
Victoria International Airport

Beaconsfield Inn

www.beaconsfieldinn.com
998 Humboldt St., Victoria, BC Canada V8V 2Z8
888-884-4044 • 250-384-4044 • Fax 250-384-4052
info@beaconsfieldinn.com

Member Since 1994

Proprietors
Mark and Diana Havin

We invite you to our award-winning Edwardian Inn built in 1905. Located only four blocks from Victoria's Inner Harbor, the Beaconsfield Inn is the ultimate in charm, luxury and romance. Enjoy antique furnishings, stately guest and common rooms, spectacular stained glass windows, feather beds with down comforters and fireplaces in all rooms. Jacuzzis in mosts rooms. The Beaconsfield Inn is situated on a quiet, tree-lined street a short 10 minute stroll to downtown and the inner harbour with all its shopping, restaurants and tourist attractions. Afternoon tea, coffee and fresh baked treats. Evening sherry hour. Awake to our gourmet full breakfasts each morning. The Beaconsfield Inn has been awarded a 5 star rating from Canada Select.

Rates
5 Deluxe Rooms, $109/$295 CDN; 4 Suites, $199/$299 CDN. Open year-round.
Number of Rooms: 9

Cuisine
Full gourmet style breakfast. Afternoon fresh baked treats, selection of teas and freshly brewed coffee. Evening sherry hour.

Nearest Airport
Victoria International. Or downtown inner harbour - Float Planes from Vancouver.

Villa Marco Polo

www.villamarcopolo.com
1524 Shasta Place, Victoria, BC Canada V8S 1X9
877-601-1524 • 250-370-1524 • Fax 250-370-1624
enquire@villamarcopolo.com

Member Since 2007

Proprietors **Eliza Livingston,
Clarke Bingham & Liam Morton**
Managing Innkeeper **Danusia Quaranta**

Escape from the ordinary...to the Villa Marco Polo Inn. Built in 1923 as a gift to a young bride, the Villa Marco Polo is an Italian Renaissance mansion that continues to be a romantic setting for special vacations. A reflecting pool visited occasionally by bald eagles, Coopers hawks, and blue herons is the focal point of a classical Italianate garden. Our suites feature double soakers, fireplaces, fine linens, luxurious beds, down pillows, hardwood floors and Persian carpets. In our Spa and Healing Space, guests can schedule facials, manicures, aromatherapy, etc. Generous gourmet breakfasts featuring locally grown produce are served in our lovely sun-splashed dining room. Enjoy afternoon tea or Italian Amarone either in the garden, or in front of the fire in our wood-paneled library. Whether a business meeting requiring WIFI and private telephones, or a celebration requiring the services of an events planner, your experience at the Villa will be memorable!

Rates
Rates range from $175 to $295. Number of Rooms: 4

Cuisine
Gourmet breakfasts feature locally grown organic produce, house-made preserves, organic maple and birch syrups from Quebec and Yukon, organic coffee from Bolivia, and fresh eggs from island farms. With prior notice, we can handle special needs.

Nearest Airport
Victoria International Airport is 28 km from the Villa.

Ontario Inn Style

Discover over 40 of Ontario's Finest Inns and Spas including several Select Registry properties. All of the innkeepers share the Select Registry's philosophy and promise of excellence.

Enjoy true Canadian hospitality along the sparkling Great Lakes, in vibrant, clean cities and throughout quaint villages and quiet rolling countryside.

Attention Spa Goers –Ontario's Finest now offers quality assured spas that feature distinctly Ontario treatments and therapies.

We look forward to welcoming you this season.

ONTARIO'S *finest* INNS · SPAS

Ask for a complimentary map & guidebook at 800-340-4667 or visit
www.ontariosfinestinns.com • www.ontariosfinestspas.com
See you soon in Ontario, Canada!

Famous for: Wine Country, Niagara Falls, Toronto, the Shaw Festival, Forests, Lakes.

🍴 🍴 🍴 ♟

Inn on the Twenty

www.innonthetwenty.com
3845 Main Street, Jordan, ON Canada L0R 1S0
800-701-8074 • 905-562-5336 • Fax 905-562-0009
info@innonthetwenty.com

Member Since 1998

Ontario

Jordan

Innkeeper/Owner
Helen Young

This is the heart of Ontario's wine country! Renovated winery buildings boast twenty-seven suites, all with fireplaces and Jacuzzi tubs; antiques and unique art abound. The Inn is located in a charming village with artisans and antique shops and our very own full service spa. Great golf, walking and bicycling opportunities as well as the sophistication of Niagara's famous Shaw Theatre and the not-to-be-missed Falls are nearby. Visit our restaurant, On the Twenty, for regional cuisine. The Niagara wine route beckons with up to forty diverse wineries within a fifteen minute drive of the Inn. Cave Spring Cellars, one of Ontario's most recognized premium wineries, is our partner and is right across the street from the Inn. Special tasting offers are available to Inn guests. A visit to Canada is a fresh experience and we are thrilled to welcome so many of our US neighbors. We are just 25 minutes from the borders at Niagara Falls and make a great en route stop to Toronto.

Rates
27 Suites: 7 two-story, 20 one-level, 5 with private garden. $159-$389. Number of Rooms: 27

Cuisine
On the Twenty offers cuisine with regional focus. Private Dining Rooms available for up to 135. Ontario wines and beers. Full bar. Cave Spring Cellars Winery on site. Tours and tastings available daily.

Nearest Airport
Buffalo, Toronto, Hamilton

SelectRegistry.com

Quebec

"La Belle Province"

Famous for: St. Lawrence Seaway, French Culture, Maple Syrup, Winter Sports, Apples, Camping.

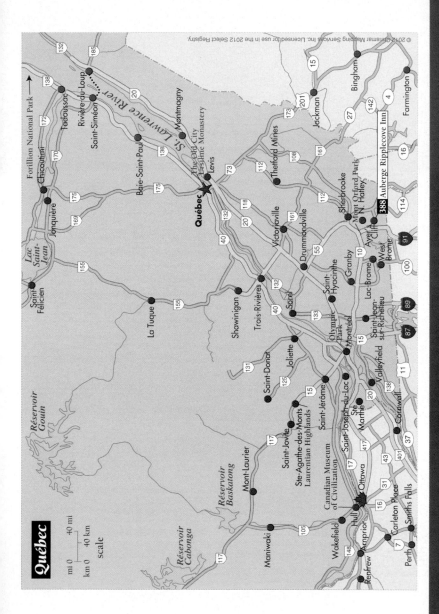

¡O¡ ¡O¡ ¡O¡ ♀

Auberge Ripplecove Inn & Spa

www.ripplecove.com
700 Ripplecove, Lake Massawippi, Ayer's Cliff, QB Canada J0B 1C0
800-668-4296 • 819-838-4296 • Fax 819-838-5541
info@ripplecove.com

Member Since 1995

Quebec

Ayer's Cliff

Innkeepers/Owners
Debra and Jeffrey Stafford

Since 1945, Ripplecove Inn has been chosen by sophisticated travelers from around the world to get away from it all in an atmosphere of romance and privacy. The Inn resides on a beautifully landscaped 12 acre peninsula alive with English gardens and century-old pines. Guests can choose from 33 designer decorated rooms, suites or lakeside cottages, many with lake view balcony and fireplace. A full service Spa facility offering massage, hydro therapy, facials, 3 private salons and a four season outdoor hot tub guarantee complete relaxation. A private beach with water craft, biking, tennis, heated outdoor pool and lake cruises are also all on site! Rated as one of Quebec's top 10 best places to dine, our Victorian dining room and lakeside terrace offer refined French and international cuisine with vintage wines accompanied by live piano music and sterling silver service. Located only 15 minutes north of the Quebec/Vermont border, Ripplecove Inn is the perfect stop over while on route to either Montreal or Quebec city via Interstate 91 through Vermont.

Rates
33 Rooms, Suites and Cottages, US $149/$365MAP/person/day including daily dinner, breakfast and gratuities. All rooms offer A/C, TV, TEL and designer decor. Most rooms offer fireplace, private lake view balcony and whirlpool bath. Number of Rooms: 33

Cuisine
Four Diamond Award french and international cuisine is served in a Victorian style lakeside dining room, pub and terrace. A 6000 bottle wine cellar has been awarded by Wine Spectator Magazine as "one of the best restaurant wine cellars in the world".

Nearest Airport
Pierre E Trudeau Airport, Dorval (Montreal), Quebec, Canada, or Burlington, Vermont.

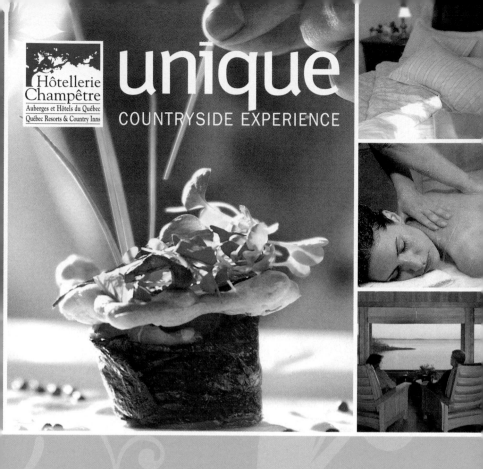

26 of Québec's finest inns and tons of delightful packages to choose from...

Book online your next dream vacation at
www.resortsquebec.com!

You are just one click away from luxurious escapes
and unrivaled pleasures!

To know more:
www.resortsquebec.com

SelectRegistry.com

Index by Inn

SelectRegistry.com

Travel Your Dreams®
with
Karen Brown's Guides

Karen Brown's
ITALY HOTELS

Karen Brown's
FRANCE HOTELS

Karen Brown's
NEW ENGLAND

Itineraries & Places to Stay • 2012

o Stay • 2012

Karen Brown's
CALIFORNIA

Karen Brown's
MID-ATLANTIC

Itinerari

Itineraries & Places to Stay • 2012

• Seventeen titles for Europe, North America & Mexico - NOW in Electronic Book Format with color photos, interactive links and maps!

• Accommodations from châteaux to cottages, inns to boutique hotels.

• Regional countryside itineraries highlight cultural & sightseeing attractions.

• Karen Brown researches the world for you. Visit our website for help in planning your trips with recommendations you can trust.

• Karen Brown is proud to recommend many Select Registry member properties in her guides and website.

KAREN · BROWN

KB

QUALITY · WELCOME · CHARM

Karen Brown's Guides
Post Office Box 70
San Mateo, CA 94401
karen@karenbrown.com

www.karenbrown.com

Credits

We appreciate the photo skills of everyone who contributed to this book. Some member inns have provided photographs without photographic credits, and other images are unidentified. If you're not listed here, we extend our thanks. We will be pleased to publish a credit if it is furnished to Select Registry. Many of the images/inns featured in the book were provided by Jumping Rocks Photography, George W. Gardner Associates, Tim Shellmer, Brad Wittman, Doug Plummer, Laurie Anderson. Other photo credits available upon request.

Select Registry, Distinguished Inns of North America, P.O. Box 150 E. Michigan Avenue, MI 49068. Phone: 800.344.5244, Fax: 269.789.0970. Copyright Select Registry, 2012. All rights reserved. Printed in the U.S.A. Select Registry assumes no liability for the accuracy of the information contained herein. At the time of this printing we assumed all information was correct. Information for individual Inn pages has been provided by the member properties. Select Registry is a membership marketing organization and has no ownership role or policy-making authority with respect to its members.

From time to time, the composition of our membership changes. For an up-to-date list of our current membership please go online at **www.selectregistry.com**. Please note that only current members are entitled to redeem Select Registry gift certificates and loyalty rewards. To assure a safe and happy trip, please call ahead to verify times, prices, Inn policies, etc.

Contributing writers: Will Carlson, Keith Kehlbeck. Canadian copy: Steve Stafford. Design: Haas-Wittmann Design. Maps: Chrismar Mapping Services Inc. Production: Cadmus Media Works. Publisher: Select Registry, Distinguished Inns of North America.

Join our loyalty program and get updates on new properties, valuable information from Select Registry and track your Quills online: **www.selectregistry.com/goldenquill**

Follow us on Facebook **www.facebook.com/SelectRegistry**

SELECT REGISTRY

DISTINGUISHED INNS OF NORTH AMERICA

Thank you for choosing a Select Registry inn.
Your comments help us to maintain the highest standards in the industry.
We appreciate feedback and the opportunity to respond
(and to facilitate communication, where appropriate, with our member properties
should something during your stay be not to your liking).
Of course, our innkeepers appreciate hearing good things from you, as well!
Please include your name, address and phone number,
so we can respond in a timely manner.
Or, if you would prefer, you can use our convenient online comment card
at www.selectregistry.com.

Name of Inn: _____ State or Province: _____ Date of visit: _____

Your name and address (please print and be aware that we require a name): _____

_____

_____

_____

Your phone number: _____

Email address: _____

Please check ONE box in each category:	Excellent	Good	Disappointing	Poor	Would not return
Bedrooms/comfort/decor	❑	❑	❑	❑	❑
Public rooms/aesthetics/furnishings	❑	❑	❑	❑	❑
Food/restaurant quality	❑	❑	❑	❑	❑
Service quality	❑	❑	❑	❑	❑
Welcome/friendliness	❑	❑	❑	❑	❑
Personality/character of the Inn	❑	❑	❑	❑	❑

Additional comments: _____

_____

_____

As a discriminating traveler who wants to go to the best Country Inns and B&Bs, I recommend the following Inns (please include name, city and state/province, and tell us why): _____

_____

_____

SELECT ✒ REGISTRY

DISTINGUISHED INNS OF NORTH AMERICA

Select Registry Gift Certificate Program

The perfect gift for that special person.
Select Registry gift certificates can be ordered online at:
www.SelectRegistry.com.
Our gift certificates are packaged with a copy
of our most recent guidebook,
and a message from you to the recipient.
VISA, MasterCard, and American Express accepted.
Expedited shipping is available for an additional charge.

Place
Postage
Here

Select Registry, Distinguished Inns of North America
501 E. Michigan Avenue
P.O. Box 150
Marshall, MI 49068